AS-Level
Chemistry

AS Chemistry is seriously tricky — no question about that.
To do well, you're going to need to revise properly and practise hard.

This book has thorough notes on all the theory you need,
and it's got practice questions... lots of them.
For every topic there are warm-up and exam-style questions.

And of course, we've done our best to make the whole thing vaguely entertaining for you.

Complete Revision and Practice

Editors:
Mary Falkner, Sarah Hilton, Paul Jordin, Sharon Keeley, Simon Little, Andy Park.

Contributors:
Antonio Angelosanto, Martin Chester, Vikki Cunningham, Ian H. Davis, John Duffy, Max Fishel, Emma Grimwood, Richard Harwood, Philippa Hulme, Lucy Muncaster, Zoe Nye, Glenn Rogers, Emma Singleton, Derek Swain, Paul Warren, Sharon Watson, Chris Workman.

Proofreaders:
Barrie Crowther, Glenn Rogers, Julie Wakeling.

Published by CGP.

This book is suitable for:

AQA, OCR A, OCR B (Salters) and Edexcel.

There are notes on the pages to tell you which bits you need to know for each unit of your syllabus.

ISBN: 978 1 84762 125 2

With thanks to Science Photo Library for permission to reproduce the photographs used on pages 65, 144 and 148.

Graph to show trend in atmospheric CO_2 Concentration and global temperature on page 147 based on data by EPICA Community Members 2004 and Siegenthaler et al 2005.

Groovy website: www.cgpbooks.co.uk
Jolly bits of clipart from CorelDRAW®
Printed by Elanders Ltd, Newcastle upon Tyne.

Based on the classic CGP style created by Richard Parsons.

Contents

The Scientific Process

'How Science Works' is all about the scientific process — how we develop and test scientific ideas.
It's what scientists do all day, everyday (well except at coffee time — never come between scientists and their coffee).

Scientists Come Up with **Theories** — Then **Test Them**...

Science tries to explain **how** and **why** things happen. It's all about seeking and gaining **knowledge** about the world around us. Scientists do this by **asking** questions and **suggesting** answers and then **testing** them, to see if they're correct — this is the **scientific process**.

1) **Ask** a question — make an **observation** and ask **why or how** whatever you've observed happens.
   E.g. Why does sodium chloride dissolve in water?

2) **Suggest** an answer, or part of an answer, by forming a **theory** or a **model** (a possible **explanation** of the observations or a description of what you think is happening actually happening).
   E.g. Sodium chloride is made up of charged particles which are pulled apart by the polar water molecules.

3) Make a **prediction** or **hypothesis** — a **specific testable statement**, based on the theory, about what will happen in a test situation.
   E.g. A solution of sodium chloride will conduct electricity much better than water does.

4) Carry out **tests** — to provide **evidence** that will support the prediction or refute it.
   E.g. Measure the conductivity of water and of sodium chloride solution.

The evidence supported Quentin's Theory of Flammable Burps.

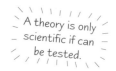

A theory is only scientific if can be tested.

...Then They **Tell** Everyone About Their **Results**...

The results are **published** — scientists need to let others know about their work. Scientists publish their results in **scientific journals**. These are just like normal magazines, only they contain **scientific reports** (called papers) instead of the latest celebrity gossip.

1) Scientific reports are similar to the **lab write-ups** you do in school. And just as a lab write-up is **reviewed** (marked) by your teacher, reports in scientific journals undergo **peer review** before they're published.

   Scientists use standard terminology when writing their reports. This way they know that other scientists will understand them. For instance, there are internationally agreed rules for naming organic compounds, so that scientists across the world will know exactly what substance is being referred to. See page 79.

2) The report is sent out to **peers** — other scientists who are experts in the **same area**. They go through it bit by bit, examining the methods and data, and checking it's all clear and logical. When the report is approved, it's **published**. This makes sure that work published in scientific journals is of a **good standard**.

3) But peer review **can't guarantee** the science is **correct** — other scientists still need to **reproduce** it.

4) Sometimes **mistakes** are made and bad work is published. Peer review **isn't perfect** but it's probably the best way for scientists to self-regulate their work and to publish **quality reports**.

...Then **Other Scientists** Will **Test** the Theory Too

1) Other scientists read the published theories and results, and try to **test the theory** themselves. This involves:
   - Repeating the **exact same experiments**.
   - Using the theory to make **new predictions** and then testing them with **new experiments**.

2) If all the experiments in the world provide evidence to back it up, the theory is thought of as **scientific 'fact'** (for now).

3) If **new evidence** comes to light that **conflicts** with the current evidence the theory is questioned all over again. More rounds of **testing** will be carried out to try to find out where the theory **falls down**.

   This is how the **scientific process works** — **evidence** supports a theory, loads of other scientists read it and test it for themselves, eventually all the scientists in the world **agree** with it and then bingo, you get to **learn** it.

   This is exactly how scientists arrived at the structure of the atom (see pages 6-7) — and how they came to the conclusion that electrons are arranged in shells and orbitals (see pages 8-9). It took years and years for these models to be developed and accepted — this is often the case with the scientific process.

The Scientific Process

If the **Evidence** Supports a Theory, It's **Accepted** — for Now

Our currently accepted theories have survived this '**trial by evidence**'. They've been tested **over and over again** and each time the results have backed them up. **BUT**, and this is a big but (teehee), they never become totally indisputable fact. Scientific **breakthroughs or advances** could provide new ways to question and test the theory, which could lead to **changes and challenges** to it. Then the testing starts all over again...

And this, my friend, is the **tentative nature of scientific knowledge** — it's always **changing** and **evolving**.

> When CFCs were first used in fridges in the 1930s, scientists thought they were problem-free — well, why not? There was no evidence to say otherwise. It was decades before anyone found out that CFCs were actually making a whopping great hole in the ozone layer. See page 144.

Evidence Comes From **Lab Experiments**...

1) Results from **controlled experiments** in **laboratories** are great.
2) A lab is the easiest place to **control variables** so that they're all **kept constant** (except for the one you're investigating).
3) This means you can draw meaningful **conclusions**.

> For example, if you're investigating how temperature affects the rate of a reaction (see pages 102-103) you need to keep everything but the temperature constant, e.g. the pH of the solution, the concentration of the solution, etc.

...But You **Can't** Always do a Lab Experiment

There are things you **can't** study in a lab. And outside the lab controlling the variables is tricky, if not impossible.

- *Are increasing CO_2 emissions causing climate change?*
  There are other variables which may have an effect, such as changes in solar activity. You can't easily rule out every possibility. Also, climate change is a very **gradual process**. Scientists won't be able to tell if their predictions are correct for donkey's years.

  See pages 146-147 for more on climate change.

- *Does drinking chlorinated tap water increase the risk of developing certain cancers?*
  There are always differences between groups of people. The best you can do is to have a **well-designed study** using **matched groups** — **choose two groups** of people (those who drink tap water and those who don't) which are **as similar as possible** (same mix of ages, same mix of diets etc). But you still can't rule out every possibility. Taking new-born identical twins and treating them identically, except for making one drink gallons of tap water and the other only pure water, might be a fairer test, but it would present huge **ethical problems**.

Samantha thought her study was very well designed — especially the fitted bookshelf.

Science Helps to Inform **Decision-Making**

Lots of scientific work eventually leads to **important discoveries** that **could** benefit humankind — but there are often **risks** attached (and almost always **financial costs**).

Society (that's you, me and everyone else) must weigh up the information in order to **make decisions** — about the way we live, what we eat, what we drive, and so on. Information is also be used by **politicians** to devise policies and laws.

- **Chlorine** is added to water in **small quantities** to disinfect it. Some studies link drinking chlorinated water with certain types of cancer (see page 75). But the risks from drinking water contaminated by nasty bacteria are far, far greater. There are other ways to get rid of bacteria in water, but they're heaps **more expensive**.
- Scientific advances mean that **non-polluting hydrogen-fuelled cars** can be made. They're better for the environment, but are really expensive. Also, it'd cost a fortune to adapt the existing filling stations to store hydrogen.
- Pharmaceutical drugs are really expensive to develop, and drug companies want to make money. So they put most of their efforts into developing drugs that they can sell for a good price. Society has to consider the **cost** of buying new drugs — the **NHS** can't afford the most expensive drugs without **sacrificing** something else.

So there you have it — how science works...

Hopefully these pages have given you a nice intro to how science works, e.g. what scientists do to provide you with 'facts'. You need to understand this, as you're expected to know how science works yourselves — for the exam and for life.

The Atom

This stuff about atoms and elements should be ingrained on your brain from GCSE. You do need to know it perfectly though if you are to negotiate your way through the field of man-eating tigers which is AS Chemistry.
These pages are for AQA (Unit 1), OCR A (Unit 1), OCR B (Unit 1) and Edexcel (Unit 1).

Atoms are made up of **Protons**, **Neutrons** and **Electrons**

All elements are made of **atoms**. Atoms are made up of 3 types of particle — **protons**, **neutrons** and **electrons**.

Electrons
1) Electrons have **–1** charge.
2) They whizz around the nucleus in **orbitals**. The orbitals take up most of the **volume** of the atom.

Nucleus
1) Most of the **mass** of the atom is concentrated in the nucleus.
2) The **diameter** of the nucleus is rather titchy compared to the whole atom.
3) The nucleus is where you find the **protons** and **neutrons**.

The mass and charge of these subatomic particles is **really small**, so **relative mass** and **relative charge** are used instead.

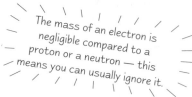

The mass of an electron is negligible compared to a proton or a neutron — this means you can usually ignore it.

Subatomic particle	Relative mass	Relative charge
Proton	1	+1
Neutron	1	0
Electron, e$^-$	$\frac{1}{2000}$	–1

Nuclear Symbols Show Numbers of **Subatomic Particles**

You can figure out the **number** of protons, neutrons and electrons from the **nuclear symbol**.

Mass number
This tells you the **total** number of **protons** and **neutrons** in the nucleus.

Element symbol

$$_Z^A X$$

Sometimes the atomic number is left out of the nuclear symbol, e.g. ^{7}Li. You don't really need it because the element's symbol tells you its value.

Atomic (proton) number
1) This is the number of **protons** in the nucleus — it identifies the element.
2) **All** atoms of the same element have the **same** number of protons.

1) For neutral **atoms**, which have no overall charge, the number of electrons is **the same as** the number of protons.
2) The number of neutrons is just **mass number minus atomic number**, i.e. 'top minus bottom' in the nuclear symbol.

Nuclear symbol	Atomic number, Z	Mass number, A	Protons	Electrons	Neutrons
$_3^7$ Li	3	7	3	3	7 – 3 = **4**
$_{35}^{80}$ Br	35	80	35	35	80 – 35 = **45**
$_{12}^{24}$ Mg	12	24	12	12	24 – 12 = **12**

"Hello, I'm Newt Ron..."

Ions have **Different** Numbers of **Protons** and **Electrons**

Negative ions have **more electrons** than protons...
E.g.

Br$^-$ The negative charge means that there's 1 more electron than there are protons. Br has 35 protons (see table above), so Br$^-$ must have 36 electrons. The overall charge = + 35 – 36 = –1.

...and **positive** ions have **fewer electrons** than protons. It kind of makes sense if you think about it.
E.g.

Mg^{2+} The 2+ charge means that there's 2 fewer electrons than there are protons. Mg has 12 protons (see table above), so Mg^{2+} must have 10 electrons. The overall charge = +12 – 10 = +2.

The Atom

Isotopes are Atoms of the Same Element with Different Numbers of Neutrons

Make sure you **learn** this definition and totally **understand** what it means —

Isotopes of an element are atoms with the same number of protons but different numbers of neutrons.

Chlorine-35 and chlorine-37 are examples of isotopes.

$35 - 17 = 18$ neutrons ⟵ **Different** mass numbers mean ⟶ $37 - 17 = 20$ neutrons
different numbers of neutrons.

$$^{35}_{17}\text{Cl}$$

The **atomic numbers** are the same.
Both isotopes have 17 protons and 17 electrons.

$$^{37}_{17}\text{Cl}$$

1) It's the **number** and **arrangement** of electrons that decides the **chemical properties** of an element. Isotopes have the **same configuration of electrons**, so they've got the **same** chemical properties.

2) Isotopes of an element do have slightly different **physical properties** though, such as different densities, rates of diffusion, etc. This is because **physical properties** tend to depend more on the **mass** of the atom.

Here's another example — naturally occurring **magnesium** consists of 3 isotopes.

^{24}Mg (79%)	^{25}Mg (10%)	^{26}Mg (11%)
12 protons	12 protons	12 protons
12 neutrons	13 neutrons	14 neutrons
12 electrons	12 electrons	12 electrons

The periodic table gives the atomic number for each element. The other number isn't the mass number — it's the relative atomic mass (see page 16). They're a bit different, but you can often assume they're equal — it doesn't matter unless you're doing really accurate work.

Practice Questions

Q1 Draw a diagram showing the structure of the atom, labelling each part.

Q2 Define the term 'isotope' and give an example.

Q3 Draw a table showing the relative charge and relative mass of the three subatomic particles found in atoms.

Q4 Using an example, explain the terms 'atomic number' and 'mass number'.

Q5 Where is the mass concentrated in an atom, and what makes up most of the volume of an atom?

Exam Questions

Q1 Hydrogen, deuterium and tritium are all isotopes of each other.
   a) Identify one similarity and one difference between these isotopes. [2 marks]
   b) Deuterium can be written ^{2}H. Determine the number of protons, neutrons and electrons in a neutral deuterium atom. [3 marks]
   c) Write a nuclear symbol for tritium, given that it has 2 neutrons. [1 mark]

Q2 This question relates to the atoms or ions A to D: A. $^{32}_{16}$S^{2-},   B. $^{40}_{18}$Ar,   C. $^{30}_{16}$S,   D. $^{42}_{20}$Ca.
   a) Identify the similarity for each of the following pairs, justifying your answer in each case.
      (i)   A and B. [2 marks]
      (ii)   A and C. [2 marks]
      (iii) B and D. [2 marks]
   b) Which two of the atoms or ions are isotopes of each other? Explain your reasoning. [2 marks]

Got it learned yet? — Isotope so...

This is a nice straightforward page just to ease you in to things. Remember that positive ions have fewer electrons than protons, and negative ions have more electrons than protons. Get that straight in your mind or you'll end up in a right mess. There's nowt too hard about isotopes neither. They're just the same element with different numbers of neutrons.

Atomic Models

Things ain't how they used to be, you know. Take atomic structure, for starters.
These pages are for AQA (Unit 1), OCR A (Unit 1) and OCR B (Unit 1).

The **Accepted Model** of the **Atom** Has **Changed** Throughout History

The model of the atom you're expected to know (the one on page 4) is one of the currently **accepted** ones.
In the past, completely different models were accepted, because they fitted the evidence available at the time:

1) Some **ancient Greeks** thought that all matter was made from **indivisible particles**.

2) At the start of the 19th century John Dalton described atoms as **solid spheres**, and said that different spheres made up the different elements.

3) But as scientists did more experiments, our currently accepted models began to emerge, with modifications or refinements being made to take account of new evidence.

The Greek word atomos means 'uncuttable'.

Experimental Evidence Showed that Atoms **Weren't Solid Spheres**

In 1897 J J Thompson did a whole series of experiments and concluded that atoms **weren't** solid and indivisible.

1) His measurements of **charge** and **mass** showed that an atom must contain even smaller, negatively charged particles. He called these particles 'corpuscles' — we call them **electrons**.

2) The 'solid sphere' idea of atomic structure had to be changed. The new model was known as the '**plum pudding model**' — a positively charged sphere with negative electrons embedded in it.

positively charged 'pudding'

delicious pudding

Rutherford Showed that the **Plum Pudding** Model Was **Wrong**

1) In 1909 Ernest Rutherford and his students Hans Geiger and Ernest Marsden conducted the famous **gold foil experiment**. They fired **alpha particles** (which are positively charged) at an extremely thin sheet of gold.

2) From the plum pudding model, they were expecting **most** of the alpha particles to be deflected **very slightly** by the positive 'pudding' that made up most of an atom.

3) In fact, most of the alpha particles passed **straight through** the gold atoms, and a very small number were deflected **backwards** (through more than 90°). This showed that the plum pudding model **couldn't be right**.

4) So Rutherford came up with a model that **could** explain this new evidence — the **nuclear model** of the atom:

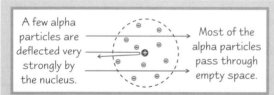

A few alpha particles are deflected very strongly by the nucleus.

Most of the alpha particles pass through empty space.

1) There is a **tiny, positively charged nucleus** at the centre of the atom, where most of the atom's mass is concentrated.

2) The nucleus is surrounded by a '**cloud**' of **negative electrons**.

3) Most of the atom is **empty space**.

Rutherford's **Nuclear Model** Was **Modified** Several Times

Rutherford's model seemed pretty convincing, but (there's always a but)... the scientists of the day didn't just say, "Well done Ernest old chap, you've got it", then all move to Patagonia to farm goats. No, they stuck at their experiments, wanting to be sure of the truth. (And it's just conceivable they wanted some fame and fortune too.)

1) Henry Moseley discovered that the charge of the nucleus **increased** from one element to another in units of one.

2) This led Rutherford to investigate the nucleus further. He finally discovered that it contained **positively charged** particles that he called **protons**. The charges of the nuclei of different atoms could then be explained — the atoms of **different elements** have a **different number of protons** in their nucleus.

3) There was still one problem with the model — the nuclei of atoms were **heavier** than they would be if they just contained protons. Rutherford predicted that there were other particles in the nucleus, that had **mass but no charge** — and the **neutron** was eventually discovered by James Chadwick.

> This is nearly always the way scientific knowledge develops — **new evidence** prompts people to come up with **new, improved ideas**. Then other people go through each new, improved idea with a fine-tooth comb as well — modern '**peer review**' (see p2) is part of this process.

Atomic Models

The *Bohr Model* Was a Further Improvement

1) Scientists realised that electrons in a 'cloud' around the nucleus of an atom would **spiral down** into the nucleus, causing the atom to **collapse**. Niels Bohr proposed a new model of the atom with four basic principles:

> 1) Electrons can only exist in **fixed orbits**, or **shells**, and not anywhere in between.
> 2) Each shell has a **fixed energy**.
> 3) When an electron moves between shells **electromagnetic radiation** is **emitted** or **absorbed**.
> 4) Because the energy of shells is fixed, the radiation will have a **fixed frequency**.

2) The frequencies of radiation emitted and absorbed by atoms were already known from experiments. The Bohr model fitted these observations — it looked good.

3) The Bohr model also explained why some elements (the noble gases) are **inert**. He said that the shells of an atom can only hold **fixed numbers of electrons**, and that an element's reactivity is due to its electrons. When an atom has **full shells** of electrons it is **stable** and does not react.

There's *More Than One* Model of Atomic Structure in Use Today

1) We now know that the Bohr model is **not perfect** — but it's still widely used to describe atoms because it's simple and explains many **observations** from experiments, like bonding and ionisation energy trends.

2) The most accurate model we have today involves complicated quantum mechanics. Basically, you can never **know** where an electron is or which direction it's going in at any moment, but you can say **how likely** it is to be at any particular point in the atom. Oh, and electrons can act as **waves** as well as particles (but you don't need to worry about the details).

3) This model might be **more accurate**, but it's a lot harder to get your head round and visualise. It **does** explain some observations that can't be accounted for by the Bohr model though. So scientists use whichever model is most relevant to whatever they're investigating.

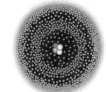

The quantum model of an atom with two shells of electrons. The denser the dots, the more likely an electron is to be there.

Practice Questions

Q1 What particle did J J Thompson discover?

Q2 Describe the model of the atom that was adopted because of Thompson's work.

Q3 Who developed the 'nuclear' model of the atom? What evidence did they have for it?

Q4 What are the names of the two particles in the nucleus of an atom?

Exam Question

Q1 Scientific theories are constantly being revised in the light of new evidence. New theories are accepted if they have been successfully tested by experiments or because they help to explain certain observations.

a) Niels Bohr thought that the model of the atom proposed by Ernest Rutherford did not describe the electrons in an atom correctly. Why did he think this and how was his model of the atom different from Rutherford's? [2 marks]

b) What happens when electrons in an atom move from one shell to another? [1 mark]

c) How did Bohr explain the lack of reactivity of the noble gases? [2 marks]

These models are tiny — even smaller than size zero, I reckon...

The process of developing a model to fit the evidence available, looking for more evidence to show if it's correct or not, then revising the model if necessary is really important. It happens with all new scientific ideas. Remember, scientific 'facts' are only accepted as true because no one's proved yet that they aren't. It <u>might</u> all be bunkum.

Electronic Structure

Those little electrons prancing about like mini bunnies decide what'll react with what — it's what chemistry's all about.
These pages are for AQA (Unit 1), OCR A (Unit 1), OCR B (Unit 1 and Unit 2) and Edexcel (Unit 1).

Electron Shells are Made Up of Sub-Shells and Orbitals

1) In the currently accepted models of the atom, electrons have **fixed energies**.
    They move around the nucleus in certain regions of the atom called **shells** or **energy levels**.

2) Each shell is given a number called the **principal quantum number**.
    The **further** a shell is from the nucleus, the **higher** its energy and the **larger** its principal quantum number.

3) This model helps to explain why electrons are **attracted** to the nucleus, but are not **drawn into it** and destroyed.

4) **Experiments** show that not all the electrons in a shell have exactly the same energy.
    The **atomic model** explains this — shells are divided up into **sub-shells** that have slightly different energies.
    The sub-shells have different numbers of **orbitals** which can each hold up to **2 electrons**.

This table shows the number of electrons that fit in each type of sub-shell.

Sub-shell	Number of orbitals	Maximum electrons
s	1	$1 \times 2 = 2$
p	3	$3 \times 2 = 6$
d	5	$5 \times 2 = 10$
f	7	$7 \times 2 = 14$

And this one shows the sub-shells and electrons in the first four energy levels.

Shell	Sub-shells	Total number of electrons	
1st	1s	2	= 2
2nd	2s 2p	$2 + (3 \times 2)$	= 8
3rd	3s 3p 3d	$2 + (3 \times 2) + (5 \times 2)$	= 18
4th	4s 4p 4d 4f	$2 + (3 \times 2) + (5 \times 2) + (7 \times 2)$	= 32

Orbitals Have Characteristic Shapes

1) An orbital is the **bit of space** which an electron moves in.
    Orbitals within the same sub-shell have the **same energy**.

2) The orbitals are defined by **mathematical equations**.
    These equations are **models** for the ways electrons move.

3) s orbitals are **spherical**. p orbitals are **dumbbell-shaped**. There are 3 p orbitals at right angles to one another.

4) There are 5 **d orbitals**, so a d sub-shell can hold **10 electrons** — you don't need to know the shapes of d orbitals.

5) The diagrams of the shapes of orbitals are simplified versions of **graphs** of the equations describing the orbitals.
    These graphs are called **electron density plots**.

s orbital   p orbitals

P_x orbital + P_y orbital + P_z orbital =

Work Out Electron Configurations by Filling the Lowest Energy Levels First

You can figure out most electronic configurations pretty easily, so long as you know a few simple rules —

1) Electrons fill up the **lowest** energy sub-shells first.

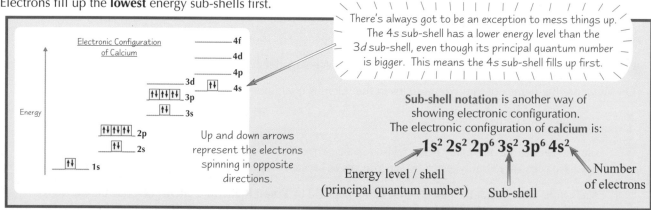

Electronic Configuration of Calcium

There's always got to be an exception to mess things up. The 4s sub-shell has a lower energy level than the 3d sub-shell, even though its principal quantum number is bigger. This means the 4s sub-shell fills up first.

Energy

Up and down arrows represent the electrons spinning in opposite directions.

Sub-shell notation is another way of showing electronic configuration.
The electronic configuration of **calcium** is:

$$1s^2\ 2s^2\ 2p^6\ 3s^2\ 3p^6\ 4s^2$$

Energy level / shell (principal quantum number)

Sub-shell

Number of electrons

2) Electrons fill orbitals **singly** before they start sharing. ⟶

See the next page for more on the s and p block.

	1s	2s	2p		
Nitrogen	↑↓	↑↓	↑	↑	↑

	1s	2s	2p		
Oxygen	↑↓	↑↓	↑↓	↑	↑

The electrons in an orbital spin in opposite directions — this is called spin-pairing.

3) For the configuration of **ions** from the **s** and **p** blocks of the periodic table, just **remove or add** the electrons to or from the highest energy occupied sub-shell. E.g. $Mg^{2+} = 1s^2\ 2s^2\ 2p^6$, $Cl^- = 1s^2\ 2s^2\ 2p^6\ 3s^2\ 3p^6$

Watch out — **noble gas symbols**, like that of argon (Ar), are sometimes used in electron configurations.
For example, calcium ($1s^2\ 2s^2\ 2p^6\ 3s^2\ 3p^6\ 4s^2$) can be written as $[Ar]4s^2$, where $[Ar] = 1s^2\ 2s^2\ 2p^6\ 3s^2\ 3p^6$.

Electronic Structure

Transition Metals Behave Unusually   *Not OCR A (Unit 1)*

1) **Chromium** (Cr) and **copper** (Cu) are badly behaved. They donate one of their **4s** electrons to the **3d sub-shell**. It's because they're happier with a **more stable** full or half-full d sub-shell.

   Cr atom (24 e⁻): $1s^2\ 2s^2\ 2p^6\ 3s^2\ 3p^6\ 3d^5\ 4s^1$ Cu atom (29 e⁻): $1s^2\ 2s^2\ 2p^6\ 3s^2\ 3p^6\ 3d^{10}\ 4s^1$

2) And here's another weird thing about transition metals — when they become **ions**, they lose their **4s** electrons **before** their 3d electrons, even though 3d is at a higher energy level.

   Fe atom (26 e⁻): $1s^2\ 2s^2\ 2p^6\ 3s^2\ 3p^6\ 3d^6\ 4s^2$ → Fe^{3+} ion (23 e⁻): $1s^2\ 2s^2\ 2p^6\ 3s^2\ 3p^6\ 3d^5$

Electronic Structure Decides the *Chemical Properties* of an Element

The number of **outer shell electrons** decides the chemical properties of an element.

1) The **s block** elements (Groups 1 and 2) have 1 or 2 outer shell electrons. These are easily **lost** to form positive ions with an **inert gas configuration**. E.g. Na — $1s^2\ 2s^2\ 2p^6\ 3s^1$ → Na^+ — $1s^2\ 2s^2\ 2p^6$ (the electronic configuration of neon).

2) The elements in Groups 5, 6 and 7 (in the p block) can **gain** 1, 2 or 3 electrons to form negative ions with an **inert gas configuration**. E.g. O — $1s^2\ 2s^2\ 2p^4$ → O^{2-} — $1s^2\ 2s^2\ 2p^6$. Groups 4 to 7 can also **share** electrons when they form covalent bonds.

3) Group 0 (the inert gases) have **completely filled** s and p sub-shells and don't need to bother gaining, losing or sharing electrons — their full sub-shells make them **inert**.

4) The **d block** elements (transition metals) tend to **lose** s and d electrons to form positive ions.

Practice Questions

Q1 Write down the sub-shells in order of increasing energy up to 4*f*.

Q2 How many electrons would full s, p and d sub-shells contain?

Q3 Draw diagrams to show the shapes of an s and a p orbital.

Q4 What does the term 'spin-pairing' mean?

Exam Questions

Q1 Potassium reacts with oxygen to form potassium oxide, K_2O.

   a) Give the electron configurations of the K atom and K^+ ion.   [2 marks]

   b) Using arrow-in-box notation, give the electron configuration of the oxygen atom.   [2 marks]

   c) Explain why it is the outer shell electrons, not those in the inner shells, which determine the chemistry of potassium and oxygen.   [2 marks]

Q2 This question concerns the electron configurations of atoms and ions.

   a) What is the electron configuration of a manganese atom?   [1 mark]

   b) Identify the element with the 4th shell configuration of $4s^2 4p^2$.   [1 mark]

   c) Suggest the identity of an atom, a positive ion and a negative ion with the configuration $1s^2\ 2s^2\ 2p^6\ 3s^2\ 3p^6$.   [3 marks]

   d) Using arrow-in-box notation, give the electron configuration of the Al^{3+} ion.   [2 marks]

She shells sub-sells on the shesore...

The way electrons fill up the orbitals is kind of like how strangers fill up seats on a bus. Everyone tends to sit in their own seat till they're forced to share. Except for the huge, scary, smelly man who comes and sits next to you. Make sure you learn the order the sub-shells are filled up, so you can write electron configurations for any atom or ion they throw at you.

Atomic Spectra

These two pages are just for people doing OCR B (Unit 1), so the rest of you can put your feet up and have a cuppa.

Electrons **Absorb or Release** Energy in **Fixed Amounts**

1) Atoms in their **ground state** have all their electrons in their **lowest** possible orbitals. Each energy level is given a **quantum number**. The quantum number, n, for 1s electrons is 1.

2) If the electrons **take in energy** from their surroundings they can move to **higher energy levels**, further from the nucleus. At higher energy levels, electrons are said to be **excited**. (More excited than you are right now, I'll bet.)

3) Electrons can also **release energy** by dropping down to a **lower energy level**.

4) The energy levels all have **certain fixed values** — they're **discrete**. Electrons can jump from one energy level to another by **absorbing or releasing** a fixed amount of energy.

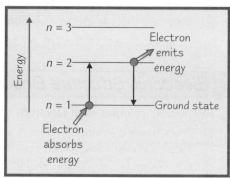

Absorption Spectra — Made Up of **Dark Lines**

1) Energy is related to **wavelength**. When **electromagnetic radiation** is passed through a gaseous element, the electrons only absorb **certain wavelengths**, corresponding to **differences between the energy levels**.

2) That means the radiation passing through has certain wavelengths missing. A spectrum of this radiation is called an **atomic absorption spectrum**.

3) The missing wavelengths show up as **dark bands** on a coloured background.

Absorption Spectrum

Emission Spectrum

Emission Spectra — Made Up of **Bright Lines**

1) When electrons **drop** to lower energy levels, they **give out** certain amounts of energy. This produces lines in the spectrum too — but this time it's called an **emission spectrum**. For any particular element, the wavelengths in an emission spectrum are the **same** as those missing in the absorption spectrum.

2) Each element has a **different** electron arrangement, so the wavelengths of radiation absorbed and emitted are different. This means the **spectrum** for each element is unique.

Spectra are Made Up of **Sets of Lines**

1) You get lots of **sets of lines** in spectra — each set represents electrons moving to or from a different energy level. So, in an emission spectrum, you get one **set of lines** produced when electrons fall to the $n = 1$ level, and another set produced when they fall to the $n = 2$ level, and so on.

2) Spectra often seem to make as much sense as bar codes. But the emission spectrum of **hydrogen** is fairly simple because hydrogen only has **one** electron that can move. It has **three important sets of lines**:

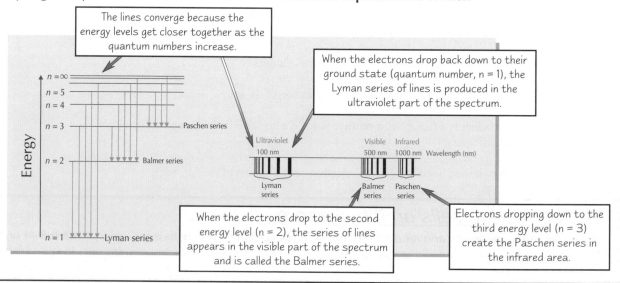

Atomic Spectra

Energy is Related to Frequency

When an electron moves to a higher or lower shell it **absorbs** or **emits** electromagnetic radiation with a certain frequency. The **amount of energy** absorbed or emitted is related to the **frequency** of the radiation by the following equation:

The **difference in energy** between two shells. The units are **joules (J)**.

$$\Delta E = h\nu$$

Don't stress too much about doing calculations with this equation — just make sure you understand the relationship between energy and frequency.

This is just a number called **Planck's constant**. The units are **joule seconds (Js)**.

This is the Greek letter nu, the symbol for the **frequency** of the radiation. The units are **hertz (Hz or s⁻¹)**.

So to find the energy of a given **frequency** of radiation you can just stick the numbers in the equation.

E.g. When an electron falls from the 3rd to the 2nd energy level of a hydrogen atom it emits visible light with a frequency of 4.57×10^{14} Hz. Planck's constant $= 6.626 \times 10^{-34}$ Js.
What is the difference in energy between the 3rd and 2nd energy levels of a hydrogen atom?

$h = 6.626 \times 10^{-34}$ Js and $\nu = 4.57 \times 10^{14}$ Hz
so $\Delta E = h\nu = (4.57 \times 10^{14}$ s$^{-1}) \times (6.626 \times 10^{-34}$ Js$) \approx \mathbf{3.0 \times 10^{-19}}$ **J**

Practice Questions

Q1 What is an excited electron?
Q2 Describe what the atomic emission spectrum of hydrogen shows.
Q3 What is the name of the state of an atom in which all the electrons are in orbitals with the lowest possible energies?
Q4 What is the name given to the set of lines produced by excited electrons falling down to a lower energy level?
Q5 Why is it possible to identify an element from its emission spectrum?

Exam Questions

Q1 The diagram below shows part of an atomic absorption spectrum of a single element.
The dark lines in the spectrum are labelled A to E.

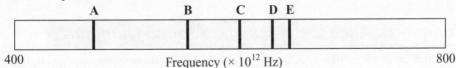

a) What happens in the atom when radiation is absorbed? [2 marks]
b) Which line in the spectrum represents the largest absorption of energy? [1 mark]
c) The same element is used to produce an atomic emission spectrum.
　　(i)　What would be different about this spectrum?
　　(ii)　What would be the same about the lines in the two spectra? [2 marks]
d) Explain why the lines get closer together from A to E. [1 mark]

Q2 The emission spectrum of the element sodium shows a set of lines in the visible part of the spectrum.
There is a strong line at a frequency 5.1×10^{14} Hz, that corresponds to the colour yellow.
What is the energy of the electron transition responsible for this line? (Planck's constant $= 6.626 \times 10^{-34}$ Js) [2 marks]

Revising spectra is like being an actor — you need to know your lines...

All this stuff about frequency and radiation sounds more like physics than chemistry, I know — but there's no avoiding the fact that the way electrons behave is a pretty major part of chemistry. Atomic spectra are pretty hard to get your head round — so go over them again and again until it's crystal clear.

Nuclear Fusion and Radiation

Another two brain-frying pages, just for you OCR B (Unit 1) folks out there...

Nuclear Fusion — Forming **Elements** in Stars

1) **Nuclear fusion** is when two nuclei combine to make one larger nucleus — it happens naturally in **stars** where there's a high temperature.

2) In stars, **hydrogen nuclei** combine to make **helium nuclei**, releasing **huge** amounts of **energy**. This is happening inside our Sun's core.

$$^2_1H + {}^1_1H \rightarrow {}^3_2He + \gamma$$

3) When the hydrogen in a star's core runs out, the **temperature** of the core starts to rise. In a big enough star it'll get **hot** enough to fuse **heavier elements**, starting with helium.

E.g. Beryllium and helium fuse to make carbon (and a gamma ray): $^8Be + {}^4He \rightarrow {}^{12}C + \gamma$

Nuclear Radiation — **Alpha**, **Beta** and **Gamma**

If an atom is **unstable**, it will **break down** to **become** stable. The **instability** could be caused by having **too many neutrons**, **not enough neutrons**, or just **too much energy** in the nucleus. The breaking down is called **radioactive decay**.

Alpha, **beta** or **gamma** radiation can be emitted. Learn the properties of these types of radiation.

	Alpha (α) Particles	Beta (β) Particles	Gamma (γ) Rays
What they are	Helium nuclei ${}^4_2He$	Fast-moving electrons ${}^0_{-1}e$	Very short wave electromagnetic waves
Penetrating power	Stopped by paper	Stopped by thin aluminium sheets	Stopped by very thick lead
Ionising ability	Strong	Moderate	Weak
Deflection in electric field	Slight	Large	Not deflected

Ionising particles **knock outer electrons** off atoms when they hit them — creating **ions**.

1) **Alpha** particles are **strongly positive** — so they can **remove electrons** from atoms. When an alpha particle hits an atom, it **transfers** some of its **energy** to the **atom**. The alpha particle **quickly ionises** lots of atoms and **loses** all its **energy**. That's why it has **low penetrating power**.

2) **Beta** particles have **lower charges** than alpha particles, but **higher speeds**. Beta particles can still **knock electrons** off atoms, but they hit atoms less frequently than alpha particles because they're smaller, so they have **better penetrating power**.

Nuclear Equations — Balance the **Mass** and **Atomic Numbers**

To find out what type of **radiation** or **element** is produced, balance the **top** and **bottom** numbers in the equation.

Example 1: What type of radiation is being lost?

$$^{14}_6C \rightarrow {}^{14}_7N + {}^{\square}_{\square}\square$$
14 – 14 = 0
6 – 7 = –1 → so radiation must be ${}^0_{-1}e$

Example 2: Which element is produced?

$$^{208}_{81}Tl \rightarrow {}^{\square}_{\square}\square + {}^0_{-1}e$$
208 – 0 = 208
81 – (–1) = 82 ← Atomic Number = Pb → ${}^{208}_{82}Pb$

Half-Life — The Time Taken for **Half** the Atoms in a sample to **Decay**

1) Radioactive decay is **random** — this means it's impossible to know when a **single atom** will decay. But like with other random events, if you look at **large numbers** of atoms, then a pattern does become clear.

2) For radioactive atoms, the pattern is best described using the idea of **half-life**. The half-life is the time taken for **half of the atoms** in a sample to decay. It's a **constant value** for any particular isotope.

3) For example, an isotope of radon has a half-life of about 4 days. This means that if you had 20 g of it now, in 4 days' time there will be only 10 g left. After 8 days there would be only 5 g, and after 12 days, 2.5 g, and so on.

Example: You have a sample containing 3 g of carbon-14 (half-life 5700 years).
How much carbon-14 would have been in the sample 22 800 years ago?
22 800 years is 4 half-lives, so there would have been 3 g × 2 × 2 × 2 × 2 = 48 g of carbon-14.

Nuclear Fusion and Radiation

Radioactive Isotopes can be used as Tracers

1) Because it's easy to **detect** radiation given out by **radioactive isotopes**, they're used as **tracers** — chemicals that can be tracked. This can be used to check how well parts of the body (or industrial equipment) are working.

2) Medical tracers can be given to a person, and as they move around the body, their position can be **detected**. For example, radioactive iodine-131 is used to check how well a person's thyroid gland is functioning.

3) Only isotopes with suitable **half-lives** can be used as medical tracers — **not too long** and **not too short**:
   - a very long half-life is **dangerous** — the patient could be exposed to radiation for a long time,
   - a very short half-life is **inconvenient** — the tracers have to be prepared, administered, and then be allowed to make their way around the body, so a tracer with a half-life of a few seconds isn't going to be much good.

   Iodine-131 has a half-life of 8 days.

One radioactive tracer too many.

   And alpha emitters are no good — they'd cause damage by ionising atoms inside the body, and anyway, they wouldn't be detectable outside the body.

Radioactive Isotopes Can be Used to Find Out How Old Stuff Is

1) Radioactive isotopes can be used to **determine** the **age** of **rocks** and **archaeological finds**.

2) **Radiocarbon dating** involves measuring how much of a particular isotope of **carbon** there is in **plant** or **animal** remains (including things made of wood, leather or bone — like arrowheads, axe handles, and so on).

3) The idea behind the technique is this...
   - All **living** things contain the **same percentage** of **carbon-14**:
     - When plants photosynthesise, they absorb carbon (in CO_2) from the atmosphere — including a small percentage of carbon-14.
     - As the carbon-14 atoms decay, they're replaced by more carbon-14 from the atmosphere.
     - Animals eat plants (or other animals that have eaten plants).
     - And the upshot is that all living things are constantly replenishing their levels of carbon-14 to match the atmosphere.
   - But as soon as they **die**, this percentage starts to **decrease** — because the carbon-14 atoms **decay**.
   - So the **less** carbon-14 in a sample of organic material, the **older** it must be.

4) You can then find the approximate **age** of the animal or plant (and therefore the arrowhead, axe handle...) with a calculation like the one on the previous page.

Practice Questions

Q1 Construct a table of the properties of alpha, beta and gamma radiation.

Q2 Why do beta particles have a higher penetrating power than alpha particles?

Q3 A certain isotope of caesium has a half-life of 30 years. Explain how scientists know that if you started with 16 million atoms of this isotope, after 150 years there would be only 0.5 million atoms left.

Q4 Why would this isotope of caesium be unsuitable for use as a medical tracer?

Exam Questions

Q1 A radioactive isotope of the element polonium underwent two stages of radioactive decay. Complete the nuclear equations to identify the type of radiation produced in the first stage of decay and the final element produced.

$$^{216}_{84}\text{Po} \rightarrow\, ^{212}_{82}\text{Pb} + {}^{\square}_{\square}\square \qquad ^{212}_{82}\text{Pb} \rightarrow {}^{\square}_{\square}\square + {}^{0}_{-1}\text{e}$$

[2 marks]

Q2 A radioactive isotope of sodium, ^{24}Na, decays by emitting a beta particle. It has a half-life of 15 hours.

a) Sodium's atomic number is 11. Give the atomic number, name and mass number of the isotope that is produced when ^{24}Na decays by beta emission. [3 marks]

b) A sample of this isotope has a decay rate of 800 counts per minute. A detector can only pick up radiation levels above 50 counts per minute. For how long will this isotope's radiation be detectable? [2 marks]

Q3 Explain why isotopes which produce gamma radiation are used in medicine and not those that produce alpha particles. [2 marks]

Radioactive tracers are like Ready Brek — you'll have a warm glow all day...

It's good to have some stuff about how useful chemistry is in real life up your sleeve for the exam — so learn those two examples of how radioactive isotopes can be used. And make sure you have the properties of alpha, beta and gamma radiation nailed down firmly in your memory. It'll be fun...I promise...and I also promise you'll win the lottery.

Ionisation Energies

This page gets a trifle brain-boggling, so I hope you've got a few aspirin handy...
These pages are for AQA (Unit 1), OCR A (Unit 1), OCR B (Unit 2) and Edexcel (Unit 1).

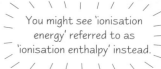

You might see 'ionisation energy' referred to as 'ionisation enthalpy' instead.

Ionisation *is the* Removal *of One or More* Electrons

When electrons have been removed from an atom or molecule, it's been **ionised**.
The energy you need to remove the first electron is called the **first ionisation energy**:

> The **first ionisation energy** is the energy needed to remove 1 electron from **each atom** in **1 mole** of **gaseous** atoms to form 1 mole of gaseous 1+ ions.

You have to put energy **in** to ionise an atom or molecule, so it's an **endothermic process** — there's more about endothermic processes on page 88.

You can write **equations** for this process — here's the equation for the **first ionisation of oxygen**:

$$O_{(g)} \rightarrow O^+_{(g)} + e^-$$ 1st ionisation energy = +1314 kJ mol^{-1}

Here are a few rather important points about ionisation energies:

1) You **must** use the gas state symbol, **(g)**, because ionisation energies are measured for gaseous atoms.
2) Always refer to **1 mole** of atoms, as stated in the definition, rather than to a single atom.
3) The **lower** the ionisation energy, the **easier** it is to form an ion.

The Factors *Affecting Ionisation Energy are...*

The **more protons** there are in the nucleus, the more positively charged the nucleus is and the **stronger the attraction** for the electrons.

Attraction falls off very **rapidly with distance**. An electron **close** to the nucleus will be **much more** strongly attracted than one further away.

Shielding

As the number of electrons **between** the outer electrons and the nucleus **increases**, the outer electrons feel less attraction towards the nuclear charge. This lessening of the pull of the nucleus by inner shells of electrons is called **shielding (or screening)**.

> A **high ionisation energy** means there's a **high attraction** between the **electron** and the **nucleus**.

There are Trends *in* First Ionisation Energies

1) The first ionisation energies of elements **down a group** of the Periodic Table **decrease**. Check out page 62 for why.
2) The first ionisation energies of elements **across a period generally increase**. But I do say **generally** — there's a bit more to it than that. Page 57 explains it in wondrous detail.

Successive Ionisation Energies *Involve Removing* Additional *Electrons*   *Not AQA*

1) You can remove **all** the electrons from an atom, leaving only the nucleus.
Each time you remove an electron, there's a **successive ionisation energy**.
2) The definition for the **second ionisation energy** is —

> The **second ionisation energy** is the energy needed to remove 1 electron from **each ion** in **1 mole** of **gaseous** 1+ ions to form 1 mole of gaseous 2+ ions.

And here's the equation for the **second ionisation of oxygen** :

$$O^+_{(g)} \rightarrow O^{2+}_{(g)} + e^-$$ 2nd ionisation energy = +3388 kJ mol^{-1}

Ionisation Energies

Successive Ionisation Energies Show **Shell Structure**   OCR A *and* Edexcel *only*

A **graph** of successive ionisation energies (like this one for sodium) provides evidence for the **shell structure** of atoms.

1) **Within each shell**, successive ionisation energies **increase**. This is because electrons are being removed from an **increasingly positive ion** — there's **less repulsion** amongst the remaining electrons, so they're **held more strongly** by the nucleus.

2) The **big jumps** in ionisation energy happen when a new shell is broken into — an electron is being removed from a shell **closer** to the nucleus.

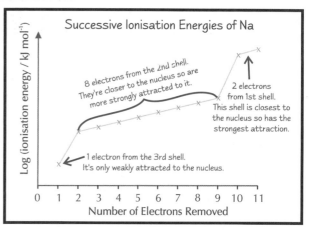

Successive Ionisation Energies of Na

8 electrons from the 2nd shell. They're closer to the nucleus so are more strongly attracted to it.

2 electrons from 1st shell. This shell is closest to the nucleus so has the strongest attraction.

1 electron from the 3rd shell. It's only weakly attracted to the nucleus.

Log (ionisation energy / kJ mol^{-1})

Number of Electrons Removed

1) Graphs like this can tell you which **group** of the periodic table an element belongs to. Just count **how many electrons are removed** before the first big jump to find the group number.

> E.g. In the graph for sodium, **one electron** is removed before the first big jump — sodium is in **group 1**.

2) These graphs can be used to predict the **electronic structure** of an element. Working from **right to left**, count how many points there are before each big jump to find how many electrons are in each shell, starting with the first.

> E.g. The graph for sodium has **2 points** on the right-hand side, then a jump, then **8 points**, a jump, and **1 final point**. Sodium has **2 electrons** in the first shell, **8** in the second and **1** in the third.

Practice Questions

Q1 Define first ionisation energy and give an equation as an example.
Q2 Describe the three main factors that affect ionisation energies.
Q3 When an atom is ionised, does it release or absorb energy?
Q4 How is ionisation energy related to the force of attraction between an electron and the nucleus of an atom?

Exam Questions

Q1 This table shows the nuclear charge and first ionisation energy for four elements.

Element	B	C	N	O
Charge of Nucleus	+5	+6	+7	+8
1st Ionisation Energy (kJ mol^{-1})	801	1087	1402	1314

a) Write an equation, including state symbols, to represent the first ionisation energy of carbon (C). [2 marks]
b) In these four elements, what is the relationship between nuclear charge and first ionisation energy? [1 mark]
c) Explain why nuclear charge has this effect on first ionisation energy. [2 marks]

Q2 This graph shows the successive ionisation energies of a certain element.
a) To which group of the periodic table does this element belong? [1 mark]
b) Give two reasons why it takes more energy to remove each successive electron. [2 marks]
c) What causes the sudden increases in ionisation energy? [1 mark]
d) What is the total number of shells of electrons in this element? [1 mark]

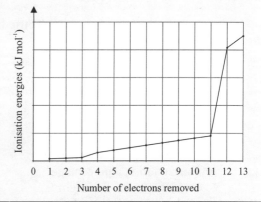

Ionisation energies (kJ mol^{-1})

Number of electrons removed

Shirt crumpled — ionise it...

When you're talking about ionisation energies in exams, always use the three main factors — shielding, nuclear charge and distance from nucleus. Recite the definition of the first and second ionisation energies to yourself until the men in white coats get to you. Then stop. I bet you can't wait until you get to that other stuff on ionisation energy I told you about.

Relative Mass

Relative mass...What? Eh?...Read on...
These pages are for AQA (Unit 1), OCR A (Units 1 and 2), OCR B (Unit 1) **and** Edexcel (Unit 1).

Relative Masses are Masses of Atoms Compared to Carbon-12

The actual mass of an atom is **very**, **very tiny**. Don't worry about exactly how tiny for now, but it's far **too small** to weigh. So, the mass of one atom is compared to the mass of a different atom. This is its **relative mass**. Here are some definitions for you to learn.

Relative atomic mass is an average, so it's not usually a whole number. Relative isotopic mass is always a whole number (at AS level anyway). E.g. a natural sample of chlorine contains a mixture of ^{35}Cl (75%) and ^{37}Cl (25%), so the relative isotopic masses are 35 and 37. But its relative atomic mass is 35.5.

The **relative atomic mass**, A_r, is the **average mass** of an atom of an element on a scale where an atom of **carbon-12** is 12.

Relative isotopic mass is the mass of an atom of an **isotope** of an element on a scale where an atom of **carbon-12** is 12.

The **relative molecular mass** (or **relative formula mass**), M_r, is the average mass of a **molecule** or **formula unit** on a scale where an atom of **carbon-12** is 12.

To find the relative molecular mass, just add up the relative atomic mass values of all the atoms in the molecule,
e.g. $M_r(C_2H_6O) = (2 \times 12) + (6 \times 1) + 16 = 46$.

Relative formula mass is used for compounds that are ionic (or giant covalent, such as SiO_2). To find the relative formula mass, just add up the relative atomic masses (A_r) of all the ions in the formula unit. (A_r of ion = A_r of atom. The electrons make no difference to the mass.) E.g. $M_r(CaF_2) = 40 + (2 \times 19) = 78$.

Relative Masses can be Measured Using a Mass Spectrometer

Not OCR A (Unit 1)

You can use a **mass spectrometer** to find out loads of stuff. It can tell you the **relative atomic mass**, **relative molecular mass**, **relative isotopic abundance**, **molecular structure** and your **horoscope** for the next fortnight.

There are **5** things that happen when a sample is squirted into a mass spectrometer.

① **Vaporisation** — the sample is turned into **gas** (**vaporised**) using an electrical heater.

② **Ionisation** — the gas particles are bombarded with **high-energy electrons** to ionise them. Electrons are knocked off the particles, leaving **positive ions**.

③ **Acceleration** — the positive ions are accelerated by an **electric field**.

④ **Deflection** — The positive ions' paths are altered with a **magnetic field**. **Lighter ions** have less momentum and are deflected **more** than heavier ions. For a given magnetic field, **only ions** with a particular **mass/charge ratio** make it to the detector.

⑤ **Detection** — the magnetic field strength is **slowly increased**. As this happens, different ions (ones with a lower mass/charge ratio) can reach the detector. A **mass spectrum** is produced.

OCR B: A time-of-flight mass spectrometer works a bit differently. The positive ions are accelerated, but then they're not deflected. Instead, the time taken for them to reach the detector is measured. This depends on an ion's mass and charge — light, highly charged ions reach the detector first, while heavier ions with a smaller charge take longer.

A Mass Spectrum

The **y-axis** gives the **abundance of ions**, often as a percentage. For an element, the **height** of each peak gives the **relative isotopic abundance**, e.g. 75.5% are the ^{35}Cl isotope.

If the sample is an **element**, each line will represent a **different isotope** of the element.

The **x-axis** units are given as a 'mass/charge' ratio. Since the charge on the ions is mostly **+1**, you can often assume the x-axis is simply the **relative mass**.

Relative Mass

A_r and Relative Isotopic Abundance can be Worked Out from a Mass Spectrum

You need to know how to calculate the **relative atomic mass** (A_r) of an element from the **mass spectrum**.   **Not OCR A (Unit 1)**

Here's how to calculate A_r for magnesium, using the mass spectrum below —

Step 1: For each peak, read the **% relative isotopic abundance** from the y-axis and the **relative isotopic mass** from the x-axis. **Multiply** them together to get the total mass for each isotope. $79 \times 24 = 1896$; $10 \times 25 = 250$; $11 \times 26 = 286$

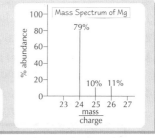

Step 2: **Add** up these totals. $1896 + 250 + 286 = 2432$

Step 3: **Divide by 100** (since percentages were used). $A_r(Mg) = \dfrac{2432}{100} = 24.32 \approx \underline{\mathbf{24.3}}$

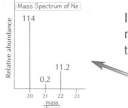

If the relative abundance is **not** given as a percentage, the total abundance may not add up to 100. In this case, don't panic. Just do steps 1 and 2 as above, but then divide by the **total relative abundance** instead of 100 — like this:

$$A_r(Ne) = \frac{(114 \times 20) + (0.2 \times 21) + (11.2 \times 22)}{114 + 0.2 + 11.2} \approx 20.18$$

Mass spectrometry is a good way to identify elements and molecules (it's kind of like fingerprinting). For instance, small mass spectrometers have been used in probes to find out what the Martian atmosphere is made of. See page 155 for more uses.

Mass Spectrometry can be used to Find Out M_r *Not OCR A (Unit 1)*

You can also get a mass spectrum for a **molecular sample**, such as ethanol (CH_3CH_2OH).

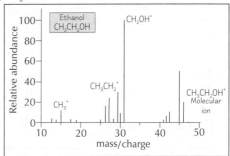

1) A **molecular ion**, $M^+_{(g)}$, is formed when the bombarding electrons remove 1 electron from the molecule. This gives the peak in the spectrum with the **highest mass** (furthest to the right, ignoring isotopes). The mass of M^+ gives $\mathbf{M_r}$ for the molecule, e.g. $CH_3CH_2OH^+$ has $M_r = 46$.

2) But it's not that simple — bombarding with electrons makes some molecules break up into fragments. These all show up on the mass spectrum, making a **fragmentation pattern**. For ethanol, the fragments you get include: CH_3^+ ($M_r = 15$), $CH_3CH_2^+$ ($M_r = 29$) and CH_2OH^+ ($M_r = 31$). Fragmentation patterns are actually pretty cool because you can use them to identify **molecules** and even their **structure**.

Practice Questions

Q1 Explain what relative atomic mass (A_r) and relative isotopic mass mean.

Q2 Explain the difference between relative molecular mass and relative formula mass.

Q3 Describe how a mass spectrometer works.

Exam Questions

Q1 Copper, Cu, exists in two main isotopic forms, ^{63}Cu and ^{65}Cu.
   a) Calculate the relative atomic mass of Cu using the information from the mass spectrum.   [2 marks]
   b) Explain why the relative atomic mass of copper is not a whole number.   [2 marks]

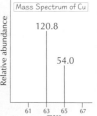

Q2 The percentage make-up of naturally occurring potassium is 93.11% ^{39}K, 0.12% ^{40}K and 6.77% ^{41}K.
   a) What method is used to determine the mass and abundance of each isotope?   [1 mark]
   b) Use the information to determine the relative atomic mass of potassium.   [2 marks]

You can't pick your relatives — you just have to learn them...

Working out M_r is dead easy — and using a calculator makes it even easier. It'll really help if you know the mass numbers for the first 20 elements or so, or you'll spend half your time looking back at the periodic table. I hope you've done the practice and exam questions, cos they pretty much cover the rest of the stuff, and if you can get them right, you've nailed it.

The Mole

It'd be handy to be able to count out atoms — but they're way too tiny. You can't even see them, never mind get hold of them with tweezers. But not to worry — using the idea of relative mass, you can figure out how many atoms you've got.
These pages are for AQA (Unit 1), OCR A (Unit 1), OCR B (Units 1 and 2) and Edexcel (Unit 1).

A *Mole* is Just a (Very Large) *Number of Particles*

1) Amount of substance is measured using a unit called the **mole** (**mol** for short) and given the symbol **n**.

2) One mole is roughly **6×10^{23} particles** (**Avogadro's number, L**).

3) It **doesn't matter** what the particles are.
   They can be atoms, molecules, penguins — **anything**.

4) Here's a nice simple formula for finding the number of moles from the number of atoms or molecules:

$$\text{Number of moles} = \frac{\text{Number of particles you have}}{\text{Number of particles in a mole}}$$

Example:
I have 1.5×10^{24} carbon atoms.
How many moles of carbon is this?

$$\text{Number of moles} = \frac{1.5 \times 10^{24}}{6 \times 10^{23}} = \textbf{2.5 moles}$$

Molar Mass is the Mass of *One Mole*

Molar mass, M, is the mass of **one mole** of something.

But the main thing to remember is:

Molar mass is just the same as the relative molecular mass, M_r
(or relative formula mass)

That's why the mole is such a ridiculous number of particles (6×10^{23}) — it's the number of particles for which the weight in g is the same as the relative molecular mass.

The only difference is you stick a 'g mol⁻¹' for grams per mole on the end...

Example: Find the molar mass of $CaCO_3$.

Relative formula mass, M_r, of $CaCO_3 = 40 + 12 + (3 \times 16) = 100$
So the molar mass, M, is **100 g mol⁻¹** — i.e. 1 mole of $CaCO_3$ weighs 100 g.

Here's another formula. This one's really important — you need it **all the time**:

$$\text{Number of moles} = \frac{\text{mass of substance}}{\text{molar mass}}$$

Example: How many moles of aluminium oxide are present in 5.1 g of Al_2O_3?

Molar mass of Al_2O_3 $= (2 \times 27) + (3 \times 16)$
$= 102 \text{ g mol}^{-1}$

Number of moles of Al_2O_3 $= \frac{5.1}{102} = \textbf{0.05 moles}$

In a Solution the *Concentration* is Measured in *mol dm⁻³*

Not OCR B (Unit 1)

1) The **concentration** of a solution is how many **moles** are dissolved per **1 dm³** of solution. The units are **mol dm⁻³** (or M).

$1 dm^3 = 1000 cm^3 = 1$ litre

2) Here's the formula to find the **number of moles**.

$$\text{Number of moles} = \frac{\text{Concentration} \times \text{Volume (in cm}^3)}{1000}$$

or just $\quad$ **Number of moles = Concentration × Volume (in dm³)**

Example: What mass of sodium hydroxide needs to be dissolved in 50 cm³ of water to make a 2 M solution?

$$\text{Number of moles} = \frac{2 \times 50}{1000} = 0.1 \text{ moles of NaOH}$$

Molar mass, M, of NaOH $= 23 + 16 + 1 = 40 \text{ g mol}^{-1}$

Mass = number of moles × M = 0.1 × 40 = **4 g**

3) A solution that has **more moles per dm³** than another is **more concentrated**.
   A solution that has **fewer moles per dm³** than another is **more dilute**.

4) For really low concentrations, you end up with **tiny** mol dm⁻³ values.
   They're a bit fiddly, so you're better off using a different unit, such as **parts per million (ppm)** — see page 142.

The Mole

Not OCR B (Unit 1)

All Gases Take Up the **Same Volume** under the Same Conditions

If temperature and pressure stay the same, **one mole** of **any** gas always has the **same volume**.
At **room temperature and pressure** (r.t.p.), this happens to be **24 dm³**, (r.t.p is 298 K (25 °C) and 101.3 kPa).
Here are two formulas for working out the number of moles in a volume of gas. Don't forget — **ONLY** use them for r.t.p.

$$\text{Number of moles} = \frac{\text{Volume in dm}^3}{24} \qquad \text{OR} \qquad \text{Number of moles} = \frac{\text{Volume in cm}^3}{24\ 000}$$

Example: How many moles are there in 6 dm³ of oxygen gas at r.t.p.?

$$\text{Number of moles} = \frac{6}{24} = \textbf{0.25 moles of oxygen molecules}$$

Ideal Gas equation — $pV = nRT$ *AQA only*

In the real world (and AQA exam questions), it's not always room temperature and pressure.
The **ideal gas equation** lets you find the **number of moles** in a certain volume at **any temperature and pressure**.

$$pV = nRT$$

Where: p = pressure (Pa)
V = volume (m³)

$1\ cm^3 = 1 \times 10^{-6}\ m^3$
$1\ dm^3 = 1 \times 10^{-3}\ m^3$

n = number of moles

The gas constant. Don't worry about what it means. Just learn it. ⟶ $R = 8.31\ \text{J K}^{-1}\text{mol}^{-1}$

T = temperature (K) $K = °C + 273$

Example:
At a temperature of 60 °C and a pressure of 250 kPa, a gas occupied a volume of 1100 cm³ and had a mass of 1.6 g.
Find its relative molecular mass.

$$n = \frac{pV}{RT} = \left(\frac{(250 \times 10^3) \times (1.1 \times 10^{-3})}{8.31 \times 333} \right) = 0.1 \text{ moles}$$

$1100\ cm^3 = 1.1 \times 10^{-3}\ m^3$

If 0.1 moles is 1.6 g, then 1 mole = $\dfrac{1.6}{0.1} = 16$ g. So the relative molecular mass (M_r) is **16**.

Practice Questions

Q1 How many molecules are there in one mole of ethane molecules?

Q2 What volume does 1 mole of gas occupy at r.t.p.?

Q3 Which has the most particles, a solution of concentration 0.1 mol dm⁻³ or an equal volume of one that is 0.1 M?

Exam Questions

Q1 Calculate the mass of 0.36 moles of ethanoic acid, CH_3COOH.   [2 marks]

Q2 What mass of H_2SO_4 is needed to produce 60 cm³ of 0.25 M solution?   [2 marks]

Q3 What volume will be occupied by 88 g of propane gas (C_3H_8) at r.t.p.?   [2 marks]

Put your back teeth on the scale and find out your molar mass...

You need this stuff for loads of the calculation questions you might get, so make sure you know it inside out. Before you start plugging numbers into formulas, make sure they're in the right units. If they're not, you need to know how to convert them or you'll be tossing marks out the window. Learn all the definitions and formulas, then have a bash at the questions.

Empirical and Molecular Formulas

Here's another page piled high with numbers — it's all just glorified maths really.

These pages are for AQA (Unit 1), OCR A (Unit 1), OCR B (Unit 1) and Edexcel (Unit 1).

Empirical and *Molecular* Formulas are **Ratios**

You have to know what's what with empirical and molecular formulas, so here goes...

1) The **empirical formula** gives just the smallest whole number ratio of atoms in a compound.

2) The **molecular formula** gives the **actual** numbers of atoms in a molecule.

3) The molecular formula is made up of a whole **number** of empirical units.

> **Example:** A molecule has an empirical formula of $C_4H_3O_2$, and a relative molecular mass of 166.
> Work out its molecular formula.
>
> First find the **empirical mass** — $(4 \times 12) + (3 \times 1) + (2 \times 16)$
> $$= 48 + 3 + 32 = 83 \text{ g}$$
>
> *Empirical mass is just like the relative formula mass... (if that helps at all...).*
>
> *Compare the empirical and relative molecular mass.*
>
> But the **relative molecular mass** is 166,
>
> so there are $\dfrac{166}{83} = 2$ empirical units in the molecule.
>
> The molecular formula must be the **empirical formula × 2**,
> so the molecular formula = $C_8H_6O_4$. So there you go.

Empirical Formulas are Calculated from **Experiments**

You need to be able to work out empirical formulas from **experimental results** too.

> **Example:** When a hydrocarbon is burnt in excess oxygen, 4.4 g of carbon dioxide and 1.8 g of water are made.
> What is the empirical formula of the hydrocarbon?
>
> *First work out how many moles of the products you have.*
>
> No. of moles of $CO_2 = \dfrac{\text{mass}}{M} = \dfrac{4.4}{12 + (16 \times 2)} = \dfrac{4.4}{44} = 0.1$ moles
>
> 1 mole of CO_2 contains 1 mole of carbon atoms, so you must have started with **0.1 moles of carbon atoms**.
>
> No. of moles of $H_2O = \dfrac{1.8}{(2 \times 1) + 16} = \dfrac{1.8}{18} = 0.1$ moles
>
> 1 mole of H_2O contains 2 moles of hydrogen atoms (H), so you must have started with **0.2 moles of hydrogen atoms**.
>
> Ratio C : H = 0.1 : 0.2 . Now you divide both numbers by the smallest — here it's 0.1.
> So, the ratio C : H = 1 : 2. So the empirical formula must be CH_2.
>
> *This works because the only place the carbon in the carbon dioxide and the hydrogen in the water could have come from is the hydrocarbon.*

As if that's not enough, you also need to know how to work out
empirical formulas from the **percentages** of the different elements.

> **Example:** A compound is found to have percentage composition 56.5% potassium,
> 8.7% carbon and 34.8% oxygen by mass. Calculate its empirical formula.
>
> *If you assume you've got 100 g of the compound, you can turn the % straight into mass, and then work out the number of moles as normal.*
>
> In **100 g** of compound there are:
>
> *Use $n = \dfrac{\text{mass}}{M}$*
>
> $\dfrac{56.5}{39} = 1.449$ moles of K $\dfrac{8.7}{12} = 0.725$ moles of C $\dfrac{34.8}{16} = 2.175$ moles of O
>
> Divide each number of moles by the **smallest number** — in this case it's 0.725.
>
> K: $\dfrac{1.449}{0.725} = 2.0$ C: $\dfrac{0.725}{0.725} = 1.0$ O: $\dfrac{2.175}{0.725} = 3.0$
>
> The ratio of K : C : O = 2 : 1 : 3. So you know the empirical formula's got to be K_2CO_3.

Empirical and Molecular Formulas

Molecular Formulas are Calculated from Experimental Data Too

Once you know the empirical formula, you just need a bit more info and you can work out the **molecular formula** too.

Example:

When 4.6 g of an alcohol, with relative molecular mass 46, is burnt in excess oxygen, it produces 8.8 g of carbon dioxide and 5.4 g of water.

Alcohols contain C, H and O.

Calculate the empirical formula for the alcohol and then its molecular formula.

The carbon in the CO_2 and the hydrogen in the H_2O must have come from the alcohol — work out the number of moles of each of these.

No. of moles of $CO_2 = \dfrac{\text{mass}}{M} = \dfrac{8.8}{44} = 0.2$ moles

1 mole of CO_2 contains 1 mole of C. So, 0.2 moles of CO_2 contains **0.2 moles of C.**

No. of moles $H_2O = \dfrac{\text{mass}}{M} = \dfrac{5.4}{18} = 0.3$ moles

1 mole of H_2O contains 2 moles of H. So, 0.3 moles of H_2O contain **0.6 moles of H.**

Mass of C = no. of moles × M = 0.2 × 12 = 2.4 g
Mass of H = no. of moles × M = 0.6 × 1 = 0.6 g
Mass of O = 4.6 − (2.4 + 0.6) = 1.6 g

Number of moles O $= \dfrac{\text{mass}}{M} = \dfrac{1.6}{16} = 0.1$ moles

Now work out the mass of carbon and hydrogen in the alcohol. The rest of the mass of the alcohol must be oxygen — so work out that too. Once you know the mass of O, you can work out how many moles there is of it.

Molar Ratio = C : H : O = 0.2 : 0.6 : 0.1 = 2 : 6 : 1

Empirical formula = C_2H_6O

When you know the number of moles of each element, you've got the molar ratio. Divide each number by the smallest.

Mass of empirical formula = (12 × 2) + (1 × 6) + 16 = 46 g

Compare the empirical and molecular mass.

In this example, the mass of the empirical formula equals the relative molecular mass, so the empirical and molecular formulas are the same.

Molecular formula = C_2H_6O

Practice Questions

Q1 Define 'empirical formula'.

Q2 What is the difference between a molecular formula and an empirical formula?

Exam Questions

Q1 Hydrocarbon X has a relative molecular mass of 78. It is found to have 92.3% carbon and 7.7% hydrogen by mass. Calculate the empirical and molecular formulae of X.   [3 marks]

Q2 When 1.2 g of magnesium ribbon is heated in air, it burns to form a white powder, which has a mass of 2 g. What is the empirical formula of the powder?   [2 marks]

Q3 When 19.8 g of an organic acid, A, is burnt in excess oxygen, 33 g of carbon dioxide and 10.8 g of water are produced.
Calculate the empirical formula for A and hence its molecular formula, if $M_r(A) = 132$.   [4 marks]

Hint: organic acids contain C, H and O.

The Empirical Strikes Back...

With this stuff, it's not enough to learn a few facts parrot-fashion, to regurgitate in the exam — you've gotta know how to use them. The only way to do that is to practise. Go through all the examples on these two pages again, this time working the answers out for yourself. Then test yourself on the practice exam questions. It'll help you sleep at night — honest.

Equations and Calculations

Balancing equations'll cause you a few palpitations — as soon as you make one bit right, the rest goes pear-shaped.
These pages are for AQA (Unit 1), OCR A (Unit 1), OCR B (Unit 1) and Edexcel (Unit 1).

Balanced Equations have Equal Numbers of each Atom on Both Sides

1) Balanced equations have the **same number** of each atom on **both** sides. They're..well...you know...balanced.

2) You can only add more atoms by adding **whole compounds**. You do this by putting a number **in front** of a compound or changing one that's already there. You **can't** mess with formulas — ever.

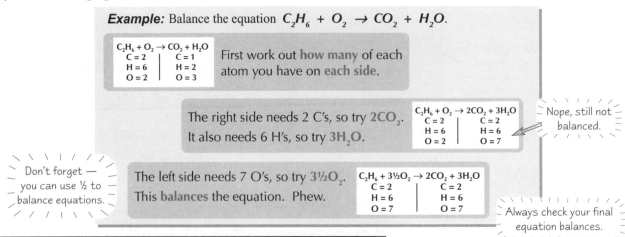

Example: Balance the equation $C_2H_6 + O_2 \rightarrow CO_2 + H_2O$.

$C_2H_6 + O_2 \rightarrow CO_2 + H_2O$

C = 2	C = 1
H = 6	H = 2
O = 2	O = 3

First work out **how many** of each atom you have on **each side**.

The right side needs 2 C's, so try **2CO$_2$**.
It also needs 6 H's, so try **3H$_2$O**.

$C_2H_6 + O_2 \rightarrow 2CO_2 + 3H_2O$

C = 2	C = 2
H = 6	H = 6
O = 2	O = 7

Nope, still not balanced.

Don't forget — you can use ½ to balance equations.

The left side needs 7 O's, so try **3½O$_2$**. This **balances** the equation. Phew.

$C_2H_6 + 3½O_2 \rightarrow 2CO_2 + 3H_2O$

C = 2	C = 2
H = 6	H = 6
O = 7	O = 7

Always check your final equation balances.

In Ionic Equations the Charges must Balance too

In ionic equations, only the **reacting particles** are included. You don't have to worry about the rest of the stuff.

Example: Balance the ionic equation $Cr_2O_7^{2-} + H^+ + e^- \rightarrow Cr^{3+} + H_2O$.

$Cr_2O_7^{2-} + e^- \rightarrow Cr^{3+} + H_2O$

Cr = 2	Cr = 1
O = 7	O = 1
H = 1	H = 2

Again, first work out **how many** of each atom you have on **each side**.

The right side needs 2 Cr's, so try **2Cr^{3+}**.
It also needs 7 O's, so try **7H$_2$O**.

$Cr_2O_7^{2-} + H^+ + e^- \rightarrow 2Cr^{3+} + 7H_2O$

Cr = 2	Cr = 2
O = 7	O = 7
H = 1	H = 14

It's not balanced yet.

The left side needs 14 H's, so try **14H$^+$**.
Now the **charges** just need balancing.

$Cr_2O_7^{2-} + 14H^+ + e^- \rightarrow 2Cr^{3+} + 7H_2O$

Cr = 2	Cr = 2
O = 7	O = 7
H = 14	H = 14

Charges on left side	Charges on right side
$(2-) + (14 \times 1+) + (1-) = 11+$	$(2 \times 3+) = 6+$

The left side needs five **additional** electrons.
So the balanced ionic equation is:
$$Cr_2O_7^{2-} + 14H^+ + 6e^- \rightarrow 2Cr^{3+} + 7H_2O$$

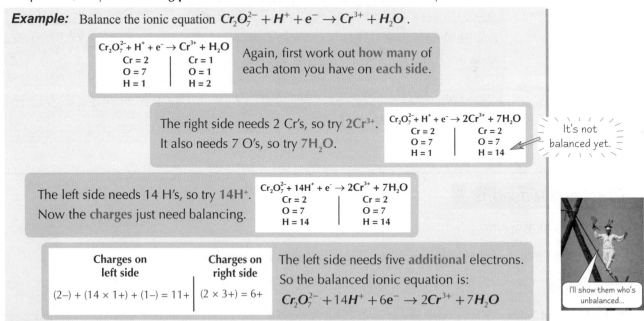

I'll show them who's unbalanced...

Balanced Equations can be used to Work out Masses

Example: Calculate the mass of iron oxide produced if 28 g of iron is burnt in air.
$$2Fe + \tfrac{3}{2}O_2 \rightarrow Fe_2O_3$$

The molar mass, M, of Fe = 56 g, so the number of moles in 28 g of Fe = $\dfrac{\text{mass}}{M} = \dfrac{28}{56} = 0.5$ moles

From the equation: 2 moles of Fe produces 1 mole of Fe$_2$O$_3$, so 0.5 moles of Fe produces 0.25 moles of Fe$_2$O$_3$.

Once you know the number of moles and the molar mass (M) of Fe$_2$O$_3$, it's easy to work out the mass.

M of Fe$_2$O$_3$ = $(2 \times 56) + (3 \times 16) = 160$ g mol^{-1}

Mass of Fe$_2$O$_3$ = no. of moles × M = $0.25 \times 160 = $ **40 g**. And that's your answer.

Equations and Calculations

That's not all... Balanced Equations can be used to Work Out Gas Volumes

It's pretty handy to be able to work out **how much gas** a reaction will produce, so that you can use **large enough apparatus**. Or else there might be a rather large bang.

> **Example:** How much gas is produced when 15 g of sodium is reacted with excess water at r.t.p.?
>
> $$2Na_{(s)} + 2H_2O_{(l)} \rightarrow 2NaOH_{(aq)} + H_{2(g)}$$
>
> M of Na = 23 g mol^{-1}, so number of moles in 15 g of Na = $\frac{15}{23}$ = 0.65 moles
>
> From the equation, 2 moles Na produces 1 mole H$_2$,
>
> so you know 0.65 moles Na produces $\frac{0.65}{2}$ = 0.326 moles H$_2$.
>
> So the volume of H$_2$ = 0.325 × 24 = **7.8 dm^3**

'Excess water' means you know all the sodium will react.

The reaction happens at room temperature and pressure, so you know 1 mole takes up 24 dm^3.

State Symbols Give a bit More Information about the Substances

State symbols are put after each compound in an equation. They tell you what **state of matter** things are in.

s = solid
l = liquid
g = gas
aq = aqueous
(solution in water)

To show you what I mean, here's an example —

$$CaCO_{3\,(s)} + 2HCl_{(aq)} \rightarrow CaCl_{2\,(aq)} + H_2O_{(l)} + CO_{2\,(g)}$$

solid   solution   solution   liquid   gas

Practice Questions

Q1 What is the state symbol for a solution of hydrochloric acid?

Q2 What is the difference between a full, balanced equation and an ionic equation?

Exam Questions

Q1 Calculate the mass of ethene required to produce 258 g of chloroethane, C$_2$H$_5$Cl.

$$C_2H_4 + HCl \rightarrow C_2H_5Cl$$

[4 marks]

Q2 15 g of calcium carbonate is heated strongly so that it fully decomposes. $CaCO_{3(s)} \rightarrow CaO_{(s)} + CO_{2(g)}$

a) Calculate the mass of calcium oxide produced. [3 marks]

b) Calculate the volume of gas produced. [3 marks]

Q3 Balance this equation: $KI + Pb(NO_3)_2 \rightarrow PbI_2 + 2KNO_3$ [1 mark]

Don't get in a state about equations...

You're probably completely fed up with all these equations, calculations, moles and whatnot...well hang in there — there's just one more double page coming up. I've said it once, and I'll say it again — practise, practise, practise... it's the only road to salvation (by the way, where is salvation anyway?). Keep going... you're nearly there.

Confirming Equations

To confirm that an equation you've written is correct, you could actually <u>do</u> the reaction — then find out how much of each reactant and product you have and check that it all adds up... always being aware of likely <u>errors</u>.

These pages are for AQA (Unit 1), OCR A (Unit 1), OCR B (Unit 1) and Edexcel (Unit 1).

A Balanced Equation Can Be *Confirmed* by *Experimental Data*

1) A balanced equation tells you **how many moles** of **products** you should expect from given amounts of **reactants**.

2) You can check whether the equation is correct with an **experiment** to **measure** the amount of each product you get. For example, here's a balanced equation for **lithium** reacting with **water**:

$$2Li_{(s)} + 2H_2O_{(l)} \rightarrow 2LiOH_{(aq)} + H_{2(g)}$$

So you'd expect <u>2 moles of lithium</u> to produce <u>2 moles</u> of lithium hydroxide and <u>1 mole</u> of hydrogen.

3) To confirm this equation, you react a **known mass of lithium** with water, and measure **how much lithium hydroxide** and **hydrogen** is actually produced.

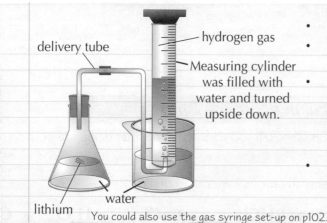

delivery tube
hydrogen gas
Measuring cylinder was filled with water and turned upside down.
lithium
water

You could also use the gas syringe set-up on p102.

- Weigh out some lithium and drop it into the conical flask.
- Fit the bung and delivery tube into the top of the flask immediately to collect the hydrogen gas as it's produced.
- The **hydrogen** displaces water from the measuring cylinder, so you can read off its volume pretty easily when the reaction has stopped (when the water level stops moving). You're going to use the volume to find the number of moles, so you have to do this at r.t.p. (see page 19).
- The **lithium hydroxide** is produced as a solution in the conical flask. It's an alkali, so to find out how much you've got, you can **titrate it** with an acid (see page 30).

The Experimental Data Is Used to *Calculate* the *Number of Moles*

1) To confirm the equation, you need to know how many **moles** of reactants and products there were. It's just a matter of using the right formulas. (See page 18-19 for more on these kinds of calculations.)

To find the number of moles of **lithium**, it's this: ⟹

$$\text{Number of moles} = \frac{\text{mass of substance}}{\text{molar mass}}$$

And to find the number of moles of **hydrogen gas** (at r.t.p.), you need this one.

$$\text{Number of moles} = \frac{\text{Volume in dm}^3}{24} \quad \text{OR} \quad \text{Number of moles} = \frac{\text{Volume in cm}^3}{24\,000}$$

...And you can find the number of moles of **lithium hydroxide** from the result of a **titration** (see page 30-31 for the calculations).

2) For example, if **0.14 g of lithium** reacted to produce **222 cm³** of hydrogen, the number of moles are calculated like this:

> Number of moles of lithium = 0.14 g ÷ 7 = **0.020 moles**
>
> Number of moles of hydrogen = 222 cm³ ÷ 24 000 = **0.00925 moles**
>
> This gives you a **moles of lithium : moles of hydrogen** ratio of **2 : 0.925**.

3) From the balanced equation for the reaction, you'd expect that ratio to be **2 : 1**. But it's hugely unlikely you'll actually get this **exact answer** from an experiment, however carefully you do it. (See the next page for some possible sources of error.) So an experimental result of 2 : 0.925 is **close enough** to say that the ratio's correct.

4) You can then do a **titration** to find out the number of moles of **lithium hydroxide** produced. Then you can work out the ratio **moles of Li : moles of LiOH**. From the equation, it should be **1 : 1**. And if that turns out to be correct too, you can be pretty sure the reaction happened as expected.

Confirming Equations

The **Accuracy** of Experimental Data is **Always Limited** by the **Methods** Used...

There are several problems with this method that can cause the result to be inaccurate.

1) Lithium has to be stored under **oil**, and it's difficult to **completely remove** the oil — so when you weigh out the lithium, the mass measured may include some oil.

2) When lithium is exposed to the **air** (after you've removed as much oil as possible), it **reacts with oxygen**, forming a surface layer of lithium oxide. So some of the 'mass of lithium' will actually be lithium oxide.

3) Some **hydrogen** will **escape** in the time between dropping the lithium into the flask and fitting the bung and delivery tube — so the volume of hydrogen recorded will be slightly lower than it should be.

These are **systematic errors** (see page 32), and they're due to the method that's used. They can be **minimised** (by cleaning as much oil from the lithium as possible, etc.) but the only way to **avoid** them is to use a **different method** (which may be impossible without complicated equipment, and might well have problems of its own).

...And the **Equipment Used**   (See page 32 for more on different types of error and how to minimise them.)

1) With **all measurements** there's a limit to the **precision** that's possible. For example, a measuring cylinder has a limited number of graduations (markings) on it — the level you're trying to read will usually be somewhere in between two graduations and you'll have to **estimate** its position by eye. The limited precision of equipment leads to **random errors** — sometimes you'll record the value as **greater** than it really is, sometimes as **smaller** than it is.

2) And of course it's no good having equipment that gives really precise readings if it's **inaccurate** — a wrongly calibrated balance that reads 0.2005 g when there's nothing on it, say, is **no good to anyone**.

3) And then there's always room for **human error** — good old-fashioned **silly mistakes**. Human errors can be systematic (e.g. always reading the top of a meniscus rather than the bottom) as well as random.

Practice Questions

Q1 Write down the formula you'd use to calculate the number of moles of hydrogen from the volume at r.t.p..

Q2 Give two systematic problems that can cause the mass of a piece of lithium to be recorded inaccurately.

Q3 Which method should you use to find out how many moles of an alkali you have?

Exam Questions

Q1 Sodium azide, NaN_3, decomposes when heated to form sodium metal, Na, and nitrogen gas, N_2.

   a) Write a balanced equation for this reaction. [2 marks]

   b) To confirm the equation, 0.325 g of sodium azide was decomposed. The nitrogen gas produced was found to have a volume of 180 cm³ at room temperature and pressure.

      i) How many moles of sodium azide were decomposed? [2 marks]

      ii) How many moles of nitrogen gas were formed? [1 mark]

      iii) What is the molar ratio of sodium azide to nitrogen? Give your answer as an integer ratio. [2 marks]

Q2 Magnesium reacts with hydrochloric acid according to this equation: $Mg_{(s)} + 2HCl_{(aq)} \rightarrow MgCl_{2(aq)} + H_{2(g)}$

   A student wanted to check that one mole of hydrogen gas is produced for every mole of magnesium that reacts. She put some hydrochloric acid into a conical flask and weighed a piece of magnesium.

   a) Describe how she could collect the hydrogen gas produced and measure its volume. [2 marks]

   b) Give two reasons why the result of this experiment is not likely to be accurate. [2 marks]

Yup, that's an equation all right...

Who'd have thought it — all that hassle just to check that a reaction happens the way you think it does. However, a bit more practice with those calculations never did anyone any harm. And that stuff about errors is really important — you need to understand the different types of error, and be able to give examples of where they happen in real experiments.

Acids and Bases

Acid's a word that's thrown around willy-nilly — but now for the truth...
These pages are for OCR A (Unit 1) — it's your lucky day. Anyone else can skip merrily on.

Acids are all about Hydrated Protons

1) When mixed with **water**, all acids **release hydrogen ions** — H^+ (these are just **protons**, but you never get them by themselves in water — they're always combined with H_2O (hydrated) to form hydroxonium ions, H_3O^+).

E.g.
$$HCl_{(g)} + water \rightarrow H^+_{(aq)} + Cl^-_{(aq)}$$
$$H_2SO_{4(l)} + water \rightarrow 2H^+_{(aq)} + SO_4^{2-}_{(aq)}$$

HCl doesn't release hydrogen ions until it meets water — so hydrogen chloride gas isn't an acid.

2) **Bases** do the opposite — they want to **grab H^+ ions**.

So,

> **Acids** put $H^+_{(aq)}$ ions into a solution — i.e. they're **proton donors**.
> **Bases** remove $H^+_{(aq)}$ ions from a solution — i.e. they're **proton acceptors**.

Acids React to Form Neutral Salts

1) Acid molecules release their hydrogen ions, so **other ions** can hop into their places. You get a **salt** if the hydrogen ions are replaced by **metal ions** or **ammonium (NH_4^+) ions**.

2) Different acids produce **different salts** — sulfuric acid (H_2SO_4) produces salts called **sulfates**, hydrochloric acid (HCl) produces **chlorides**, and nitric acid (HNO_3) produces **nitrates**. *Learn the formulas for these acids.*

3) Not only that, but there are a few different things acids can react with that result in salts — read on...

Acids can React with Metals and Carbonates

When acids react with **metals** and **carbonates**, **salts** are produced.

> Metal + Acid → Metal Salt + Hydrogen
>
> E.g. $Mg_{(s)} + H_2SO_{4(aq)} \rightarrow MgSO_{4(aq)} + H_{2(g)}$
>
> Or the ionic equation: $Mg_{(s)} + 2H^+_{(aq)} \rightarrow Mg^{2+}_{(aq)} + H_{2(g)}$

It's often easier to see what acids are doing in ionic equations. Have a look at pages 22 and 23 if you've forgotten what they are.

> Metal Carbonate + Acid → Metal Salt + Carbon Dioxide + Water
>
> E.g. $Na_2CO_{3(s)} + 2HCl_{(aq)} \rightarrow 2NaCl_{(aq)} + CO_{2(g)} + H_2O_{(l)}$
>
> Ionic equation: $O^{2-} + 2H^+_{(aq)} \rightarrow H_2O_{(l)}$

Professor Redmond's final classroom demonstration...

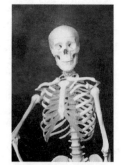

Effects of submersion in a bath of conc. H_2SO_4.

Acids React with Bases too

1) When **acids** react with **bases**, they **neutralise** each other.
2) **Metal oxides**, **metal hydroxides** and **ammonia** are common **bases**.

> Metal Oxide + Acid → Salt + Water
>
> E.g. $MgO_{(s)} + 2HCl_{(aq)} \rightarrow MgCl_{2(aq)} + H_2O_{(l)}$
>
> Ionic equation: $O^{2-} + 2H^+_{(aq)} \rightarrow H_2O_{(l)}$

The magnesium ion takes the place of the hydrogen ion of the acid to form a salt.

The O^{2-} ion accepts two H^+ ions which have been donated by the acid.

Acids and Bases

Alkalis are Soluble Bases

1) An **alkali** is just a base that dissolves in water.
2) **Sodium hydroxide (NaOH)** and **potassium hydroxide (KOH)** are the alkalis you're most likely to meet.
3) Alkalis **release OH⁻** ions in water. These OH⁻ ions are more than happy to accept an **H⁺ ion** (a proton) from an acid to form a **water molecule**.

The ionic equation shows that a proton is transferred from the acid to the hydroxide ion. This ionic equation is the same for all reactions between metal hydroxides and acids.

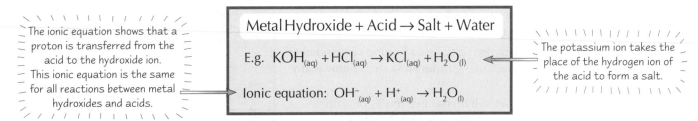

Metal Hydroxide + Acid → Salt + Water

E.g. $KOH_{(aq)} + HCl_{(aq)} \rightarrow KCl_{(aq)} + H_2O_{(l)}$

Ionic equation: $OH^-_{(aq)} + H^+_{(aq)} \rightarrow H_2O_{(l)}$

The potassium ion takes the place of the hydrogen ion of the acid to form a salt.

Ammonia Reacts with Acids to Form Ammonium Salts

1) Ammonia, NH_3, is a **base** — in fact it dissolves in water, so **aqueous ammonia** is an **alkali**.
2) It'll happily **accept a proton** from an acid to form an **ammonium ion** (NH_4^+) — this can then form an **ammonium salt**.

Here's how ammonia reacts with nitric acid (HNO_3) and sulfuric acid

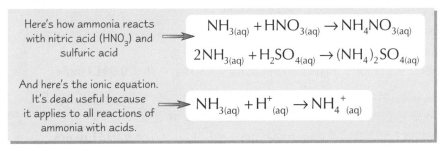

$NH_{3(aq)} + HNO_{3(aq)} \rightarrow NH_4NO_{3(aq)}$

$2NH_{3(aq)} + H_2SO_{4(aq)} \rightarrow (NH_4)_2SO_{4(aq)}$

And here's the ionic equation. It's dead useful because it applies to all reactions of ammonia with acids.

$NH_{3(aq)} + H^+_{(aq)} \rightarrow NH_4^+_{(aq)}$

Practice Questions

Q1 What are the formulas for: a) sulfuric acid, b) potassium hydroxide, c) ammonia, d) ammonium ion?

Q2 Sulfuric acid, H_2SO_4, reacts with calcium carbonate, $CaCO_3$. State the gas given off and the salt formed.

Q3 Write an ionic equation for the reaction between a metal hydroxide and an acid.

Q4 Explain what an alkali is.

Exam Question

Q1 Chloric(VII) acid, $HClO_4$, and sulfuric acid, H_2SO_4, are both strong acids.

a) Write a balanced equation, including state symbols, for the reaction between chloric(VII) acid and calcium carbonate, $CaCO_3$. [3 marks]

b) Sulfuric acid reacts with lithium metal, potassium hydroxide and ammonia.
   i) Write a balanced ionic equation for the reaction with lithium. [2 marks]
   ii) Write a balanced equation for the reaction with potassium hydroxide. [2 marks]
   iii) Write a balanced equation for the reaction with aqueous ammonia. [2 marks]

It's a stick-up — your protons or your life...

Remember — all acids have protons to give away and bases just love to take them. It's what makes them acids and bases. It's like how bus drivers drive buses...it's what makes them bus drivers. Learn the formulas for the common acids — hydrochloric, sulfuric and nitric, and the common alkalis — sodium hydroxide, potassium hydroxide and aqueous ammonia.

Salts

Some salts are <u>hydrated</u> — their lattices contain water molecules as well as the usual positive and negative ions.
This page is for OCR A (Unit 1) and Edexcel (Unit 1).

Salts Can Be Anhydrous or Hydrated   *OCR A only*

1) All solid salts consist of a **lattice** of positive and negative ions.
   In some salts, **water molecules** are incorporated in the lattice too.

2) The water in a lattice is called **water of crystallisation**.
   A solid salt containing water of crystallisation is **hydrated**.
   A salt is **anhydrous** if it doesn't contain water of crystallisation.

3) **One mole** of a particular hydrated salt always has the **same number
   of moles** of water of crystallisation — its **formula** shows **how many**
   (it's always a whole number).

4) For example, **hydrated copper sulfate** has **five** moles of water
   for every mole of the salt. So its formula is $CuSO_4.5H_2O$. ◄— Notice that there's a dot between $CuSO_4$ and $5H_2O$.

5) Many hydrated salts **lose** their water of crystallisation **when heated**, to become **anhydrous**.
   If you know the mass of the salt when hydrated and anhydrous, you can work its formula out like this:

> Here's a tiny part of the lattice in a hydrated salt.
>
> Water molecules are **polar**. They're held in place in the lattice because they're attracted to the ions.

Example:

Heating 3.210 g of hydrated magnesium sulfate, $MgSO_4.XH_2O$, forms 1.567 g of anhydrous magnesium sulfate.
Find the value of **X** and write the formula of the hydrated salt.

First you find the number of moles of water lost.

Mass of water lost:	$3.210 - 1.567$	$= 1.643$ g
Number of moles of water lost:	mass ÷ molar mass	$= 1.643$ g ÷ 18 = **0.0913 moles**

Then you find the number of moles of anhydrous salt.

Molar mass of $MgSO_4$:	$24 + 32 + (4 \times 16)$	$= 120$ g mol^{-1}
Number of moles (in 1.567 g):	mass ÷ molar mass	$= 1.567 ÷ 120 = $ **0.0131 moles**

Now you work out the ratio of moles of anydrous salt to moles of water in the form 1 : n.

From the experiment,   **0.0131 moles of salt : 0.0913 moles of water**,

So,   **1 mole of salt :** $\dfrac{0.0913}{0.0131} = $ **6.99 moles of water**.

You might be given the percentage of the mass that is water — use the method on p20.

X must be a whole number, and some errors are to be expected in any experiment, so you
can safely round off your result — so the formula of the hydrated salt is $MgSO_4.7H_2O$.

Preparing a Salt — Mix the Right Stuff, Crystallise, Filter   *Edexcel only*

Here's how to prepare **hydrated ammonium iron(II) sulfate** from
iron, **ammonia** and **sulfuric acid**.

Ammonium iron(II) sulfate, $(NH_4)_2Fe(SO_4)_2$, is a double salt because it's got two cations.

Here's the balanced equation. It looks worse than it is, I promise.

$$Fe_{(s)} + 2NH_{3\,(aq)} + 2H_2SO_{4\,(aq)} + 6H_2O_{(l)} \rightarrow (NH_4)_2Fe(SO_4)_2.6H_2O_{(s)} + H_{2\,(g)}$$

1) Add a known mass of **iron filings** to an excess of **warm sulfuric acid** and stir until they've all reacted.
   You've now got **iron(II) sulfate solution**.

2) Add **just enough** ammonia solution to **react completely** with the iron.
   (From the reaction equation, you need twice as many moles of ammonia
   as of iron — you need to work out what amounts to use.)

3) Leave the solution to evaporate — **blue-green crystals** of the salt will form.
   Some solution will remain (because you started with an excess of acid).

4) Collect the crystals by **filtering**.

5) To **dry** the crystals, press them between two pieces of filter paper to
   absorb as much water as possible.

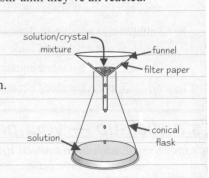

Salts

This page is for AQA (Unit 1), OCR A (Unit 2), OCR B (Unit 2) and Edexcel (Unit 1).

Percentage Yield Is Never 100%

1) The **theoretical yield** is the **mass of product** that **should** be formed. It assumes **no** chemicals are 'lost' in the process.

2) You can use the **masses of reactants** and a **balanced equation** to calculate the theoretical yield for a reaction.

3) For example, here's how to calculate the theoretical yield of **hydrated ammonium iron(II) sulfate**. Say you react **1.40 g** of iron filings:

$$Fe_{(s)} + 2NH_{3\ (aq)} + 2H_2SO_{4\ (aq)} + 6H_2O_{(l)} \rightarrow (NH_4)_2Fe(SO_4)_2.6H_2O_{(s)} + H_{2\ (g)}$$

- Number of moles of **iron** (A_r = 56) reacted = mass ÷ molar mass = 1.40 ÷ 56 = **0.025 moles**.
  From the equation, 'moles of iron : moles of ammonium iron(II) sulfate' is 1:1, so 0.025 moles of product should form.
- Molar mass of $(NH_4)_2Fe(SO_4)_2.6H_2O_{(s)}$ = 392, so **theoretical yield** = 0.025 × 392 = **9.8 g**.

4) For any reaction, the **actual** mass of product (the **actual yield**) will always be **less** than the theoretical yield. There are many reasons for this. For example, sometimes not all the 'starting' chemicals react fully. And some chemicals are always 'lost', e.g. some solution gets left on filter paper, or is lost during transfers between containers.

5) So, in the ammonium iron(II) sulfate experiment, the theoretical yield was 9.8 g... but you won't actually **get** 9.8 g — not all the product forms crystals, for example, so some is left in solution and is 'lost' that way.

6) In this case, to find the **actual yield** you just **weigh the crystals**. Then you can work out the **percentage yield**.

$$\text{Percentage yield} = \frac{\text{Actual Yield}}{\text{Theoretical Yield}} \times 100\%$$

So if the actual yield of hydrated ammonium iron(II) sulfate crystals was **5.2 g**:

$$\text{Percentage yield} = (5.2 \div 9.8) \times 100\% = 53\%$$

Practice Questions

Q1 What is the difference between a hydrated and an anhydrous salt?

Q2 Why can water molecules become fixed in an ionic lattice?

Q3 Why is it never possible to prepare a salt with a 100% yield?

Q4 Write down the formula for calculating percentage yield.

Exam Questions

Q1 A sample of hydrated calcium sulfate, $CaSO_4.XH_2O$, was prepared by reacting calcium hydroxide with sulfuric acid. 1.883 g of hydrated salt was produced. This was then heated until all the water of crystallisation was driven off and the product was then reweighed. Its mass was 1.133 g.

    a) How many moles of anhydrous calcium sulfate were produced?   [2 marks]

    b) What mass of water was present in the hydrated salt?   [1 mark]

    c) Calculate the value of **X** in the formula $CaSO_4.XH_2O$. (**X** is an integer.)   [3 marks]

Q2 Copper(II) sulfate pentahydrate, $CuSO_4.5H_2O$, was prepared by adding excess copper(II) oxide to 50 cm³ of hot 0.2 mol dm⁻³ sulfuric acid. The equation for the reaction is:

$$CuO_{(s)} + H_2SO_{4\ (aq)} + 4H_2O_{(l)} \rightarrow CuSO_4.5H_2O_{(aq)}$$

The solution was filtered to remove any unreacted solid and allowed to evaporate until crystals of product formed. The crystals were collected and dried with filter paper. The dry crystals had a mass of 1.964 g.

    a) How many moles of sulfuric acid were used?   [1 mark]

    b) What was the percentage yield for the reaction?   [4 marks]

Percentage Revision Yield = Pages Learnt ÷ Pages Read × 100%

Ah, salts. Back in the day, there was only one kind of salt you needed to know about and it usually went on your fish and chips. Alas, those innocent days are gone for ever. Now you need to know about hydrated double salts as well as your bog-standard anhydrous salts — how to write their formulas, how to make dry samples and how to do pesky sums.

Titrations

*Titrations are used to find out the **concentration** of acid or alkali solutions.*
They're also handy when you're making salts of soluble bases.
These pages are for AQA (Unit 1), OCR A (Unit 1), OCR B (Unit 2) and Edexcel (Unit 2).

Titrations need to be done Accurately

1) **Titrations** allow you to find out **exactly** how much acid is needed to **neutralise** a quantity of alkali.

2) You measure out some **alkali** using a pipette and put it in a flask, along with some **indicator**, e.g. **phenolphthalein**.

3) First of all, do a rough titration to get an idea where the **end point** is (the point where the alkali is **exactly neutralised** and the indicator changes colour). Add the **acid** to the alkali using a **burette** — giving the flask a regular **swirl**.

4) Now do an **accurate** titration. Run the acid in to within 2 cm³ of the end point, then add the acid **dropwise**. If you don't notice exactly when the solution changed colour you've **overshot** and your result won't be accurate.

5) **Record** the amount of acid used to **neutralise** the alkali. It's best to **repeat** this process a few times, making sure you get the same answer each time.

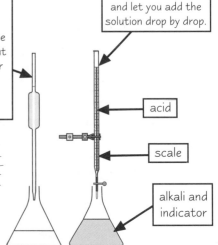

Pipette
Pipettes measure only one volume of solution. Fill the pipette about 3 cm above the line, then take the pipette out of the solution (or the water pressure will hold up the level). Now drop the level down carefully to the line.

Burette
Burettes measure different volumes and let you add the solution drop by drop.

acid

scale

alkali and indicator

You can also do titrations the other way round — adding alkali to acid.

Indicators Show you when the Reaction's Just Finished

Indicators change **colour**, as if by magic. In titrations, indicators that change colour quickly over a **very small pH range** are used so you know **exactly** when the reaction has ended.

The main two indicators for **acid/alkali reactions** are —

> **methyl orange** —- turns **yellow** to **red** when adding acid to alkali.
> **phenolphthalein** —- turns **red** to **colourless** when adding acid to alkali.

Universal indicator is no good here — its colour change is too gradual.

You can Calculate Concentrations from Titrations

Now for the calculations...

Example: 25 cm³ of 0.5 M HCl was used to neutralise 35 cm³ of NaOH solution. Calculate the concentration of the sodium hydroxide solution.

First write a **balanced equation** and decide **what you know** and what you **need to know**:

$$HCl + NaOH \rightarrow NaCl + H_2O$$
25 cm³   35 cm³
0.5 M   ?

It's just the formula from page 18.

Now work out how many **moles of HCl** you have:

$$\text{Number of moles HCl} = \frac{\text{concentration} \times \text{volume (cm}^3)}{1000} = \frac{0.5 \times 25}{1000} = 0.0125 \text{ moles}$$

From the equation, you know 1 mole of HCl neutralises 1 mole of NaOH.
So 0.0125 moles of HCl must neutralise **0.0125** moles of NaOH.

Now it's a doddle to work out the **concentration of NaOH**.

$$\text{Concentration of NaOH}_{(aq)} = \frac{\text{moles of NaOH} \times 1000}{\text{volume (cm}^3)} = \frac{0.0125 \times 1000}{35} = \textbf{0.36 mol dm}^{-3}$$

If you're asked for the concentration in g dm⁻³, you need to now use the formula from p18 — number of moles = mass ÷ M_r

Titrations

You use a *Pretty Similar Method* to Calculate *Volumes* for Reactions

This is usually used for **planning experiments**.

You need to use this formula again, but this time **rearrange** it to find the volume. $\longrightarrow$

$$\text{number of moles} = \frac{\text{concentration} \times \text{volume (cm}^3)}{1000}$$

Example: 20.4 cm³ of a 0.5 M solution of sodium carbonate reacts with 1.5 M nitric acid. Calculate the volume of nitric acid required to neutralise the sodium carbonate.

Like before, first write a **balanced equation** for the reaction and decide **what you know** and what you **want to know**:

$$Na_2CO_3 + 2HNO_3 \rightarrow 2NaNO_3 + H_2O + CO_2$$
20.4 cm³   ?
0.5 M   1.5 M

Now work out how many **moles** of Na_2CO_3 you've got:

$$\text{No. of moles of } Na_2CO_3 = \frac{\text{concentration} \times \text{volume (cm}^3)}{1000} = \frac{0.5 \times 20.4}{1000} = 0.0102 \text{ moles}$$

1 mole of Na_2CO_3 neutralises 2 moles of HNO_3, so 0.0102 moles of Na_2CO_3 neutralises **0.0204 moles of HNO_3.**

Now you know the number of moles of HNO_3 and the concentration, you can work out the **volume**:

$$\text{Volume of } HNO_3 = \frac{\text{number of moles} \times 1000}{\text{concentration}} = \frac{0.0204 \times 1000}{1.5} = 13.6 \text{ cm}^3$$

Practice Questions

Q1 Describe the procedure for doing a titration.

Q2 What colour change would you expect to see if you added enough hydrochloric acid to a conical flask containing sodium hydroxide and methyl orange?

Exam Questions

Q1 Calculate the concentration of a solution of ethanoic acid, CH_3COOH, if 25.4 cm³ of it is neutralised by 14.6 cm³ of 0.5 M sodium hydroxide solution. **$CH_3COOH + NaOH \rightarrow CH_3COONa + H_2O$** [3 marks]

Q2 You are supplied with 0.75 g of calcium carbonate and a solution of 0.25 M sulfuric acid. What volume of acid will be needed to neutralise the calcium carbonate?
$CaCO_3 + H_2SO_4 \rightarrow CaSO_4 + H_2O + CO_2$ [4 marks]

Burettes and pipettes — big glass things, just waiting to be dropped...

Titrations are annoyingly fiddly. But you do get to use big, impressive-looking equipment and feel like you're doing something important. It's really tempting to rush it and let half the acid gush into the alkali first. But it's totally not worth it, cos you'll just have to do it again. Yep, this is definitely one of those slow-and-steady-wins-the-race situations.

More About Titrations

Thought you were done with titrations? Well they're not finished with you yet...
These pages are for Edexcel (Unit 2).

Uncertainty *is the Amount of* Error *Your* Measurements *Might Have*

The results you get from a titration won't be completely perfect.

1) When you do a **titration**, you need to know how to work out how much **error** there could be in your **measurements**.

2) The **maximum possible error** is a useful measure of **uncertainty**.

   - The **uncertainty** in your measurements **varies** for different equipment. For example, the scale on a 50 cm³ **burette** has marks every **0.1 cm³**. You should be able to tell which mark the level's closest to, so any reading you take won't be more than **0.05 cm³** out (as long as you don't make a daft mistake). The **uncertainty** of a reading from the burette is the **maximum error** you could have — so that's **0.05cm³**.

   - There's **uncertainty** when you weigh stuff, too. Even electronic scales don't give an **exact mass**. If the mass is measured to the **nearest 0.01 g**, the real mass could be up to **0.005 g smaller or larger**.

   - Pieces of equipment for measuring out **liquid** — things like fixed-volume pipettes and volumetric flasks — have uncertainties in the **volumes** they measure. These depend on how well made the equipment is. The manufacturers provide these **uncertainty values**.

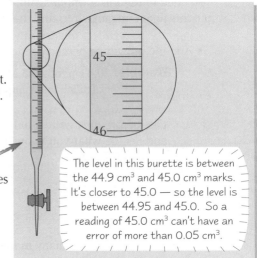

The level in this burette is between the 44.9 cm³ and 45.0 cm³ marks. It's closer to 45.0 — so the level is between 44.95 and 45.0. So a reading of 45.0 cm³ can't have an error of more than 0.05 cm³.

You Can Minimise *Some* Uncertainties

1) One obvious way to **reduce errors** in your measurements is to buy the most **precise equipment** available. In real life there's not much you can do about this one — you're stuck with whatever your school or college has got. But there are other ways to **lower the uncertainty** in your titrations.

2) A bit of clever **planning** can improve your results. Think about the readings from a **burette**. You take **two readings** to work out a titre (the volume of liquid delivered from the burette) — the **initial volume** and the **final volume**. Each reading has an uncertainty of **0.05 cm³**. The titre is the second reading minus the first, so the titre will have a total uncertainty of **0.1 cm³**. (The second could be up to 0.05 cm³ too high, and the first up to 0.05 cm³ too low.)

3) For any reading or measurement you can calculate the **percentage uncertainty** using the equation:

$$\text{percentage uncertainty} = \frac{\text{uncertainty}}{\text{reading}} \times 100$$

Percentage uncertainty is sometimes called percentage error.

4) If you use a burette to measure **10 cm³** of liquid the percentage uncertainty is (0.1/10) × 100 = **1%**. But if you measure **20 cm³** of liquid the uncertainty is (0.1/20) × 100 = **0.5%**. Hey presto — you've just halved the uncertainty. The percentage uncertainty can be reduced by planning a titration so that a **larger volume** will be measured by the burette.

5) The same principle can be applied to other measurements such as **weighing solids** — if you plan to weigh a small mass, the **percentage uncertainty** will be large.

Errors *Can Be* Systematic *or* Random

1) **Systematic errors** are the same every time you repeat the experiment. They may be caused by the **set-up** or **equipment** you're using. If the 10.00 cm³ pipette you're using to measure out a sample for titration actually only measures 9.95 cm³, your sample will be about 0.05 cm³ too small **every time** you repeat the experiment.

2) **Random errors** vary — they're what make the results a bit **different** each time you repeat an experiment. The errors when you make a reading from a burette are random. You have to estimate or round the level when it's between two marks — so sometimes your figure will be **above** the real one, and sometimes it will be **below**.

This should be a photo of a scientist. I don't know what happened — it's a random error...

3) **Repeating an experiment** and finding the mean of your results Telps to deal with **random errors**. The results that are bit high will be **cancelled out** by the ones that are a bit low. (Your results will be more **reliable**.) But repeating your results won't get rid of any **systematic errors**. (Your results won't get more **accurate**.)

4) For more about accuracy and reliability see page 160.

More About Titrations

The **Total Uncertainty** in a Result Should be Calculated

1) In chemical analysis, knowing the **uncertainty** in the **final result** can be really important. For instance, if you were analysing the alcohol level of a driver's blood and found that it was just above the legal limit, this data would be no use to the police if the uncertainty was large enough that the driver could have been just under the limit.

2) In **titrations**, here's how you find the **total uncertainty in the final result**:
   - Find the **percentage uncertainty** for each bit of equipment.
   - Add the individual percentage uncertainties together. This gives the **percentage uncertainty in the final result**.
   - Use this to work out the **actual total uncertainty** in the final result.

Example: 10.00 cm³ of KOH solution is neutralised by 27.3 cm³ of HCl of known concentration.
The volume of KOH has an uncertainty of 0.06 cm³. The volume of HCl has an uncertainty of 0.1 cm³.
The concentration of the KOH is calculated to be 1.365 mol dm⁻³.
What is the uncertainty in this concentration?

First work out the **percentage uncertainty** for each **volume measurement**:

The KOH volume of 10.00 cm³ has an uncertainty of 0.06 cm³:
$$\text{percentage uncertainty} = \frac{0.06}{10.00} \times 100 = \mathbf{0.60\%}$$

The HCl volume of 27.3 cm³ has an uncertainty of 0.1 cm³:
$$\text{percentage uncertainty} = \frac{0.1}{27.3} \times 100 = \mathbf{0.37\%}$$

Find the **percentage uncertainty in the final result**: Total percentage uncertainty = 0.60% + 0.37% = **0.97%**

You're not done yet — you still have to calculate the **uncertainty** in the final result.

Uncertainty in the final answer is 0.97% of 1.365 mol dm⁻³ = **0.013 mol dm⁻³**

So the actual concentration may be 0.013 mol dm⁻³ bigger or smaller than 1.365 mol dm⁻³.

Practice Questions

Q1 If the uncertainty of a reading from a burette is 0.05 cm³, why is the uncertainty of a titre quoted as being 0.1 cm³?

Q2 Write down the equation for the percentage uncertainty of a measurement.

Q3 Does repeating the same experiment several times improve the reliability or the accuracy of the results?

Exam Questions

Q1 The table shows the data recorded from a titration experiment.

Run	Initial volume (cm³)	Final volume (cm³)	Titre (cm³)
Rough	1.1	5.2	4.1
1	1.2	4.3	3.1

   a) Suggest a way to make the data more reliable. [1 mark]

   b) Each reading recorded in the experiment has an uncertainty of 0.05 cm³.
   Calculate the percentage uncertainty in the **titre** in Run 1. [2 marks]

   c) Explain how you could reduce the percentage error in these titre values by changing the concentration of the solution in the burette. [2 marks]

Q2 The concentration of a solution of sodium hydroxide is measured by titration against 0.100 M hydrochloric acid.
25.00 cm³ of NaOH solution requires 19.25 cm³ of HCl for neutralisation.

   a) Calculate the concentration of the NaOH. [3 marks]

   b) The volume of NaOH was measured using a pipette with an uncertainty of 0.06 cm³.
   The titre reading from the burette has an uncertainty of 0.1 cm³.
   By combining percentage uncertainties calculate the uncertainty in the concentration of the NaOH. [4 marks]

I used to be uncertain, but now I'm not sure...

Typical... you think you've done a nice, accurate experiment and all they care about is how wrong it is. If you get a question about uncertainty, make sure you read it carefully. If the question asks for the uncertainty in the final answer, they want the uncertainty in the same units as the result. If you only work out the total <u>percentage</u> uncertainty, you'll miss out.

Atom Economy and Percentage Yield

How to make a subject like chemistry even more exciting — introduce the word 'economy'...
These pages are for AQA (Unit 1), OCR A (Unit 2) and OCR B (Unit 2) and Edexcel (Unit 1).

Atom Economy is a Measure of the Efficiency of a Reaction

1) The **efficiency** of a reaction is often measured by the **percentage yield** (see p29).
This tells you how wasteful the **process** is — it's based on how much of the product is lost because of things like reactions not completing or losses during collection and purification.

2) But percentage yield doesn't measure how wasteful the **reaction** itself is. A reaction that has a 100% yield could still be very wasteful if a lot of the atoms from the **reactants** wind up in **by-products** rather than the **desired product**.

3) **Atom economy** is a measure of the proportion of reactant **atoms** that become part of the desired product (rather than by-products) in the **balanced** chemical equation. It's calculated using this formula:

$$\% \text{ atom economy} = \frac{\text{molecular mass of desired product}}{\text{sum of molecular masses of all products}} \times 100$$

Look out — those cheeky scamps at **AQA** like to use a **different formula** (don't worry, it gives the same result):

$$\% \text{ atom economy} = \frac{\text{mass of desired product}}{\text{total mass of reactants}} \times 100$$

You can use the masses in grams, or their relative molecular masses.

Addition Reactions have a 100% Atom Economy

1) In an **addition reaction** the reactants **combine** to form a **single product**.
The atom economy for addition reactions is **always 100%** since no atoms are wasted.

2) For example, ethene (C_2H_4) and hydrogen react to form ethane (C_2H_6) in an addition reaction:

$$C_2H_4 + H_2 \rightarrow C_2H_6$$

The **only product** is ethane — the desired product. So **none** of the reactant atoms are wasted.

Substitution Reactions have a Lower Atom Economy than Addition Reactions

1) A **substitution reaction** is one where some atoms from one reactant are **swapped** with atoms from another reactant. This type of reaction **always** results in **at least two products** — the desired product and at least one by-product.

2) An example is the reaction of bromomethane (CH_3Br) with sodium hydroxide (NaOH) to make methanol (CH_3OH):

$$CH_3Br + NaOH \rightarrow CH_3OH + NaBr$$

Here the Br atoms have **swapped places** with the OH groups. This is **more wasteful** than an addition reaction because the Na and Br atoms are not part of the desired product.

3) The **atom economy** for this reaction is:

$$\% \text{ atom economy} = \frac{\text{molecular mass of desired product}}{\text{sum of molecular masses of all products}} \times 100$$

Always make sure you're using a balanced equation.

$$= \frac{M_r(CH_3OH)}{M_r(CH_3OH) + M_r(NaBr)} \times 100$$

$$= \frac{(12 + (3 \times 1) + 16 + 1)}{(12 + (3 \times 1) + 16 + 1) + (23 + 80)} \times 100 = \frac{32}{32 + 103} \times 100 = \mathbf{23.7\%}$$

Using the **AQA formula** you get the same result from a different calculation:

$$\% \text{ atom economy} = \frac{\text{mass of desired product}}{\text{total mass of reactants}} \times 100$$

The relative molecular masses have been used here.
Use the numbers of moles from the balanced equation.

$$= \frac{(12 + (3 \times 1) + 16 + 1)}{(12 + (3 \times 1) + 80) + (23 + 16 + 1)} \times 100 = \frac{32 \text{ g}}{135 \text{ g}} \times 100 = \mathbf{23.7\%}$$

(See... it really does give the same answer — because the total mass of the reactants is always the same as the total mass of the products. And you didn't believe me...)

Atom Economy and Percentage Yield

Reactions can Have **High Percentage Yields** and **Low Atom Economies**

Example: 0.475 g of CH_3Br reacts with excess NaOH in this reaction: $CH_3Br + NaOH \rightarrow CH_3OH + NaBr$
0.153 g of CH_3OH is produced. What is the percentage yield?

Number of moles = mass of substance ÷ molar mass
Moles of CH_3Br = 0.475 ÷ (12 + 3 × 1 + 80) = 0.475 ÷ 95 = **0.005 moles**
The reactant : product ratio is 1 : 1, so the maximum number of moles of CH_3OH is **0.005**.
Theoretical yield = 0.005 × $M_r(CH_3OH)$ = 0.005 × (12 + (3 × 1) + 16 + 1) = 0.005 × 32 = **0.160 g**

$$\text{percentage yield} = \frac{\text{actual yield}}{\text{theoretical yield}} \times 100 = \frac{0.153}{0.160} \times 100 = \mathbf{95.6\%}$$

This reaction has a **very high percentage yield**, but as we've already seen, the **atom economy** is **low**.

It is Important to Develop Reactions with **High Atom Economies**

1) Companies in the chemical industry will often choose to use reactions with high atom economies. Keeping atom economy as high as possible has **environmental** and **economic benefits**. There's more about this on p152.

2) A **low atom economy** means there's lots of **waste** produced. It costs money to **separate** the desired product from the waste products and more money to dispose of the waste products **safely** so they don't harm the environment. (Finding uses for the by-products helps against this).

3) If a large proportion of the mass of the reactants ends up as waste rather than ending up as useful products, the reactants are being used **inefficiently**. This is costly to the company (who have to buy a large mass of reactant chemicals to make the product). It also lowers the **sustainability** of the process. Many raw materials are in limited supply, so it makes sense to use them efficiently so they last as long as possible.

Practice Questions

Q1 How many products are there in an addition reaction?

Q2 Does the percentage yield for a reaction always have the same value as the percentage atom economy?

Q3 Why do reactions with high atom economy save chemical companies money and cause less environmental impact?

Exam Questions

Q1 Reactions 1 and 2 below show two possible ways of preparing the compound chloroethane (C_2H_5Cl):

    1 $C_2H_5OH + PCl_5 \rightarrow C_2H_5Cl + POCl_3 + HCl$
    2 $C_2H_4 + HCl \rightarrow C_2H_5Cl$

a) Which of these is an addition reaction? [1 mark]

b) Calculate the atom economy for reaction 1. (Atomic masses: C = 12, H = 1, O = 16, P = 31, Cl = 35.5) [3 marks]

c) Reaction 2 has an atom economy of 100%. Explain why this is, in terms of the products of the reaction. [1 mark]

Q2 Phosphorus trichloride (PCl_3) reacts with chlorine to give phosphorus pentachloride (PCl_5):

     $PCl_3 + Cl_2 \rightleftharpoons PCl_5$ (Atomic masses: P = 31, Cl = 35.5)

a) If 0.275 g of PCl_3 reacts with 0.142 g of chlorine, what is the theoretical yield of PCl_5? [2 marks]

b) When this reaction is performed 0.198 g of PCl_5 is collected. Calculate the percentage yield. [1 mark]

c) Changing conditions such as temperature and pressure will alter the percentage yield of this reaction. Will changing these conditions affect the atom economy? Explain your answer. [2 marks]

I knew a Tommy Conomy once... strange bloke...

These pages shouldn't be too much trouble — you've survived worse already. Make sure you get plenty of practice using the atom economy formula — and make sure you learn the right one for your exam board. And don't get mixed up between percentage yield (which is to do with the process) and atom economy (which is to do with the reaction).

Ionic Bonding

Every atom's aim in life is to have a full outer shell of electrons. Once they've managed this, that's it — they're happy.
These pages are for AQA (Unit 1), OCR A (Unit 1), OCR B (Units 1 and 2) and Edexcel (Unit 1).

Compounds are Atoms of Different Elements Bonded Together

1) When different elements join or bond together, you get a **compound**.
2) There are two main types of bonding in compounds — **ionic** and **covalent**. You need to make sure you've got them **both** totally sussed.

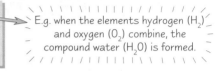
E.g. when the elements hydrogen (H_2) and oxygen (O_2) combine, the compound water (H_2O) is formed.

Ionic Bonding is when Ions are Stuck Together by Electrostatic Attraction

1) Ions are formed when electrons are **transferred** from one atom to another.

2) The simplest ions are single atoms which have either lost or gained 1, 2 or 3 electrons so that they've got a **full outer shell**. Here are some examples of ions:

A sodium atom (Na) **loses** 1 electron to form a sodium ion (Na^+) $Na \rightarrow Na^+ + e^-$
A magnesium atom (Mg) **loses** 2 electrons to form a magnesium ion (Mg^{2+}) $Mg \rightarrow Mg^{2+} + 2e^-$
A chlorine atom (Cl) **gains** 1 electron to form a chloride ion (Cl^-) $Cl + e^- \rightarrow Cl^-$
An oxygen atom (O) **gains** 2 electrons to form an oxide ion (O^{2-}) $O + 2e^- \rightarrow O^{2-}$

3) You **don't** have to remember what ions **most elements** form — nope, you just look at the periodic table.
Elements in the same **group** all have the same number of **outer electrons**. So they have to **lose or gain** the same number to get the full outer shell that they're aiming for. And this means that they form ions with the **same charges**.

4) **Electrostatic attraction** holds positive and negative ions together — it's **very** strong. When atoms are held together like this, it's called **ionic bonding**.

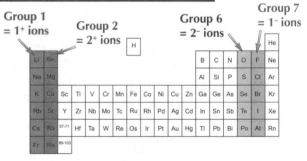

Sodium Chloride and Magnesium Oxide are Ionic Compounds

1) The formula of sodium chloride is **NaCl**. It just tells you that sodium chloride is made up of **Na^+ ions** and **Cl^- ions** (in a 1:1 ratio).

2) You can use '**dot-and-cross**' diagrams to show how ionic bonding works in sodium chloride —

Here, the dots represent the Na electrons and the crosses represent the Cl electrons (all electrons are really identical, but this is a good way of following their movement).

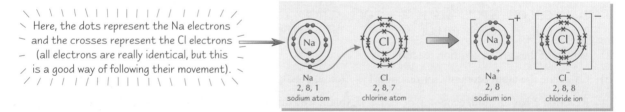

Na
2, 8, 1
sodium atom

Cl
2, 8, 7
chlorine atom

Na^+
2, 8
sodium ion

Cl^-
2, 8, 8
chloride ion

3) **Magnesium oxide**, MgO, is another good example:

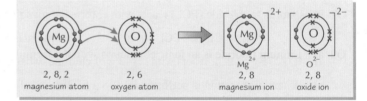

2, 8, 2
magnesium atom

2, 6
oxygen atom

Mg^{2+}
2, 8
magnesium ion

O^{2-}
2, 8
oxide ion

Dot (cross)

The positive charges in the compound **balance** the negative charges exactly — so the total overall charge is **zero**. This is a dead handy way of checking the formula.
- In **NaCl**, the single + charge on the Na^+ ion balances the single minus charge on the Cl^- ion.
- In **$MgCl_2$**, the 2+ charge on the Mg^{2+} ion balances the minus charges on the two Cl^- ions.

Ionic Bonding

Sodium Chloride has a *Giant Ionic Lattice* Structure

1) Ionic crystals are giant lattices of ions. A **lattice** is just a **regular structure**.

2) The structure's called '**giant**' because it's made up of the same basic unit repeated over and over again.

3) In **sodium chloride**, the Na^+ and Cl^- ions are packed together. The sodium chloride lattice is **cube** shaped — different ionic compounds have different shaped structures, but they're all still giant lattices.

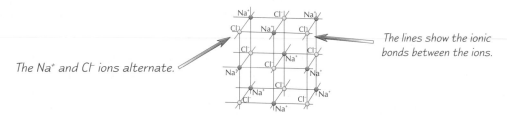

The Na^+ and Cl^- ions alternate.

The lines show the ionic bonds between the ions.

The structure of ionic compounds decides their **physical properties**...

Ionic Structure Explains the *Behaviour* of Ionic Compounds

1) **Ionic compounds conduct electricity when they're molten or dissolved — but not when they're solid.**
   The ions in a liquid are free to move (and they carry a charge).
   In a solid they're fixed in position by the strong ionic bonds.

2) **Ionic compounds have high melting points.**
   The giant ionic lattices are held together by strong electrostatic forces. It takes loads of energy to overcome these forces, so melting points are very high (801 °C for sodium chloride).

3) **Ionic compounds dissolve in water.**
   Water molecules are polar — part of the molecule has a small negative charge, and the other bits have small positive charges (see p48). The water molecules pull the ions away from the lattice and cause it to dissolve.

Practice Questions

Q1 What's a compound?

Q2 Draw a dot-and-cross diagram showing the bonding between magnesium and oxygen.

Q3 What type of force holds ionic substances together?

Q4 What happens when a current is passed through a dissolved ionic compound?

Exam Questions

Q1 a) Draw a labelled diagram to show the structure of sodium chloride. [3 marks]

b) What is the name of this type of structure? [1 mark]

c) Would you expect sodium chloride to have a high or a low melting point?
   Explain your answer. [4 marks]

Q2 a) Lithium fluoride is an ionic compound with the formula LiF. Draw a dot and cross
   diagram to show how LiF is formed from one lithium atom and one fluorine atom. [4 marks]

b) Solid lead bromide does not conduct electricity, but molten lead bromide does.
   Explain this with reference to ionic bonding. [5 marks]

Any old ion, any old ion, any any any old ion...

This stuff's easy marks in exams. Just make sure you can draw dot-and-cross diagrams showing the bonding in ionic compounds, and you're sorted. Remember — atoms are lazy. It's easier to lose two electrons to get a full shell than it is to gain six, so that's what an atom's going to do. Practise drawing sodium chloride too, and don't stop till you're perfect.

More on Ions and Ionic Bonding

Just when you thought it was safe to go back to revision — another page on ions and ionic bonding.
And once you've got an idea of how the theory behind ionic bonding works, you'll need some evidence to back it up.

These pages are for OCR A (Unit 1), OCR B (Unit 2) and Edexcel (Unit 1).

Models of Ionic Bonding Have Their Limitations

In the **dot-and-cross model** of ionic bonding, an **ionic bond** is formed when an electron jumps from one atom to another. The **positive ion** and the **negative ion** stay stuck together thanks to the **electrostatic attraction**.

Like most things in life though it's not really quite as simple as that.

1) Most bonds aren't **purely ionic** or **purely covalent** but somewhere in between. This is down to **bond polarisation** (see page 49). Most compounds end up with a **mixture** of ionic and covalent properties.

2) The **dot-and-cross model** makes it look as if a substance like sodium chloride is made up of **1 sodium ion** bonded to **1 chloride ion**. It's actually a **giant ionic lattice** made up of equal numbers of the two ions.

Not All Ions are Made from Single Atoms

All the **ions** that you saw on the last page were formed from **single atoms**.

There are lots of ions that are made up of a group of atoms with an overall charge. These are called **compound ions**. You'll come across some of them pretty often in AS Chemistry, so you need to know their formulas.

Nitrate NO_3^-	Carbonate CO_3^{2-}	Sulfate SO_4^{2-}	Ammonium NH_4^+

The Size of an Ion Depends On Its Atomic Number and Charge

Edexcel only

The **size** of an ion usually means its **ionic radius**.
There are two **trends** in ionic radii that you need to know about.

1) The **ionic radius increases** as you go **down a group**.

Ion	Ionic radius (nm)
Li^+	0.060
Na^+	0.095
K^+	0.133
Rb^+	0.148

All these **Group 1** ions have the **same charge**.
As you go down the group the **ionic radius increases** as the **atomic number increases**.
This is because **extra electron shells** are added.

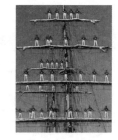

Class 5B wished Mr Evans had come up with a simpler way to illustrate trends in ionic radius.

2) **Isoelectronic ions** are ions of different atoms with the **same number of electrons**. The **ionic radius** of a set of **isoelectronic ions decreases** as the **atomic number increases**.

Ion	Number of electrons	Number of protons	Ionic radius (nm)
N^{3-}	10	7	0.171
O^{2-}	10	8	0.140
F^-	10	9	0.136
Na^+	10	11	0.095
Mg^{2+}	10	12	0.065
Al^{3+}	10	13	0.050

As you go through this series of ions the number of **electrons** **stays the same**, but the number of **protons increases**.

This means that the electrons are **attracted** to the **nucleus** more strongly, pulling them in a little, so the **ionic radius decreases**.

More on Ions and Ionic Bonding

There are Different Kinds of Evidence for the Existence of Ions   *Edexcel only*

The last three pages have all been about the **theory** behind what an ion is and how ionic bonding happens.

Scientists develop **models** of ionic bonding based on **experimental evidence** — they're an attempt to **explain observations** about how ionic compounds behave. You need to know about the kinds of **evidence** that these models are based on.

1) **When ionic compounds are molten or dissolved they conduct electricity.**
   This is evidence for the presence of charged particles which can carry a charge when liquid or in solution.

   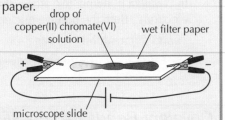

   You can demonstrate this using the **migration of coloured ions** on filter paper.

   When you **electrolyse** a **green** solution of **copper(II) chromate(VI)** the filter paper turns **blue** at the **cathode** and **yellow** at the **anode**.

   Copper(II) ions are **blue** in solution and chromate(VI) ions are **yellow**. Copper(II) chromate(VI) solution is **green** because it contains **both** ions.

   When you pass a current through the solution, the **positive** ions move to the **cathode** and the **negative** ions move to the **anode**.

2) **Electron density maps** look like contour maps. The lines on the map join parts of the molecule that have the **same density** of electrons.

   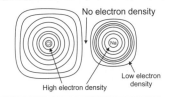

   The electron density map of an **ionic** crystal shows that there are **spaces** between the ions where the density of electrons is **zero**. This shows that the atoms have **no shared electrons** — the bonding electrons have moved from one atom to the other.

   Electron density maps are made using X-ray crystallography. A beam of X-rays is fired at a crystal and the electrons in the crystal scatter the X-rays. The pattern of scattering gives a picture of the electron density throughout the crystal — this is the electron density map.

3) The **physical properties** of ionic compounds provide evidence that supports the theory of ionic bonding.

   1) They have **high melting points** — this tells you that the atoms are held together by a **strong attraction**. Positive and negative ions are strongly attracted, so the **model** fits the **evidence**.

   2) They are **soluble** in **water** but **not** in **non-polar solvents** — this tells you that the particles are **charged**. The ions are **pulled apart** by **polar molecules** like water, but **not** by **non-polar** molecules. Again, the **model** of ionic structures fits this evidence.

   There's more on the properties of ionic compounds on page 37.

Practice Questions

Q1 Write the formula of a nitrate ion and the formula of an ammonium ion.

Q2 Explain why an aluminium ion is smaller than a magnesium ion even though they are isoelectronic.

Q3 Explain how an electron density map of NaCl shows that electrons are not being shared between the atoms.

Exam Questions

Q1 a) The ions O^{2-} and Na^+ have the same number of electrons as an element in Group 0. Which element?   [1 mark]

   b) Explain the difference in ionic radius between the two ions and the Group 0 atom.   [4 marks]

Q2 The apparatus shown in the diagram is set up. After a while a purple streak is seen moving towards the anode.

   a) What does this experiment show about the colour of potassium ions?   [1 mark]

   b) How does this experiment show that ions are charged particles?   [2 marks]

This sentence was printed using Copper(II) Chromate(VI) solution...

...which means that the left-hand side of this page must be positive, and the right-hand side must be negative. Weird. Anyhow, the migration of coloured ions is a great piece of evidence that you can use, say in an exam, to back up all this theory about what an ion is. And what is it that you need to back up a theory? Dedication? Nope. Evidence. That's what you need.

Covalent Bonding

And now for covalent bonding — this is when atoms share electrons with one another so they've all got full outer shells.
These pages are for AQA (Unit 1), OCR A (Unit 1), OCR B (Units 1 and 2) and Edexcel (Unit 1).

Molecules are Groups of Atoms **Bonded** Together

Molecules are the **smallest parts** of compounds that can take part in chemical reactions.
They're formed when **2 or more** atoms covalently bond. It doesn't matter if the atoms are the **same** or **different** —
chlorine gas (Cl_2), carbon monoxide (CO), water (H_2O) and ethanol (C_2H_5OH) are all molecules.

In covalent bonding, two atoms **share** electrons, so they've **both** got full outer shells of
electrons. Both the positive nuclei are attracted **electrostatically** to the shared electrons,
so the bond is pretty strong.

E.g. two hydrogen atoms bond covalently
to form a molecule of hydrogen.

Covalent bonding happens
between non-metals.
Ionic bonding is between
a metal and a non-metal.

Covalent Bonds can be **Sigma** (σ) **Bonds**...   *Edexcel only*

1) The two hydrogen atoms above each have an electron in an **s orbital** (see page 8 for more on orbitals).
   When the hydrogen atoms form an H_2 molecule, their s orbitals overlap to make a σ **bond** (sigma bond).

2) The two s orbitals overlap in a straight line — this gives the
   highest possible electron density between the two nuclei.
   This is a **single** covalent bond and is shown as a single line
   between the atoms, like this: H — H

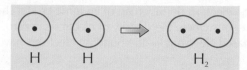

...or **Pi** (π) **Bonds**

1) A π **bond** is formed when two electrons in **p orbitals** overlap.

2) It has **two parts** to it — one 'above' and one 'below' the molecular axis.
   This is because the π orbitals which overlap are **dumbbell shaped**.

3) The π bond is **less tightly bound** to the two nuclei than the σ bond. This means
   π bonds are **weaker** than σ bonds and molecules with π bonds are **more reactive**.

Atoms don't just form single bonds — **double** or even **triple covalent bonds** can form too.
An example of a compound with a double bond is **ethene**, C_2H_4.

Its carbon-carbon **double** bond is drawn as C=C, but
you're not really going to get little equals signs holding
atoms together. The double bond is actually
made up of a σ **bond** plus a π **bond**.

Ethene's π bond makes it a lot **more reactive**
than ethane, which has only got σ bonds.

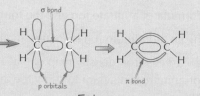

Ethene

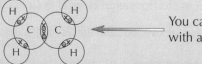

You can also show ethene's bonding
with a **dot-and-cross diagram**.

There are **Limitations** to **Models** of **Covalent Bonding**

There are some problems with the **dot-and-cross** model of covalent bonding.

1) The **dot-and-cross** model only illustrates how the atoms in a compound **share** their electron pairs.
   It can't explain anything about the **lengths** of the covalent bonds formed, or the overall **shape** of a molecule.

2) Most bonds aren't **purely ionic** or **purely covalent** but somewhere in between.
   Thanks to **bond polarisation** (see page 48-49) most compounds have a **mixture** of ionic and covalent properties.

3) Some compounds that use covalent bonding end up with **more than eight electrons** in their outer shell
   (see the next page for more about this).

Covalent Bonding

Make sure you can Draw the Bonding in these Molecules

These diagrams don't show all the electrons in the molecules — just the ones in the **outer shells**:

Chlorine, Cl_2

Hydrogen chloride, HCl

Carbon dioxide, CO_2

Nitrogen, N_2
(nitrogen's a triple-bonder.)

Ammonia, NH_3

Water, H_2O

Methane, CH_4

Oxygen, O_2

Most atoms bond so that they have either 2 or 8 electrons in their outer shell.   *OCR A only*
BUT... there are a few pesky exceptions to make life that bit trickier —

A few compounds have **less** than
8 electrons in their outer shell...

In boron trifluoride, boron only
has 6 electrons in its outer shell.

...and a few compounds can use d orbitals
to 'expand the octet'. This means they have
more than 8 electrons in their outer shell.

In sulfur hexafluoride, sulfur has
12 electrons in its outer shell.

Dative Covalent Bonding is where Both Electrons come from One Atom

The **ammonium ion** (NH_4^+) is formed by dative (or coordinate) covalent bonding — it's an example the examiners love.
It forms when the nitrogen atom in an ammonia molecule **donates a pair of electrons** to a proton (H^+) —

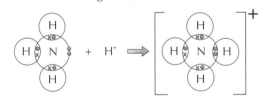
+ H^+ ⟹

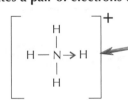

or

Dative covalent bonding is shown
in diagrams by an arrow, pointing
away from the 'donor' atom.

Practice Questions

Q1 a)   When two or more atoms are joined by covalent bonds, they form a _____.

   b)   In covalent bonding, electrons are _____ between atoms.

Q2 Draw a dot-and-cross diagram to show the arrangement of the outer electrons in a molecule of hydrogen chloride.

Exam Questions

Q1 Methane, CH_4, is an organic molecule.

   a)   What type of bonding would you expect it to have?   [1 mark]

   b)   Draw a dot-and-cross diagram showing the arrangement of <u>all</u> the electrons in a molecule of methane.   [2 marks]

Q2 In terms of covalent bonds, explain why ethene is more reactive than ethane.   [3 marks]

Q3 a)   What type of bonding is present in the ammonium ion (NH_4^+)?   [1 mark]

   b)   Explain how this type of bonding occurs.   [2 marks]

<u>Steak and kidney — a great pie bond...</u>

More pretty diagrams to learn here folks — practise till you get every single dot and cross in the right place. It's totally amazing to think of these titchy little atoms sorting themselves out so they've got full outer shells of electrons. Remember — covalent bonding happens between two non-metals, whereas ionic bonding happens between a metal and a non-metal.

Giant Covalent Structures

Atoms can form giant structures as well as piddling little molecules — well...'giant' in molecular terms anyway.
Compared to structures like the Eiffel Tower or even your granny's carriage clock, they're still unbelievably tiny.

These pages are for AQA (Unit 1), OCR A (Unit 1), OCR B (Units 1 and 2) and Edexcel (Units 1 and 2).

Diamond, Graphite and Silicon(IV) Oxide have Giant Molecular Structures

1) **Giant molecular** structures have a huge network of **covalently** bonded atoms.
   (They're sometimes called **macromolecular structures** too.)
2) The reason **carbon** and silicon atoms can form this type of structure is that they can
   each form four strong, covalent bonds.

Diamond is the Hardest known Substance

Diamond is made up of **carbon atoms**.
Each carbon atom is **covalently bonded** to **four** other carbon atoms.
The atoms arrange themselves in a **tetrahedral** shape — its crystal lattice structure.

Diamond

Because of its **strong covalent** bonds:

1) Diamond is extremely **hard** — it's used in diamond-tipped drills and saws.
2) **Vibrations** travel easily through the stiff lattice, so it's a **good thermal conductor**.
3) Diamond has a **very high melting point** — it actually sublimes at over 3800 K.
4) It **can't conduct** electricity — all the outer electrons are held in localised bonds.
5) It won't dissolve in **any** solvent.

'Sublimes' means it changes straight from a solid to a gas, skipping the liquid stage.

You can 'cut' diamond to form gemstones. Its structure
makes it refract light a lot, which is why it sparkles.

Graphite is another Allotrope of Carbon

Allotropes are different forms of the **same element** in the **same state**. Graphite is another **allotrope** of **carbon**.

The carbon atoms are arranged in sheets of flat hexagons covalently bonded with three σ bonds each. The fourth outer electron of each carbon atom is delocalised.

Graphite

The sheets of hexagons are bonded together by weak van der Waals forces.

Graphite's **structure** means it has some **different properties** from diamond.

1) The weak bonds **between** the layers in graphite are easily broken, so the sheets can slide over each other — graphite feels **slippery** and is used as a **dry lubricant** and in **pencils**.
2) The 'delocalised' electrons in graphite aren't attached to any particular carbon atoms and are **free to move** along the sheets, so an **electric current** can flow.
3) The layers are quite **far apart** compared to the length of the covalent bonds, so graphite is **less dense** than diamond and is used to make **strong, lightweight** sports equipment.
4) Because of the **strong covalent bonds** in the hexagon sheets, graphite also has a **very high melting point** (it sublimes at over 3900 K).
5) Like diamond, graphite is **insoluble** in any solvent.
   The covalent bonds in the sheets are **too difficult** to break.

Giant Covalent Structures

Silicon(IV) Oxide has a Tetrahedral Arrangement

OCR B (Unit 2) only

1) **Silicon dioxide** or **silica** (SiO_2) is found as **quartz** or **sand** (sand's not pure — it's got lots of bits of other stuff in too).

2) Each silicon atom **covalently bonds** with **four oxygen atoms** in a **tetrahedral** arrangement to form a big **crystal lattice**.

3) Its structure **isn't** exactly the same as diamond's, because the oxygen atoms can only bond with **two silicon atoms**.

4) Like diamond, silica is a **hard crystalline solid** with a **high melting point**. It is **insoluble** in any solvent. This is down to its strong **covalent bonds**.

5) Silica **doesn't conduct electricity** — all of its bonding electrons are used for making covalent bonds.

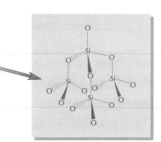

The Properties of Giant Structures Provide Evidence for Covalent Bonding

All of these giant structures have some properties in common — thanks to their covalent bonds:

1) They are all **insoluble** in **polar solvents** like water, which shows that they **don't contain ions**.

2) They form **hard crystals** with very **high melting points**. This is down to their network of very strong covalent bonds.

3) They **don't conduct electricity**. All their bonding electrons are used to form **covalent bonds**, and they contain **no charged particles**. The exception to this rule is graphite, which can conduct electricity because of the **delocalised electrons** within its sheets of atoms.

Electron Density Maps Give Evidence for Covalent Bonding

Edexcel (Unit 1) only

On page 39 you saw what the **electron density map** of an ionic compound looks like. The electron density map of a **covalently bonded molecule** looks very different.

This time you can see an area of **high electron density** between the two atoms. It shows that they're **sharing electrons** — the atoms have a **covalent bond** between them.

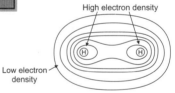

Practice Questions

Q1 How are the carbon sheets in graphite held together?

Q2 In silica, how many oxygen atoms are bonded to each silicon atom?

Q3 Are the melting points of diamond, graphite and silicon dioxide high or low? Explain why this is.

Exam Questions

Q1 Carbon can be found as the allotropes diamond and graphite.

   a) What type of structure do diamond and graphite display?   [1 mark]

   b) Draw diagrams to illustrate the structures of diamond and graphite.   [2 marks]

   c) Compare and explain the electrical conductivities of diamond and graphite in terms of their structure and bonding.   [4 marks]

Q2 Diamond and silica have similar physical properties.

   Give two properties that are shared by diamond and silica.

   Explain why these materials display each property in terms of their molecular structure.   [4 marks]

Carbon is a girl's best friend...

Examiners love giving you questions on diamond and graphite. Close the book and do a quick sketch of each allotrope, together with a list of their properties — then look back at the page and see what you missed. It might be less fun than ironing your underwear, but it's much more useful and the only way to make sure you sparkle in the exam.

Nanostructures and Metallic Bonding

There's a third allotrope of carbon that you need to know about — and this one's really really really tiny...
This page is for Edexcel (Unit 2).

The *Fullerenes* are a Group of *Carbon Allotropes*

1) **Fullerenes** are **molecules** of **carbon** shaped like **hollow balls** or **tubes**.
Each carbon atom forms **three** covalent bonds with its neighbours, leaving
free electrons that can **conduct** electricity.

2) Fullerenes are **nanoparticles**. Nanoparticles are generally up to 100 nanometres across.

3) The first fullerene to be discovered was **buckminsterfullerene**, which has **60** carbon
atoms joined to make a **ball** — its molecular formula is C_{60}. It occurs naturally in soot.

4) Many fullerenes are **soluble** in **organic solvents**, and form brightly coloured solutions.

5) Because they're hollow, fullerenes can be used to '**cage**' other molecules.
The fullerene structure forms around another molecule, which is then trapped inside.
This could be used as a way of **delivering a drug** into specific cells of the body.

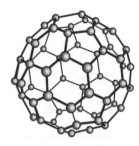

Buckminsterfullerene

A **carbon nanotube** is like a single layer of graphite rolled up into a tiny hollow cylinder.

1) All those covalent bonds make carbon
nanotubes **very strong**. They can be used to
to reinforce graphite in tennis rackets and to
make stronger, lighter building materials.

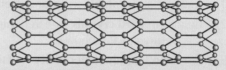

2) Nanotubes **conduct** electricity, so they can be used as tiny wires in **circuits** for computer chips.

3) The ends of a nanotube can be '**capped**', or closed off, to create a large molecular cage structure.

All these applications of fullerenes are examples of **nanotechnology**.
Nanotechnology is concerned with the development and use of **materials** and **devices** that are made from **nanoparticles**.
At this tiny scale, materials often have very **different properties** from '**bulk**' forms of the same substance.

There's a Debate About the *Safety* of *Nanotechnology*

When someone comes up with a **new** way to use **nanotechnology** there are often questions about whether it's **safe**.
As with all practical applications of science it's a question of weighing up any **risks** against the possible **benefits**:

1) You don't want to stop a **useful** new technology being developed.
A new nanotechnology could improve people's **health** or **quality of life**.

2) But you also don't want people to be using a product that could **harm** them.
So all new products and technologies are **thoroughly tested** before anyone is allowed to use them.

3) Some people question whether any nanotechnology has been tested enough to **prove** that it's **safe**.
Others think that where the **benefit** is big enough, we should take the **risk** of starting to use some
nanotechnologies that appear to be safe.

Example — Nanoparticles in Transparent Sunscreen Creams

1) Many **sunscreen** creams contain nanoparticles of **zinc oxide** and
titanium dioxide. These particles **reflect UV light**, but at this size
they appear **transparent** — so you can have a **see-through sunscreen**.

2) People are much more likely to use sunscreen if it's see-through.
And it's really important that they do, because it reduces their
risk of getting **skin cancer**.

3) Scientists have found that some nanoparticles seem to be able to **pass through** the **skin**
and into **cells**. And if they can do that, there's a possibility that they could **damage** the cells.

4) Researchers studying the sunscreens **don't think** that these nanoparticles are capable of getting
through the skin. But some people think we should **avoid using them** until we're **absolutely
sure** that they're not harmful.

Nanostructures and Metallic Bonding

This page is for AQA (Unit 1), OCR A (Unit 1), OCR B (Units 1 and 2) and Edexcel (Unit 1).

Metals *have Giant Structures Too*

Metal elements exist as **giant metallic lattice structures**.

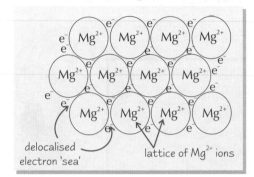

delocalised
electron 'sea'

lattice of Mg^{2+} ions

1) The outermost shell of electrons of a metal atom is **delocalised** — the electrons are free to move about the metal. This leaves a **positive metal ion**, e.g. Na^+, Mg^{2+}, Al^{3+}.

2) The positive metal ions are **attracted** to the **delocalised** negative electrons. They form a lattice of closely packed positive ions in a **sea** of delocalised electrons — this is **metallic bonding**.

Metallic bonding explains why metals do what they do —

1) The **number of delocalised electrons per atom** affects the melting point. The **more** there are, the **stronger** the bonding will be and the **higher** the melting point. Mg^{2+} has **two** delocalised electrons per atom, so it's got a **higher melting point** than Na^+, which only has **one**. The **size** of the metal ion and the **lattice structure** also affect the melting point.

2) As there are **no bonds** holding specific ions together, the metal ions can "**creep**" when the structure is pulled, so metals are **malleable** (a posh word for bendable) and **ductile** (can be drawn into a wire).

3) The delocalised electrons can pass **kinetic energy** to each other, making metals **good thermal conductors**.

4) Metals are **good electrical conductors** because the **delocalised electrons** can carry a **current**.

5) Metals are **insoluble**, except in **liquid metals**, because of the **strength** of the metallic bonds.

Practice Questions

Q1 What are fullerenes?

Q2 Describe the structure of a nanotube.

Q3 Explain why metals can be bent into shape without breaking.

Q4 Why are metals good electrical conductors?

Exam Questions

Q1 a) Explain what is meant by metallic bonding. Draw a diagram to illustrate your explanation.   [4 marks]

   b) Explain why calcium has a higher melting point than potassium.   [4 marks]

Q2 a) Describe the structure of buckminsterfullerene.   [3 marks]

   b) Buckminsterfullerene is an **allotrope** of carbon.
       What is meant by the term allotrope?   [1 mark]

   c) Carbon nanotubes are a member of the fullerene family. Explain one potential use of carbon nanotubes.   [2 marks]

Y'all say howdy to buckminsterfullerene — the state molecule of Texas...

No really, it is. Not that you're going to get any marks for knowing that*. But you'll probably get some for knowing about its structure and uses. That goes for carbon nanotubes too. And you should definitely know the properties of metals and how they are explained by metallic bonding. Because they're things that examiners love asking questions about.

*Unless you're appearing on a seriously obscure quiz show.

Shapes of Molecules

Chemistry would be heaps more simple if all molecules were flat. But they're not.
These pages are for AQA (Unit 1), OCR A (Unit 1), OCR B (Units 1 and 2) and Edexcel (Unit 2).

Molecular Shape depends on Electron Pairs around the Central Atom

Molecules and molecular ions come in loads of **different shapes**.
The shape depends on the **number of pairs** of electrons in the outer shell of the central atom.

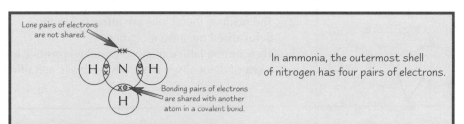

Lone pairs of electrons are not shared.

Bonding pairs of electrons are shared with another atom in a covalent bond.

In ammonia, the outermost shell of nitrogen has four pairs of electrons.

A lone pear

Electron Pairs exist as Charge Clouds

Bonding pairs and lone pairs of electrons exist as **charge clouds**. A charge cloud is an area where you have a really **big chance** of finding an electron pair. The electrons don't stay still — they **whizz around** inside the charge cloud.

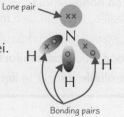

Lone pair

Bonding pairs

- The charge cloud for a **bonding pair** is 'sausage' shaped (for a sigma bond), because the electrons are attracted towards two different nuclei.
- The charge cloud for a **lone pair** is more 'football' shaped, because the electrons are pulled closer to the nucleus of the **central atom**.

Here's ammonia again, but this time with charge clouds shown.

Electron Charge Clouds Repel Each Other

1) Electrons are all **negatively charged**, so it's pretty obvious that the charge clouds will **repel** each other as much as they can.

2) This sounds straightforward, but the **shape** of the charge cloud affects **how much** it repels other charge clouds. Lone-pair charge clouds repel **more** than bonding-pair charge clouds.

3) So, the **greatest** angles are between **lone pairs** of electrons, and bond angles between bonding pairs are often **reduced** because they are pushed together by lone-pair repulsion.

Lone-pair/lone-pair bond angles are the biggest.	*Lone-pair/bonding-pair bond angles are the second biggest.*	*Bonding-pair/bonding-pair bond angles are the smallest.*

4) This is known by the long-winded name '**Valence-Shell Electron-Pair Repulsion Theory**'.

The central atoms in these molecules all have **four pairs** of electrons in their outer shells, but they're all **different shapes**.

H — C — H   109.5°

Methane — no lone pairs

The lone pair repels the bonding pairs

N — H   107°

Ammonia — 1 lone pair

2 lone pairs reduce the bond angle even more

O   104.5°

Water — 2 lone pairs

In a molecule diagram, use wedges to show that a bond sticks out of the page towards you, and a broken (or dotted) line to show a bond goes behind the page.

5) These rules mean that the **shapes and bond angles** of loads of molecules can be predicted.

Shapes of Molecules

Practise *Drawing* these Molecules

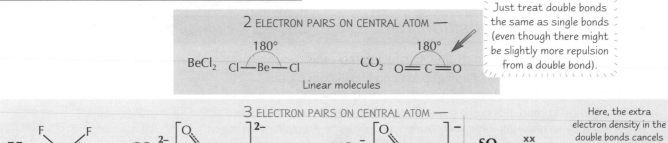

2 ELECTRON PAIRS ON CENTRAL ATOM —

$BeCl_2$ 180°   Cl—Be—Cl CO_2 180°   O=C=O

Linear molecules

> Just treat double bonds the same as single bonds (even though there might be slightly more repulsion from a double bond).

3 ELECTRON PAIRS ON CENTRAL ATOM —

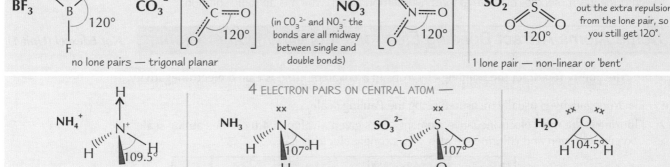

BF_3 120°   no lone pairs — trigonal planar

$CO_3{}^{2-}$ 120°

$NO_3{}^{-}$ 120° (in $CO_3{}^{2-}$ and $NO_3{}^{-}$ the bonds are all midway between single and double bonds)

SO_2 120°   1 lone pair — non-linear or 'bent'

Here, the extra electron density in the double bonds cancels out the extra repulsion from the lone pair, so you still get 120°.

4 ELECTRON PAIRS ON CENTRAL ATOM —

$NH_4{}^{+}$ 109.5°   no lone pairs — tetrahedral

NH_3 107°   1 lone pair — trigonal pyramidal

$SO_3{}^{2-}$ 107°

H_2O 104.5°   2 lone pairs — non-linear or 'bent'

> Some central atoms can use d orbitals and can 'expand the octet' — which means they can have more than eight bonding electrons. E.g. in PCl_5, phosphorus has 10 electrons in its outermost shell, while in SF_6, sulfur has 12.

5 ELECTRON PAIRS ON CENTRAL ATOM —

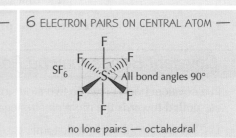

PCl_5 120°   90°   no lone pairs — trigonal bipyramidal

6 ELECTRON PAIRS ON CENTRAL ATOM —

SF_6 All bond angles 90°   no lone pairs — octahedral

Practice Questions

Q1 What is a lone pair of electrons?

Q2 What is a charge cloud?

Q3 What shape is the charge cloud for a bonding pair of electrons?

Q4 Write down the order of the strength of repulsion between different kinds of electron pairs.

Q5 Draw a tetrahedral molecule.

Exam Question

Q1 Nitrogen and boron can form the chlorides NCl_3 and BCl_3.

   a) Draw 'dot and cross' diagrams to show the bonding in NCl_3 and BCl_3.   [2 marks]

   b) Draw the shapes of the molecules NCl_3 and BCl_3.
      Show the approximate values of the bond angles on the diagrams and name each shape.   [6 marks]

   c) Explain why the shapes of NCl_3 and BCl_3 are different.   [3 marks]

These molecules ain't square...

In the exam, those evil examiners might try to throw you by asking you to predict the shape of an unfamiliar molecule. Don't panic — it'll be just like one you do know, e.g. PH_3 is the same shape as NH_3. Make sure you can draw every single molecule on this page. Yep, that's right — from memory. And you need to know what the shapes are called too.

Polarisation of Molecules and Ions

Opposites attract, like Jack Sprat and his wife — that's all you need to know. Well OK, that's not true, so get learnin'...
These pages are for AQA (Unit 1), OCR A (Unit 1), OCR B (Unit 2) and Edexcel (Units 1 and 2).

There's a Gradual *Transition* from Ionic to Covalent Bonding   *Not Edexcel (Unit 1)*

1) Very few compounds come even close to being **purely ionic**.

2) Only bonds between atoms of a **single** element, like diatomic gases
such as hydrogen (H_2) or oxygen (O_2), can be **purely covalent**.

3) So really, most compounds come somewhere **in between** the two extremes —
meaning they've often got ionic **and** covalent properties, e.g. covalent hydrogen
chloride gas molecules dissolve to form hydrochloric acid, which is an ionic solution.

$$HCl_{(g)} \xrightarrow{H_2O} H^+_{(aq)} + Cl^-_{(aq)}$$

Some Atoms *Attract* Bonding Electrons More than Other Atoms   *Not Edexcel (Unit 1)*

The ability to attract the bonding electrons in a covalent bond is called electronegativity.

1) Electronegativity is usually measured using the **Pauling scale**.

2) **Fluorine** is the most electronegative element — it's given a value of **4.0** on the Pauling scale.
Oxygen, nitrogen and chlorine are also very strongly electronegative.

Element	H	C	N	Cl	O	F
Electronegativity	2.1	2.5	3.0	3.0	3.5	4.0

3) Electronegativity **increases across periods** and **decreases down groups** (ignoring the noble gases).

Covalent Bonds may be Polarised by *Differences* in *Electronegativity*

In a covalent bond between two atoms of **different** electronegativities, the bonding electrons   *Not Edexcel (Unit 1)*
are **pulled towards** the more electronegative atom. This makes the bond **polar**.

1) The covalent bonds in diatomic gases (e.g. H_2, Cl_2) are
non-polar because the atoms have **equal** electronegativities
and so the electrons are equally attracted to both nuclei.

2) Some elements, like carbon and hydrogen, have pretty **similar**
electronegativities, so bonds between them are essentially **non-polar**.

3) In a **polar bond**, the difference in electronegativity between the two atoms
causes a **dipole**. A dipole is a **difference in charge** between the two atoms
caused by a shift in **electron density** in the bond.

Permanent polar bonding

4) So what you need to **remember** is that the greater the **difference** in electronegativity, the **more polar** the bond.

Polar Bonds *Don't* always make *Polar Molecules*   *OCR B and Edexcel (Unit 2) only*

Whether a molecule has a **permanent dipole** depends on its **shape** and the **polarity** of its bonds.

1) So in a simple molecule, such as **hydrogen chloride**, the
polar bond gives the whole molecule a permanent dipole
— it's a **polar molecule**.

$$\overset{\delta+}{H} \overset{\circ}{\underset{x}{-}} \overset{\delta-}{Cl}$$
polar

'δ' (delta) means 'slightly', so
'δ+' means 'slightly positive'.

2) A more complicated molecule may have **several polar bonds**.
If the polar bonds are arranged so they point in opposite directions,
they'll **cancel each other out** — the molecule is **non-polar** overall.

No dipole overall.

$$\overset{\delta-}{O} = \overset{\delta+}{C} = \overset{\delta-}{O}$$

3) If the polar bonds all
point in roughly the
same direction, then the
molecule will be **polar**.

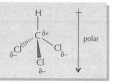

polar

4) **Lone pairs of electrons** on the
central atom also have an effect
on the overall polarity and may
cancel out the dipole created by
the bonding pairs.

No dipole overall.

Polarisation of Molecules and Ions

Ions *can be* Polarised *too* — Edexcel (Unit 1) only

> A **cation** is a positive ion, an **anion** is a negative ion, and an **onion** is the edible bulb of the Allium cepa plant.

What normally happens in ionic compounds is that the **positive charge** on the **cation** attracts electrons towards it from the **anion** — this is **polarisation** again.

1) **Small** cations with a **large charge** are **very polarising** because they have a **high charge density** — the positive charge is concentrated in the ion. So the cation can pull electrons towards itself.

2) **Large anions** are **polarised more easily** than small anions because their electrons are further away from the nucleus. So the electrons on large anions can be pulled away more easily towards cations.

3) If a compound contains a cation with a **high polarising ability** and an anion which is **easily polarised**, some of the anion's electron charge cloud will be dragged towards the positive cation.

4) If the compound is polarised enough, a **covalent bond** with a **dipole** is formed. It's now a **polar molecule**.

> How polarising a cation is depends on its charge density. The charge density is just the charge/volume ratio.
>
> Charge density = $\dfrac{\text{charge}}{\text{volume}}$

Increasing the positive charge leads to more polarisation —

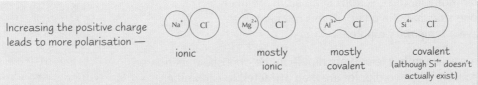

ionic   mostly ionic   mostly covalent   covalent (although Si^{4+} doesn't actually exist)

- The more a **covalent bond** is polarised, the more **ionic character** it gains.
- The more an **ionic bond** is polarised, the more **covalent character** it gains.
- You can work out why some compounds have **weird properties** by thinking about how **polarised** the compound is.

Practice Questions

Q1 What are the only bonds which can be purely covalent?

Q2 What is the most electronegative element?

Q3 What is a dipole?

Q4 What sort of ion is easily polarised?

Exam Questions

Q1 Many covalent molecules have a permanent dipole, due to differences in electronegativities.
    a) Define the term electronegativity.   [2 marks]

    b) Draw the shapes and predict the overall polarity of the following molecules, marking any bond polarities clearly on your diagram:
      (i) Br_2 (ii) H_2O (iii) CCl_4 (iv) NH_3 [8 marks]

Q2 Metal/non-metal compounds are usually ionic, yet solid aluminium chloride exhibits many covalent characteristics. Explain why.   [4 marks]

Enough of this chemistry rubbish. Here are some interesting facts...

If you chop the head off a beetle, it wouldn't die of being beheaded, but actually starvation. It's true. If you ate 14 lbs of almonds, you'd die of cyanide poisoning. It's true! Daddy-long-legs are actually the most poisonous insects in the world, but they can't pierce the skin... it's TRUE. Every night, the human body sweats enough to fill a swimming pool. It's true...

Intermolecular Forces

Intermolecular forces hold molecules together. They're pretty important, cos we'd all be gassy clouds without them.
These pages are for AQA (Unit 1), OCR A (Unit 1), OCR B (Unit 2) and Edexcel (Unit 2).

Intermolecular Forces are **Very Weak**

Intermolecular forces are forces **between** molecules. They're much **weaker** than covalent, ionic or metallic bonds. There are three types you need to know about:

1) **Instantaneous dipole-induced dipole** or **van der Waals** forces (this is the weakest type)
2) **Permanent dipole-dipole interactions**
3) **Hydrogen bonding** (this is the strongest type)

Sometimes the term 'van der Waals forces' is considered to include all three types of intermolecular force.

Van der Waals Forces are Found Between **All** Atoms and Molecules

Van der Waals forces cause **all** atoms and molecules to be **attracted** to each other.

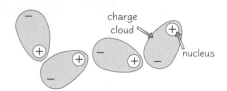

1) **Electrons** in charge clouds are always **moving** really quickly. At any particular moment, the electrons in an atom are likely to be more to one side than the other. At this moment, the atom would have a **temporary dipole**.

2) This dipole can cause **another** temporary dipole in the opposite direction on a neighbouring atom. The two dipoles are then **attracted** to each other.

Edexcel: These are sometimes called 'London forces'.

3) The second dipole can cause yet another dipole in a **third atom**. It's kind of like a domino rally.

4) Because the electrons are constantly moving, the dipoles are being **created** and **destroyed** all the time. Even though the dipoles keep changing, the **overall effect** is for the atoms to be **attracted** to each another.

Stronger **Van der Waals Forces** mean *Higher Melting and Boiling Points*

1) Not all van der Waals forces are the same strength — larger molecules have **larger electron clouds**, meaning **stronger** van der Waals forces.

2) Molecules with greater **surface areas** also have stronger van der Waals forces because they have a **bigger exposed electron cloud**.

3) When you **boil** a liquid, you need to **overcome** the intermolecular forces, so that the particles can **escape** from the liquid surface. It stands to reason that you need **more energy** to overcome **stronger** intermolecular forces, so liquids with stronger van der Waals forces will have **higher boiling points**.

4) Melting solids also involves **overcoming intermolecular forces**, so solids with stronger van der Waals forces will have **higher melting points** too.

5) Alkanes show this nicely — **long-chain alkanes** melt and boil at **higher** temperatures than short-chain alkanes. Also, **straight-chain alkanes** have **more surface area** than branched alkanes, so the melting and boiling temperatures of straight-chain alkanes are **higher**. For more details and some nice diagrams have a squiz at page 81.

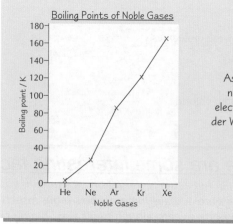

As you go down the group of noble gases, the number of electrons increases. So the van der Waals forces increase, and so do the boiling points.

Intermolecular Forces

Polar Molecules have Permanent Dipole-Dipole Forces

The $\delta+$ and $\delta-$ charges on **polar molecules** cause **weak electrostatic forces** of attraction **between** molecules.

E.g. hydrogen chloride gas has polar molecules.

$$\overset{\delta+}{H}-\overset{\delta-}{Cl}\cdots\overset{\delta+}{H}-\overset{\delta-}{Cl}\cdots\overset{\delta+}{H}-\overset{\delta-}{Cl}$$

Even though they're weak, the forces are still much stronger than van der Waals forces.

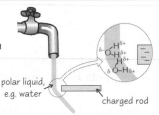

Now this bit's pretty cool:

If you put an **electrostatically charged rod** next to a jet of a polar liquid, like water, the liquid will **move** towards the rod. I wouldn't believe me either, but it's true. It's because **polar liquids** contain molecules that have **permanent dipoles**. It doesn't matter if the rod is **positively** or **negatively** charged. The polar molecules in the liquid can **turn around** so the oppositely charged end is attracted towards the rod.

You can use this experiment to find out if the molecules in a jet of liquid are **polar or non-polar**.

polar liquid, e.g. water

charged rod

Hydrogen Bonding is the Strongest Intermolecular Force

1) Hydrogen bonding **only** happens when **hydrogen** is covalently bonded to **fluorine**, **nitrogen** or **oxygen**.

2) Fluorine, nitrogen and oxygen are very **electronegative**, so they draw the bonding electrons away from the hydrogen atom. The bond is so **polarised**, and hydrogen has such a **high charge density** because it's so small, that the hydrogen atoms form weak bonds with **lone pairs of electrons** on the fluorine, nitrogen or oxygen atoms of **other molecules**.

3) Molecules which have hydrogen bonding are usually **organic**, containing **-OH** or **-NH** groups. **Water** and **ammonia** both have hydrogen bonding.

A lone pair of electrons on the oxygen is attracted to the hydrogen.

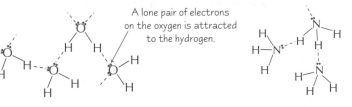

4) Hydrogen bonding has a **huge effect** on the properties of substances.

- They have **higher boiling and melting points** than other similar molecules because of the **extra energy** needed to break the hydrogen bonds.

  This is the case with **water**, and also **hydrogen fluoride**, which has a much **higher boiling point** than the other hydrogen halides.

- Ice has more hydrogen bonds than liquid water, and hydrogen bonds are relatively **long**. So the H_2O molecules in ice are further apart on average, making ice **less dense** than liquid water.

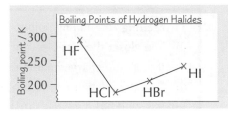

Boiling Points of Hydrogen Halides

Practice Questions

Q1 What's the strongest type of intermolecular force?

Q2 Which noble gas has the highest boiling point and why?

Q3 What is a hydrogen bond?

Exam Question

Q1 a) Name three types of intermolecular force. [3 marks]

Water, H_2O, boils at 373 K.

b) Water is a Group 6 hydride. This graph shows the boiling points of some Group 6 hydrides. State and explain the overall trend in boiling points for Group 6 hydrides. Why is water's boiling point higher than expected in comparison to other Group 6 hydrides? [5 marks]

c) Draw a labelled diagram showing the intermolecular bonding that takes place in water. [2 marks]

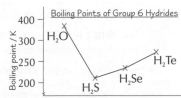

Boiling Points of Group 6 Hydrides

Van der Waal — a German hit for Oasis...

Just because intermolecular forces are a bit wimpy and weak, don't forget they're there. It'd all fall apart without them. Learn the three types — van der Waals, permanent dipole-dipole forces and hydrogen bonds. I bet fish are glad that water forms hydrogen bonds. If it didn't, their water would boil. (And they wouldn't have evolved in the first place.)

Properties of Structures

Lots of this stuff you should already be able to recite in your sleep, but just in case it's fallen out of your brain, here it is...
These pages are for AQA (Unit 1), OCR A (Unit 1), OCR B (Units 1 and 2) and Edexcel (Units 1 and 2).

The **Physical Properties** of Solids, Liquids and Gases Depend on **Particles**

1) A typical **solid** has its particles very **close** together. This gives it a high density, and makes it **incompressible**. The particles **vibrate** about a **fixed point** and can't move about freely.

2) A typical **liquid** has a similar density to a solid and is virtually **incompressible**. The particles move about **freely** and **randomly** within the liquid, allowing it to flow.

3) In **gases**, the particles have **loads more** energy and are much **further apart**. So the density is generally pretty low and it's **very compressible**. The particles move about **freely**, with not a lot of attraction between them, so they'll quickly **diffuse** to fill a container.

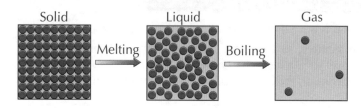

Solid → Melting → Liquid → Boiling → Gas

The jelly state* occurs in solids when the particles start feeling a bit tired and wobbly.

Don't write this in the exam, cos I just made it up, like...

The Physical Properties of a **Solid** Depend on the **Nature** of its Particles

Here are some handy points that'll make AS chemistry a little less painful —

1) **Melting** and **boiling** points depend on **attraction** between particles.
2) The **closer** the particles, the **greater** the density.
3) If there are **charged** particles that are **free** to move, then it'll conduct electricity.
4) Solubility depends on the **type** of particles present.
5) If a solid has a regular structure, it's called a **crystal**. The structure is a **crystal lattice**.

Covalent Bonds **Don't** Break during **Melting** and **Boiling***

This is something that confuses loads of people — prepare to be enlightened...

1) To **melt** or **boil** a simple covalent compound you only have to overcome the **van der Waals forces** or **hydrogen bonds** that hold the molecules together.

2) You **don't** need to break the much stronger covalent bonds that hold the atoms together in the molecules.

3) That's why simple covalent compounds have relatively **low melting** and **boiling points**. For example:

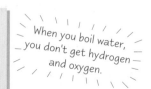

When you boil water, you don't get hydrogen and oxygen.

Chlorine, Cl_2, has **stronger** covalent bonds than bromine, Br_2.
But under normal conditions, chlorine is a **gas** and bromine a **liquid**.
Bromine has the higher boiling point because its molecules are **bigger**, giving stronger van der Waals forces.

Except for giant molecular substances, like silicon dioxide.

Properties of Structures

Learn the **Properties** of the Main Substance Types

Make sure you know this stuff like the back of your spam —

Bonding	Examples	Melting and boiling points	Typical state at STP	Does solid conduct electricity?	Does liquid conduct electricity?	Is it soluble in water?
Ionic	NaCl MgCl$_2$	High	Solid	No (ions are held firmly in place)	Yes (ions are free to move)	Yes
Simple molecular (covalent)	CO$_2$ I$_2$ H$_2$O	Low (have to overcome van der Waals forces or hydrogen bonds, not covalent bonds)	Liquid or gas (water is liquid because it has hydrogen bonds)	No	No	Depends on how polarised the molecule is
Giant molecular (covalent)	Diamond Graphite SiO$_2$	High	Solid	No (except graphite)	— (will generally sublime)	No
Metallic	Fe Mg Al	High	Solid	Yes (delocalised electrons)	Yes (delocalised electrons)	No

Practice Questions

Q1 Describe the motion of particles in solids, liquids and gases.

Q2 Why do gases diffuse to fill the space available?

Q3 What is a solid with a regular structure called?

Q4 What types of bonds must be overcome in order for a substance to boil or melt?

Q5 Do ionic compounds conduct electricity?

Q6 Why can metals conduct electricity?

Exam Questions

Q1

Substance	Melting point	Electrical conductivity of solid	Electrical conductivity of liquid	Solubility in water
A	High	Poor	Good	Soluble
B	Low	Poor	Poor	Insoluble
C	High	Good	Good	Insoluble
D	Very High	Poor	Poor	Insoluble

a) Identify the type of structure present in each substance, A to D. [4 marks]

b) Which substance is most likely to be:
(i) diamond, (ii) aluminium, (iii) sodium chloride and (iv) iodine? [4 marks]

Q2 Explain the electrical conductivity of magnesium, sodium chloride and graphite.
In your answer you should consider the structure and bonding of each of these materials. [14 marks]

Gases — like flies in jam jars...

You need to learn the info in the table above. With a quick glance in my crystal ball, I can almost guarantee you'll need a bit of it in your exam...let me look a bit closer and tell you which bit....mmm....nah. It's clouded over. You'll have to learn the lot. Sorry. Tell you what — close the book and see how much of the table you can scribble out from memory.

The Periodic Table

As far as Chemistry topics go, the Periodic Table is a bit of a biggie. So much so that they even want you to know the history of it. So make yourself comfortable and I'll tell you a story that began... oh, about 200 years ago...

This page is for OCR A (Unit 1) and OCR B (Unit 1).

In the *1800s*, Elements Could Only Be Grouped by *Atomic Mass*

1) In the early 1800s, there were only two ways to categorise elements — by their **physical and chemical properties** and by their **relative atomic mass**. (The modern Periodic Table is arranged by proton number, but back then, they knew nothing about protons or electrons. The only thing they could measure was relative atomic mass.)

2) An English chemist called **John Newlands** had the first good stab at arranging the elements in 1863. He noticed that if he arranged the elements in order of **mass**, similar elements appeared at regular intervals — every **eighth element** was similar. He called this the **law of octaves**, and he listed some known elements in rows of seven so that the similar elements lined up in columns.

Li	Be	B	C	N	O	F
Na	Mg	Al	Si	P	S	Cl

3) Newlands presented his ideas to other scientists — but they **weren't convinced**. The problem was, the pattern **broke down** on the third row, with transition metals like Fe, Cu and Zn messing it up completely.

Dmitri Mendeleev Created the *First Accepted Version*

1) In 1869, Russian chemist **Dmitri Mendeleev** produced a much better table which wasn't far off the one we have today.

2) Like Newlands, he arranged all the known elements by atomic mass (with a few exceptions). But unlike everyone else, he **left some gaps** in the table where the next element didn't seem to fit. By putting in gaps, he could keep elements with similar chemical properties in the same group.

	Group 1	Group 2	Group 3	Group 4	Group 5	Group 6	Group 7
Period 1	H						
Period 2	Li	Be	B	C	N	O	F
Period 3	Na	Mg	Al	Si	P	S	Cl
Period 4	K Cu	Ca Zn	* *	Ti *	V As	Cr Se	Mn Br
Period 5	Rb Ag	Sr Cd	Y In	Zr Sn	Nb Sb	Mo Te	* I

What do you think of the table? I made it myself...

Oh, Dmitri, I love it....

3) Mendeleev was being quite **bold** leaving gaps — Newlands and others who'd tried arranging the elements had assumed that they'd all been discovered. They'd also assumed that all the substances they were arranging **were elements**. (Both these assumptions turned out to be wrong. Oops.)

> Mendeleev realised that knowledge of the elements was far from complete, and presented his 'best guess' based on the evidence available. It's still the case today that scientific knowledge is **tentative** — we know that our understanding of many areas of science is **incomplete** and that ideas might have to change quite radically in the future.

4) Mendeleev **predicted** the properties of the missing elements by comparing them with other elements in the same group. If his ideas were correct then his predictions would turn out to be correct.

5) For example, Mendeleev left a gap in the table below silicon and predicted several of the properties of the missing element. He called the missing element **ekasilicon**.

   In 1886, a German chemist, Winkler, discovered the element we now call germanium, and it fitted Mendeleev's predictions for eka-silicon almost perfectly.

6) More new elements were discovered that fitted, as predicted, into the gaps in the table. This showed that old Dmitri had been right about the periodic patterns in the elements.

	ekasilicon	germanium
atomic mass	72	72.59
density (g/cm³)	5.5	5.35
melting point	high	947 °C
colour	grey	grey

The Periodic Table

This page is for AQA (Unit 1), OCR A (Unit 1), OCR B (Unit 1) and Edexcel (Unit 1).

The **Modern Periodic Table** arranges Elements by **Proton Number**

The modern Periodic Table doesn't look **totally** different from Mendeleev's, but there have been changes:

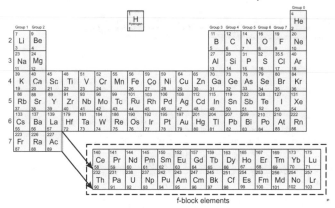

f-block elements

1) The elements are arranged according to **atomic number** rather than by mass.

2) This fixes a few elements that Mendeleev had put out of place using atomic mass.

3) It has a whole new group — the **noble gases** (Group 0, or 8), which were discovered in the 1890s.

4) The final big change was a result of the work of **Glenn Seaborg**. He suggested how the **f-block** elements fit into the Periodic Table (though they're usually shown separated from the main part of the table).

1) The modern Periodic Table is arranged into **periods** (rows) and **groups** (columns).

2) All the elements **within a period** have the same number of **electron shells** (if you don't worry about the sub-shells)
   — the elements of Period 1 (hydrogen and helium) both have 1 electron shell.
   — the elements in Period 2 have 2 electron shells. And so on down the table...

3) All the elements **within a group** have the same number of **electrons in their outer shell**. This means they have similar chemical properties. The group number tells you the number of electrons in the outer shell, e.g. Group 1 elements have 1 electron in their outer shell, Group 4 elements have 4 electrons, and so on...

Practice Questions

Q1 In what ways is Newlands' 'Periodic Table' not as good as Mendeleev's?

Q2 In what order did Mendeleev originally set out the elements?

Q3 In what order are the elements set out in the modern Periodic Table? Who was the first to do this?

Q4 What is the name given to the columns in the Periodic Table?

Q5 What is the name given to the rows in the Periodic Table? *(Err, hello — <u>easy</u> questions alert.)*

Exam Questions

Q1 John Newlands' attempt at arranging the elements was based on his law of octaves.

   a) What property of the elements did John Newlands base his arrangement on?   [1 mark]

   b) Why was his law known as the law of 'octaves'?   [2 marks]

   c) What was the problem with his law?   [1 mark]

Q2 Dmitri Mendeleev's Periodic Table arranged the elements in the same way as John Newlands' but with one important difference.

   a) What was the important difference?   [1 mark]

   b) Describe the steps which led from this difference to the conclusion that Mendeleev's table was probably correct.   [2 marks]

*Periodic — probably the best table in the world**

The Periodic Table is pretty fundamental to chemistry — it's good to know about the major steps in its development. The general principle about how science progresses is important too — people make observations and develop models to fit them — then other people test the models and try to improve them or show that they're wrong.

Periodic Trends

These pages are about trends in properties that occur as you move across a period, and repeat themselves in each period. E.g. metal to non-metal is a trend that occurs going left to right. You might have to explain why some trends occur — it's to do with sub-shells and other hard-sounding things, but it's all pretty logical.

These two pages are for AQA (Unit 1), OCR A (Unit 1), OCR B (Unit 2) and Edexcel (Unit 1).

You can use the Periodic Table to work out *Electron Configurations*

The Periodic Table can be split into an **s block**, **d block** and **p block** like this: Doing this shows you which sub-shells all the electrons go into.

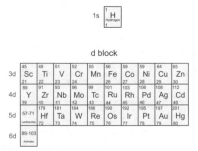
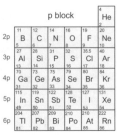

See page 8 if this sub-shell malarkey doesn't ring a bell.

1) The **s-block** elements have an outer shell electron configuration of s^1 or s^2.

   Examples Lithium ($1s^2\ 2s^1$) and magnesium ($1s^2\ 2s^2\ 2p^6\ 3s^2$)

2) The **p-block** elements have an outer shell configuration of s^2p^1 to s^2p^6.

   Example Chlorine ($1s^2\ 2s^2\ 2p^6\ 3s^2\ 3p^5$)

3) The **d-block** elements have electron configurations in which d sub-shells are being filled.

   Example Cobalt ($1s^2\ 2s^2\ 2p^6\ 3s^2\ 3p^6\ 3d^7\ 4s^2$)

   Even though the 3d sub-shell fills last in cobalt, it's not written at the end of the line.

When you've got the periodic table **labelled** with the **shells** and **sub-shells** like the one up there, it's pretty easy to read off the electron structure of any element by starting at the top and working your way across and down until you get to your element.

<u>A wee apology...</u>
This bit's really hard to explain clearly in words. If you're confused, just look at the examples until you get it...

Example

Electron structure of phosphorus (P):

Period 1 — $1s^2$ *Complete sub-shells*
Period 2 — $2s^2\ 2p^6$
Period 3 — $3s^2\ 3p^3$ *Incomplete outer sub-shell*

So the full electron structure of phosphorus is
   $1s^2\ 2s^2\ 2p^6\ 3s^2\ 3p^3$

Atomic Radius **Decreases** across a Period

1) As the number of protons increases, the **positive charge** of the nucleus increases. This means electrons are **pulled closer** to the nucleus, making the atomic radius smaller.

2) The extra electrons that the elements gain across a period are added to the **outer energy level** so they don't really provide any extra shielding effect (shielding works with inner shells mainly).

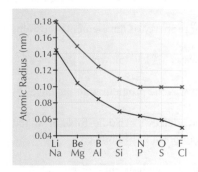

Electronegativity **Increases** across a Period   *Not AQA*

1) **Electronegativity** measures how strongly an **atom** attracts **electrons** in a covalent bond (see page 48).

2) The **higher** the electronegativity of an atom, the greater its attraction for **bonding electrons**.

3) Elements on the far **left** of the periodic table have 1 or 2 outer trelectrons and would rather **give these away** (to achieve a full outer shell of a lower energy level) than grab another atom's electrons. So they have **low** electronegativity.

4) Elements near the far **right** of the periodic table only need a few electrons to complete their outer shell, so they have a strong desire to **grab** another atom's electrons. These have a **high** electronegativity.

Periodic Trends

*Ionisation Energy Generally **Increases** across a Period*

Don't forget — there are **3 main things** that affect the size of ionisation energies:

1) **Atomic radius** — the further the outer shell electrons are from the positive nucleus, the less they'll be attracted towards the nucleus. So, the ionisation energy will be **lower**.

2) **Nuclear charge** — the **more protons** there are in the nucleus, the more it'll attract the outer electrons — it'll be harder to remove the electrons, so the ionisation energy will be **higher**.

3) **Electron shielding** — the inner electron shells **shield** the outer shell electrons from the attractive force of the nucleus. Because more inner shells give more shielding, the ionisation energy will be **lower**.

The graph below shows the first ionisation energies of the elements in **Periods 2 and 3**.

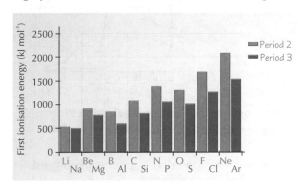

1) As you **move across** a period, the general trend is for the ionisation energies to **increase** — i.e. it gets harder to remove the outer electrons.

2) This is because the number of protons is increasing, which means a stronger **nuclear attraction**.

3) All the extra electrons are at **roughly the same** energy level, even if the outer electrons are in different orbital types.

4) This means there's generally little **extra shielding** effect or **extra distance** to lessen the attraction from the nucleus.

5) But, there are **small drops** between Groups 2 and 3, and 5 and 6. Tell me more, I hear you cry. Well, all right then...

Electronic Structure Explains the Drop between Groups 2 and 3   *Not OCR A*

 Be $1s^2\,2s^2$ 1st ionisation energy = 900 kJ mol^{-1}
B $1s^2\,2s^2\,2p^1$ 1st ionisation energy = 799 kJ mol^{-1}

1) The crucial difference here is that while beryllium's outer electron is in the **2s sub-shell**, boron's outer electron is in the **2p sub-shell**.

2) The 2p sub-shell has a **slightly higher** energy than the 2s. So boron's outer electron is, on average, just a little bit **further** from the nucleus.

3) That little extra distance means there's not as much attraction between the nucleus and the outer electron. And the **2s² electrons** give the 2p sub-shell some **partial shielding**.

4) The combination of these two factors **overrides** the effect of the increased nuclear charge, resulting in a slight **drop** in ionisation energy.

> The same thing happens with magnesium and aluminium, but in the **third** energy level: Aluminium has one **3p electron**, which is, on average, slightly further away from the nucleus than the 3s electrons, and also **partially shielded** by the 3s electrons. These two factors override the larger nuclear charge, so the first ionisation energy of aluminium is **lower** than magnesium's.

*The Drop between Groups 5 and 6 is due to **Electron Repulsion***   *Not OCR A*

 N $1s^2\,2s^2\,2p^3$ 1st ionisation energy = 1400 kJ mol^{-1}
O $1s^2\,2s^2\,2p^4$ 1st ionisation energy = 1310 kJ mol^{-1}

1) This time the outer electrons for both elements are in the **same sub-shell**, so there's no difference in the shielding or the distance from the nucleus. But the key is how the sub-shells are filled.

2) The 2p sub-shell has three **orbitals** (see p8), and nitrogen has one electron in each of them. One of oxygen's 2p orbitals has **two electrons** in it. These two electrons **repel** each other — making it **easier** to remove one of them.

3) The first ionisation energy of **sulfur** is lower than that of **phosphorus** for exactly the same reason.

Periodic Trends

This page is for AQA (Unit 1), OCR A (Unit 1), OCR B (Unit 1) and Edexcel (Unit 1).

Melting and Boiling Points are linked to **Bond Strength** and **Structure**

Periods 2 and 3 show similar trends in their melting and boiling points. These trends are linked to changes in **structure** and **bond strength**.

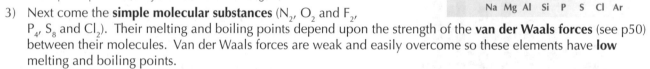

1) For the **metals** (Li and Be, Na, Mg and Al), melting and boiling points **increase** across the period because the **metal-metal bonds** get stronger. The bonds get stronger because the metal ions have an increasing number of **delocalised electrons** and a decreasing **ionic radius**. This leads to a higher **charge density**, which attracts the ions together more strongly.

2) The elements with **macromolecular** structures have **strong covalent bonds** linking all their atoms together. **A lot** of energy is needed to break these bonds. So, for example, carbon (as graphite or diamond) and silicon have the **highest** melting and boiling points in their periods. (*The carbon data in the graph opposite is for graphite — diamond has an even higher boiling point. But neither of them actually melts or boils at atmospheric pressure, they sublime from solid to gas.*)

3) Next come the **simple molecular substances** (N_2, O_2 and F_2, P_4, S_8 and Cl_2). Their melting and boiling points depend upon the strength of the **van der Waals forces** (see p50) between their molecules. Van der Waals forces are weak and easily overcome so these elements have **low** melting and boiling points.

4) More atoms in a molecule mean stronger van der Waals forces. For example, in Period 3 sulfur is the **biggest molecule** (S_8), so it's got higher melting and boiling points than phosphorus or chlorine.

5) The noble gases (neon and argon) have the **lowest** melting and boiling points because they exist as **individual atoms** (they're monatomic) resulting in **very weak** van der Waals forces.

Practice Questions

Q1 Name three factors that affect the size of ionisation energies.

Q2 How does the ionisation energy change as you go across a period?

Q3 Why is there a drop in ionisation energies between Groups 2 and 3, going across a period?

Q4 Explain the drop in ionisation energies between Groups 5 and 6.

Q5 Why does phosphorus have a lower melting point than magnesium?

Exam Questions

Q1 Explain the meaning of the term periodicity, as applied to the properties of rows of elements in the periodic table. [2 marks]

Q2 Explain why the melting point of magnesium is higher than that of sodium. [3 marks]

Q3 The first ionisation energies of the elements lithium to neon are given below in kJ mol⁻¹:

Li	Be	B	C	N	O	F	Ne
519	900	799	1090	1400	1310	1680	2080

   a) Explain why the ionisation energies show an overall tendency to increase across the period. [3 marks]

   b) Explain the irregularities in this trend for:

      i) Boron   ii) Oxygen [4 marks]

Q4 State and explain the trend in atomic radius across Period 3. [4 marks]

Q5 Explain why the first ionisation energy of neon is greater than that of sodium. [2 marks]

Periodic trends — my mate Dom's always a decade behind...

He still thinks Oasis, Blur and REM are the best bands around. The sad muppet. But not me. Oh no sirree, I'm up with the times — April Lavigne... Linkin' Pork... Christina Agorrilla. I'm hip, I'm with it. Da ga da ga da ga da ga.. ooaarrr ooup *   <small>* Obscure reference to Austin Powers: International Man of Mystery. You should watch it — it's better than doing Chemistry.</small>

Oxidation and Reduction

This next bit has more occurrences of "oxidation" than the Beatles' "All You Need is Love" features the word "love".

These three pages are for AQA (Unit 2), OCR A (Unit 1), OCR B (Unit 2) and Edexcel (Unit 2) .

If Electrons are Transferred, it's a **Redox Reaction**

1) A **loss** of electrons is called **oxidation**. A **gain** in electrons is called **reduction**.

2) Reduction and oxidation happen **simultaneously** — hence the term "**redox**" reaction.

3) An **oxidising agent accepts** electrons and gets reduced.

4) A **reducing agent donates** electrons and gets oxidised.

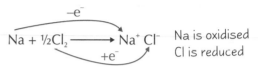

$$Na + \tfrac{1}{2}Cl_2 \xrightarrow{\; -e^- \;} Na^+ Cl^-$$

with $+e^-$ below the arrow

Na is oxidised
Cl is reduced

Sometimes it's Easier to Talk about **Oxidation States** ◄— (They're also called oxidation <u>numbers</u>.)

1) Oxidation state (or number) is a way of showing the charge an atom *would have* if all its bonds were totally ionic.

2) Here's the nice simple bit:

> • When **metals** react and form ions they normally lose electrons and are oxidised to form positive ions. This **increases** their oxidation number.
>
> • **Non-metals** normally react by gaining electrons — they're reduced to negative ions. This **decreases** their oxidation number.

3) And here's the harder bit — there are several **rules** for working out oxidation states. Take a deep breath...

> 1) All atoms are treated as **ions** for this, even if they're covalently bonded.
>
> 2) Uncombined **elements** have an oxidation state of **0**.
>
> 3) Elements just bonded to **identical atoms**, like O_2 and H_2, also have an oxidation state of **0**.
>
> 4) The oxidation state of a simple **monatomic ion**, e.g. Na^+, is the same as its **charge**.
>
> 5) In **compounds** or **compound ions**, the **overall oxidation state** is just the ion charge.
>
> SO_4^{2-} — overall oxidation state = -2,
> oxidation state of O = -2 (total = -8), ◄— *Within an ion, the most electronegative element has a negative oxidation state (equal to its ionic charge). Other elements have more positive oxidation states.*
> so oxidation state of S = **+6**
>
> 6) The sum of the oxidation states for a **neutral compound** is 0.
>
> Fe_2O_3 — overall oxidation state = **0**, oxidation state of O = -2
> (total = -6), so oxidation state of **Fe = +3**
>
> 7) Combined **oxygen** is nearly always -2, except in peroxides, where it's -1,
> (and in the fluorides OF_2, where it's +2, and O_2F_2, where it's +1 (and O_2 where it's 0).
>
> In H_2O, oxidation state of O = -2, but in H_2O_2, oxidation state of H has to be **+1** (an H atom can only lose one electron), so oxidation state of O = -1
>
> 8) Combined **hydrogen** is +1, except in metal hydrides where it is -1 (and H_2 where it's 0).
>
> In **HF**, oxidation state of H = +1, but in **NaH**, oxidation state of H = -1

4) Oxidation states are sometimes shown in chemical names as **Roman numerals**. This is because some elements can have several oxidation states — there's more about this on the next page.

E.g. copper has oxidation state **+2** in **copper(II) sulfate** and
manganese has oxidation state **+7** in a **manganate(VII) ion** (MnO_4^-)

Hands up if you like
Roman numerals...

Oxidation and Reduction

Oxidation States go *Up* or *Down* as Electrons are *Lost* or *Gained*

1) The oxidation state for an atom will **increase by 1** for each **electron lost**.

2) The oxidation state will **decrease by 1** for each **electron gained**.

3) Elements can also be **oxidised and reduced** at the same time — this is called **disproportionation**.

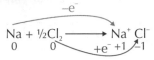

$$Na + \tfrac{1}{2}Cl_2 \longrightarrow Na^+ Cl^-$$

Oxidation No.   0   0   +1 −1

Example:
Chlorine and its ions undergo disproportionation reactions:

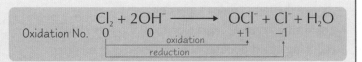

$$Cl_2 + 2OH^- \longrightarrow OCl^- + Cl^- + H_2O$$

Oxidation No.   0   0   *oxidation*   +1   −1
                        reduction

You Can *Combine Half-Equations* into Full Reaction Equations

1) **Ionic half-equations** show oxidation or reduction.

2) You can **combine** half-equations for different oxidising or reducing agents together to make **full equations** for reactions.

> Magnesium burns in oxygen to form magnesium oxide.
> Magnesium is oxidised: $Mg \rightarrow Mg^{2+} + 2e^-$
> Oxygen is reduced: $\tfrac{1}{2}O_2 + 2e^- \rightarrow O^{2-}$
> Combining the half-equations gives: $Mg + \tfrac{1}{2}O_2 \rightarrow MgO$
>
> *(The electrons balance on each side so they aren't included in the full equation.)*

You Can Work Out *Oxidation States* from *Formulas* or *Systematic Names*

1) Many elements can have **more than one** oxidation state. For example, **iron** can form Fe^{2+} or Fe^{3+} ions. So it's not good enough to call a substance 'iron oxide' — the name has to show which oxidation state the Fe atoms are in.

2) **Systematic names** of compounds make it clear which oxidation state such elements are in.
E.g. iron(III) oxide is formed from Fe^{3+} and O^{2-} ions, whereas iron(II) oxide contains Fe^{2+} ions and O^{2-}.

3) This systematic naming process doesn't just apply to ionic substances.

> For example, **silicon** can exist in **several oxidation states**.
>
> The compound SiO_2 contains **two oxygen atoms** for every **one silicon atom**. The oxygen atoms are in oxidation state **–2** (giving $-2 \times 2 = -4$), so the silicon must be in oxidation state **+4** (to make the overall oxidation number for the compound **0**).

> So its systematic name is silicon(IV) oxide — but it's often called silicon dioxide.
>
> (Silicon(II) oxide is SiO — its overall oxidation number is O too.)

4) Many common substances contain **compound ions** (see page 38). For example, the sulfate, carbonate and nitrate ions are all compound ions. Their systematic names tell you the oxidation states of the atoms that make them up. Take **potassium sulfate(VI)** for example:

- The **ate** ending in 'sulfate' shows that the ion contains oxygen as well as sulfur (just as a nitrate ion contains nitrogen and oxygen, a carbonate ion contains carb... OK, you've got it, I'll stop). **BUT...**

- **Sulfate(VI)** tells you that the **sulfur** has oxidation state **+6**. (The oxidation state applies to the sulfur not the oxygen, because oxygen is always –2.)

5) Several ions have widely used common names that are different from their correct systematic names. For example, the systematic name for the compound ion SO_3^{2-} is **sulfate(IV)**. (Oxygen is –2, and $2 \times 3 = -6$, so sulfur must have oxidation state +4 to give the overall state of –2.) But this ion is often called the **sulfite** ion.
   In the old naming system, compound ions of oxygen and an element with two possible oxidation states had names ending in either '-ate' or '-ite'. The '-ite' ending indicated one less oxygen atom (i.e. the 'other' atom was in its lower oxidation state).

6) You might have to work out the systematic name for a compound, given its formula. Here's how:

> **Example:** Give the systematic name of the compound KNO_3.
>
>   Potassium always forms K^+ ions. The nitrate ion must be NO_3^-.
>   Each oxygen atom in the NO_3^- ion has oxidation state –2. This gives $3 \times -2 = -6$.
>   The ion has an overall state of **–1**, so the nitrogen must be in the **+5** state.
>
>   So the compound is called **potassium nitrate(V)**.

It's called the nitrate(V) ion.

Oxidation and Reduction

Many Metals Reduce Dilute Acids

1) **Dilute acids** contain hydrogen ions, H^+, in solution.
2) Many metals react with dilute acid to produce hydrogen gas. This is a redox reaction:
   - The metal atoms are **oxidised**, losing electrons and forming soluble metal ions.
   - The hydrogen ions in solution are **reduced**, gaining electrons and forming hydrogen molecules.
3) For example, magnesium reacts with dilute hydrochloric acid like this:

$$Mg_{(s)} + 2HCl_{(aq)} \rightarrow MgCl_{2\,(aq)} + H_{2\,(g)}$$

Magnesium is oxidised: $Mg_{(s)} \rightarrow Mg^{2+}_{(aq)} + 2e^-$

Hydrogen ions are reduced: $2H^+_{(aq)} + 2e^- \rightarrow H_{2\,(g)}$

Notice that the chloride ions don't change oxidation state — they're still chloride ions, with oxidation state –1. That's why you don't need to include them in the ionic half-equations.

If you use **sulfuric acid** instead of hydrochloric acid, exactly the same process of **oxidation** and **reduction** takes place.

$$Mg_{(s)} + H_2SO_{4\,(aq)} \rightarrow MgSO_{4\,(aq)} + H_{2\,(g)}$$

Magnesium is oxidised: $Mg_{(s)} \rightarrow Mg^{2+}_{(aq)} + 2e^-$

Hydrogen ions are reduced: $2H^+_{(aq)} + 2e^- \rightarrow H_{2\,(g)}$

The electrons in the two half-equations should balance.

Practice Questions

Q1 What is a reducing agent?
Q2 What is the usual oxidation number for oxygen combined with another element?
Q3 What is disproportionation?
Q4 What happens to the hydrogen ions when metals react with acids?

Exam Questions

Q1 When hydrogen iodide gas is bubbled through warm concentrated sulfuric acid, hydrogen sulfide and iodine are produced.

a) Balance the equation below for the reaction.

$$H_2SO_{4\,(aq)} + HI_{(g)} \rightarrow H_2S_{(g)} + I_{2\,(s)} + H_2O_{(l)}$$ [1 mark]

b) State the oxidation number of sulfur in H_2SO_4 and in H_2S.   [2 marks]

c) Write a half-equation to show the conversion of iodide, I^-, into iodine, I_2.   [1 mark]

d) Write a half-equation to show the conversion of sulfuric acid into hydrogen sulfide.   [2 marks]

e) In this reaction, which is the reducing agent? Give a reason.   [2 marks]

Q2 If sodium hydroxide is added to aqueous solutions of iron(II) sulfate and iron(III) sulfate, precipitates of the corresponding hydroxides are formed.

a) Write the formulae for:

(i) iron(II) sulfate,   (ii) iron(II) hydroxide,   (iii) iron(III) sulfate,   (iv) iron(III) hydroxide.   [4 marks]

b) Most iron(II) compounds are green in colour but most iron(III) compounds are orange/brown.
Suggest why iron-containing rocks that form in contact with air are more likely to be orange/brown.   [1 mark]

Redox — relax in a lovely warm bubble bath...

Ionic equations are so evil even Satan wouldn't mess with them. But if they're on your specification, you can't ignore them. Have a flick back to p22 if they're freaking you out.

And while we're on the oxidation page, I suppose you ought to learn the most famous memory aid thingy in the world...

OIL RIG
- **O**xidation **I**s **L**oss
- **R**eduction **I**s **G**ain
(of electrons)

Group 2 — The Alkaline Earth Metals

Group 2, a.k.a. the alkaline earth metals, is in the "s block" of the periodic table. There's a whopping total of six pages about them and their compounds, so we've got a lot to do — best get on...

This page is for AQA (Unit 2), OCR A (Unit 1), OCR B (Units 1 and 2) and Edexcel (Unit 2).

1) Know the Electron Configurations

Element	Atom	Ion
Be	$1s^2\,2s^2$	$1s^2$
Mg	$1s^2\,2s^2\,2p^6\,3s^2$	$1s^2\,2s^2\,2p^6$
Ca	$1s^2\,2s^2\,2p^6\,3s^2\,3p^6\,4s^2$	$1s^2\,2s^2\,2p^6\,3s^2\,3p^6$

Group 2 elements all have two electrons in their outer shell (s^2).

They lose their two outer electrons to form **2+ ions**. Their ions then have every atom's dream electronic structure — that of a **noble gas**.

If you forget these electron configurations, you can always look at the Periodic Table and work them out — see p56.

2) Atomic Radius and Ionic Radius Increase Down the Group

1) This is because of the extra **electron shells** as you go down the group.
2) Ionic radius is smaller than atomic radius for Group 2 elements because the loss of the outer electron(s) results in the loss of the **outer shell**.

3) Ionisation Energy Decreases Down the Group

1) Each element down Group 2 has an **extra electron shell** compared to the one above.
2) The extra inner shells **shield** the outer electrons from the attraction of the nucleus.
3) Also, the extra shell means that the outer electrons are **further away** from the nucleus, which greatly reduces the nucleus's attraction.

> Both of these factors make it **easier** to remove outer electrons, resulting in a **lower ionisation energy**.

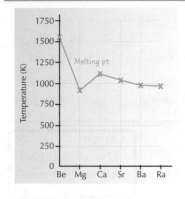

Mr Kelly has one final attempt at explaining electron shielding to his students...

The positive charge of the nucleus does increase as you go down a group (due to the extra protons), but this effect is overridden by the effect of the extra shells.

4) Reactivity Increases Down the Group

1) As you go down the group, the **ionisation energies** decrease. This is due to the increasing atomic radius and shielding effect (see above).
2) When Group 2 elements react they **lose electrons**, forming positive ions (**cations**). The easier it is to lose electrons (i.e. the lower the first and second ionisation energies), the more reactive the element, so **reactivity increases** down the group.

5) Melting Points Generally Decrease Down the Group

1) The Group 2 elements have typical **metallic structures**, with the electrons of their outer shells being **delocalised**.
2) Going down the group the metallic ions get **bigger** — so they have a smaller **charge/volume ratio**. But the number of delocalised electrons per atom doesn't change (it's always 2) — so the delocalised electrons get more **spread out**.
3) These two factors mean there's reduced attraction of the positive ions to the 'sea' of delocalised electrons. So it takes **less energy** to break the bonds, which means lower melting points generally down the group. However, there's a big 'blip' at magnesium, because the crystal structure (the arrangement of the metallic ions) changes.

Group 2 — The Alkaline Earth Metals

This page is for AQA (Unit 2), OCR A (Unit 1), OCR B (Unit 1), Edexcel (Unit 2).

Group 2 Elements React with **Water**, **Oxygen** and **Chlorine**

When Group 2 elements react, they are **oxidised** from a state of **0** to **+2**, forming M^{2+} ions.
This is because Group 2 atoms contain 2 electrons in their outer shell.

$$M \rightarrow M^{2+} + 2e^- \qquad \text{E.g.} \qquad Ca \rightarrow Ca^{2+} + 2e^-$$
Oxidation state: 0   +2   0   +2

1) **GROUP 2 ELEMENTS REACT WITH WATER TO PRODUCE HYDROXIDES**

The Group 2 metals react with water to give a **metal hydroxide and hydrogen**.
They get **increasingly** reactive down the group because the **ionisation energies** decrease.

$$M_{(s)} + 2H_2O_{(l)} \rightarrow M(OH)_{2\,(aq)} + H_{2\,(g)}$$
Oxidation state: 0   +2
e.g. $$Ca_{(s)} + 2H_2O_{(l)} \rightarrow Ca(OH)_{2\,(aq)} + H_{2\,(g)}$$

Be	doesn't react
Mg	VERY slowly
Ca	steadily
Sr	fairly quickly
Ba	rapidly

2) **THEY BURN IN OXYGEN WITH CHARACTERISTIC FLAME COLOURS**

...and form solid white oxides.

Magnesium burns with a brilliant white flame, and the others burn with their characteristic **flame colours** (see p67).

$$2M_{(s)} + O_{2\,(g)} \rightarrow 2MO_{(s)}$$
Oxidation state of metal: 0   +2
Oxidation state of oxygen: 0   –2

e.g.

$$2Ca_{(s)} + O_{2\,(g)} \rightarrow 2CaO_{(s)}$$
0   +2
0   –2

3) **THEY REACT WITH CHLORINE** *Edexcel (Unit 2) only*

...forming white solid chlorides.

$$M_{(s)} + Cl_{2\,(g)} \rightarrow MCl_{2\,(s)}$$
Ox. state of metal: 0   +2

e.g.

$$Ca_{(s)} + Cl_{2\,(g)} \rightarrow CaCl_{2\,(s)}$$
0   +2

Practice Questions

Q1 Which is the least reactive metal in Group 2?

Q2 Why does reactivity with water increase down Group 2?

Q3 Which of the following increases in size down Group 2?   **ionic radius, first ionisation energy, boiling point**

Q4 What is the oxidation state of Mg in: a) $MgCl_2$ b) MgO ?

Exam Questions

Q1 Use the electron configurations of magnesium and calcium to help explain the difference in their first ionisation energies.
[5 marks]

Q2 Calcium can be burned in chlorine gas.
a) Write an equation for the reaction. [1 mark]
b) State the change in oxidation state of calcium. [1 mark]
c) Predict the appearance of the product. [2 marks]
d) What type of bonding would the product have? [1 mark]

Q3 The table shows the atomic radii of three elements from Group 2.

Element	Atomic radius (nm)
X	0.089
Y	0.198
Z	0.176

a) Predict which element would react most rapidly with water. [1 mark]
b) Explain your answer. [2 marks]

I'm not gonna make it. You've gotta get me out of here, Doc...

We're deep in the dense jungle of Inorganic Chemistry now. Those carefree days of Section Three are well behind us. It's now an endurance test and you've just got to keep going. By now, all the facts are probably blurring into one, all the compounds looking the same. It's tough, but you've got to stay awake, stay focused and keep learning. That's all you can do.

Compounds of Group 2 Metals

Another page, and more juicy, squidgy facts about those jolly nice Group 2 fellas.
This time we're looking at their cuddly compounds...   *(Sorry, just trying to liven things up a bit.)*

This page is for AQA (Unit 2), OCR A (Unit 1), OCR B (Unit 1) and Edexcel (Unit 2).

Group 2 Oxides and Hydroxides are **Bases**

THEY FORM ALKALINE SOLUTIONS IN WATER...

1) The **oxides** of the Group 2 metals react readily with **water** to form **metal hydroxides**, which dissolve. The **hydroxide ions, OH⁻**, make these solutions **strongly alkaline**.

2) Magnesium oxide is an exception — it only reacts slowly and the hydroxide isn't very soluble.

$$CaO_{(s)} + H_2O_{(l)} \rightarrow Ca^{2+}_{(aq)} + 2OH^-_{(aq)}$$

3) The oxides form **more strongly alkaline** solutions as you go down the group, because the hydroxides get more soluble.

...AND THEY NEUTRALISE ACIDS

Because they're **bases**, both the oxides and hydroxides will **neutralise** dilute acids, forming solutions of the corresponding salts.

$$MgO_{(s)} + 2HCl_{(aq)} \rightarrow H_2O_{(l)} + MgCl_{2\,(aq)}$$

$$Mg(OH)_{2\,(s)} + 2HCl_{(aq)} \rightarrow 2H_2O_{(l)} + MgCl_{2\,(aq)}$$

Solubility Trends Depend on the **Compound Anion**   *not OCR A*

Generally, compounds of Group 2 elements that contain **singly charged** negative ions (e.g. OH⁻) **increase** in solubility down the group, whereas compounds that contain **doubly charged** negative ions (e.g. SO_4^{2-} and CO_3^{2-}) **decrease** in solubility down the group.

Group 2 element	hydroxide (OH⁻)	sulfate (SO_4^{2-})	carbonate (CO_3^{2-})
magnesium	least soluble	most soluble	most soluble
calcium			
strontium			
barium	most soluble	least soluble	least soluble

Compounds like magnesium hydroxide which have **very low** solubilities are said to be **sparingly soluble**.

Most sulfates are soluble in water, but **barium sulfate** is **insoluble**.

The test for sulfate ions makes use of this property...

Test for sulfate ions

If a solution of a soluble barium compound, such as barium chloride or barium nitrate, is added to a solution containing sulfate ions then a white precipitate of barium sulfate is formed.

$$Ba^{2+}_{(aq)} + SO_4^{2-}_{(aq)} \rightarrow BaSO_{4\,(s)}$$

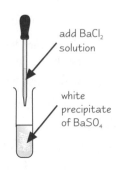

add BaCl₂ solution

white precipitate of BaSO₄

Compounds of Group 2 Metals

Group 2 Compounds are used to **Neutralise Acidity**   *AQA and OCR A*

Group 2 elements are known as the **alkaline earth metals**, and many of their common compounds are used for neutralising acids. Here are a couple of common examples:

1) Calcium hydroxide (slaked lime, $Ca(OH)_2$) is used in **agriculture** to neutralise acid soils.

2) Magnesium hydroxide ($Mg(OH)_2$) is used in some indigestion tablets as an **antacid**.

> In both cases, the ionic equation for the neutralisation is
> $$H^+_{(aq)} + OH^-_{(aq)} \rightarrow H_2O_{(l)}$$

Barium Sulfate is Used in 'Barium Meals'   *AQA only*

X-rays are great for finding broken bones, but they pass straight through soft tissue — so soft tissues, like the digestive system, don't show up on conventional X-ray pictures.

1) Barium sulfate is **opaque** to X-rays — they won't pass through it. It's used in '**barium meals**' to help diagnose problems with the oesophagus, stomach or intestines.

2) A patient swallows the barium meal, which is a suspension of **barium sulfate**. The barium sulfate **coats** the tissues, making them show up on the X-rays, showing the structure of the organs.

CHRIS PRIEST / SCIENCE PHOTO LIBRARY

Practice Questions

Q1 Name two properties of a Group 2 oxide that show it to be a base.

Q2 Which is less soluble, barium sulfate or magnesium sulfate?

Q3 How is the solubility of magnesium hydroxide often described?

Q4 Name a use of magnesium hydroxide.

Exam Questions

Q1 Hydrochloric acid can be produced in excess quantities in the stomach, causing indigestion. Antacid tablets often contain sodium hydrogencarbonate ($NaHCO_3$), which reacts with the acid to form a salt, carbon dioxide and water.

a) Write an equation for the neutralisation of hydrochloric acid with sodium hydrogencarbonate. [1 mark]

b) What discomfort could be caused by the carbon dioxide produced? [1 mark]

c) From your knowledge of Group 2 compounds, choose an alternative antacid that would not give this problem and write an equation for its reaction with hydrochloric acid. [2 marks]

Q2 Describe how you could use barium chloride solution to distinguish between solutions of zinc chloride and zinc sulfate. Give the expected observations and an appropriate balanced equation including state symbols. [4 marks]

Q3 Identify which of the following solutions would be most likely to give the results described for each test below. Give an explanation for each of your answers.

Solutions: $BaCl_2(aq)$ $BeCl_2(aq)$ $MgCl_2(aq)$ $MgSO_4(aq)$

Test A   No precipitate formed on addition of sodium hydroxide solution. [2 marks]

Test B   White precipitate formed on addition of $BaCl_2(aq)$ [2 marks]

Bored of Group 2 trends? Me too. Let's play noughts and crosses...

x	0	
0	x	x
0		0

Noughts and crosses is pretty rubbish really, isn't it?
It's always a draw. Ho hum. Back to Chemistry then, I guess...

Compounds of S-Block Metals

These pages are about Groups 1 and 2, starting with the thermal stability of their carbonates and nitrates.
So — quick, get your vest and long johns on before you topple over — we haven't even started yet.

These pages are for OCR A *(Unit 1),* OCR B *(Unit 2)* **and** Edexcel *(Unit 2).*

Thermal Stability of Carbonates and Nitrates Changes Down the Group

Thermal decomposition is when a substance **breaks down** (decomposes) when **heated**.
The more thermally stable a substance is, the more heat it will take to break it down.

1) **Thermal stability increases down a group**

   The carbonate and nitrate ions are **large** and can be made **unstable** by the presence of a **positively charged ion** (a cation). The cation **polarises** the anion, distorting it. The greater the distortion, the less stable the anion.

   Large cations cause **less distortion** than small cations. So the further down the group, the larger the cations, the less distortion caused and the **more stable** the carbonate/nitrate anion. Phew... that was hard.

2) **Group 2 compounds are less thermally stable than Group 1 compounds**

   The greater the **charge** on the cation, the greater the **distortion** and the **less stable** the carbonate/nitrate ion becomes. Group 2 cations have a **2+** charge, compared to a **1+** charge for Group 1 cations. So Group 2 carbonates and nitrates are less stable than those of Group 1.

Group 1	Group 2
Group 1 carbonates* are **thermally stable** — you can't heat them enough with a Bunsen to make them decompose (though they do decompose at higher temperatures). *except Li_2CO_3 which decomposes to Li_2O and CO_2 (there's always one...)	Group 2 carbonates decompose to form the **oxide** and **carbon dioxide**. $MCO_{3\,(s)} \longrightarrow MO_{(s)} + CO_{2\,(g)}$ e.g. $CaCO_{3\,(s)} \longrightarrow CaO_{(s)} + CO_{2\,(g)}$ calcium carbonate calcium oxide
Group 1 nitrates** decompose to form the **nitrite** and **oxygen**. $2MNO_{3\,(s)} \longrightarrow 2MNO_{2\,(s)} + O_{2\,(g)}$ e.g. $2KNO_{3\,(s)} \longrightarrow 2KNO_{2\,(s)} + O_{2\,(g)}$ potassium nitrate potassium nitrite **except $LiNO_3$ which decomposes to form Li_2O, NO_2 and O_2.	Group 2 nitrates decompose to form the **oxide**, **nitrogen dioxide** and **oxygen**. $2M(NO_3)_{2\,(s)} \longrightarrow 2MO_{(s)} + 4NO_{2\,(g)} + O_{2\,(g)}$ e.g. $2Ca(NO_3)_{2\,(s)} \longrightarrow 2CaO_{(s)} + 4NO_{2\,(g)} + O_{2\,(g)}$ calcium nitrate calcium oxide nitrogen dioxide

OCR A and OCR B:
The stability of Group 2 carbonates only.

Here's How to Test the Thermal Stability of Nitrates and Carbonates

How easily nitrates decompose can be tested by measuring...

- how long it takes until **oxygen** is produced (i.e. to relight a glowing splint)
  OR
- how long it takes until a **brown gas (NO_2)** is produced.
  This needs to be done in a fume cupboard because NO_2 is **toxic**.

How easily carbonates decompose can be tested by measuring...

- how long it takes for **carbon dioxide** to be produced.
  You test for carbon dioxide using limewater — which is a saturated solution of calcium hydroxide. This turns cloudy with carbon dioxide, because a precipitate of calcium carbonate is formed.

Compounds of S-Block Metals

S-Block Ions have Distinctive *Flame Colours*   *Edexcel (Unit 2) only*

...not all of them, but quite a few. For compounds containing the ions below, flame tests can help **identify them**.

Flame colours of s-block metals and their compounds

Li	red		
Na	orange/yellow		
K	lilac	Ca	brick-red
Rb	red	Sr	crimson
Cs	blue	Ba	green

Here's how to do a flame test:

1) Mix a small amount of the compound you're testing with a few drops of **concentrated hydrochloric acid**.
2) Heat a piece of **platinum** or **nichrome wire** in a hot Bunsen flame to clean it.
3) Dip the wire into the compound/acid mixture. Hold it in a very hot flame and note the colour produced.

The explanation

The **energy** absorbed from the flame causes electrons to move to **higher energy levels**. The colours are seen as the electrons fall back down to lower energy levels, releasing energy in the form of **light**. The **wavelengths** of light released determine the **colour** — they depend on the energy **differences** between the energy levels, which are different for each atom.

(It's never enough just to say, "ooh that's nice." Oh no, chemists have to have an explanation for everything, even colour.)

Practice Questions

Q1 Write an equation for the thermal decomposition of calcium carbonate.

Q2 What is the trend in the thermal stability of the nitrates of Group 1 elements?

Q3 Describe two ways that you could test how easily the nitrates of Group 2 decompose.

Q4 Which s-block metal ions are indicated by the following flame colours?
   a) lilac   b) brick-red   c) orange/yellow

Exam Questions

Q1 When heated, **X**, a compound of calcium, produces a gas **A** and a solid **B**.
The gas **A** is bubbled through a solution of limewater to give a cloudy precipitate of **C**.
Give the formulae of the substances **A**, **B**, **C** and **X**.   [4 marks]

Q2 a) Write a balanced equation for the thermal decomposition of sodium nitrate.   [1 mark]
   b) How could you test for the gas produced in the thermal decomposition?   [1 mark]
   c) Place the following in order of ease of thermal decomposition (easiest first).
      magnesium nitrate   **potassium nitrate**   **sodium nitrate**
      Explain your answer.   [3 marks]

Q3 a) When a substance is heated, what changes occur within the atom that give rise to a coloured flame?   [2 marks]
   b) A compound gives a blue colour in a flame test.
      What s-block metal ions might this compound contain?   [1 mark]

"So that was lithium, now let's try..." "SCHTOP! — this flame is not reddy yet..."

Here at CGP, we like to test our flames slowly. So they burn <u>real smooth</u> *with their characteristic colours...*
[OK — s-block metals — that's Groups 1 and 2. Lots of trends here. Just learn them. And learn the explanation for each one (not like a parrot – so you understand it).
Then learn the flame colours and that explainy bit about line emission spectra and energy levels.] CGP — we only test flames when they're ready...

Group 7 — The Halogens

Finally we can wave goodbye to those pesky s-block elements. Here come the halogens.

These pages are for AQA (Unit 2), OCR A (Unit 1), OCR B (Unit 2) and Edexcel (Unit 2).

Halogens are the *Highly Reactive Non-Metals* of Group 7

The word halogen should be used when describing the atom (X) or molecule (X_2), but the word halide is used to describe the negative ion (X^-).

The table below gives some of the main properties of the first 4 halogens.

halogen	formula	colour	physical state	electronic structure	electronegativity
fluorine	F_2	pale yellow	gas	$1s^2\ 2s^2\ 2p^5$	increases
chlorine	Cl_2	green	gas	$1s^2\ 2s^2\ 2p^6\ 3s^2\ 3p^5$	up
bromine	Br_2	red-brown	liquid	$1s^2\ 2s^2\ 2p^6\ 3s^2\ 3p^6\ 3d^{10}\ 4s^2\ 4p^5$	the
iodine	I_2	grey	solid	$1s^2\ 2s^2\ 2p^6\ 3s^2\ 3p^6\ 3d^{10}\ 4s^2\ 4p^6\ 4d^{10}\ 5s^2\ 5p^5$	group

1) **Their boiling points increase down the group**
   This is due to the increasing strength of the **van der Waals forces** as the size and relative mass of the atoms increases. This trend is shown in the changes of **physical state** from chlorine (gas) to iodine (solid). (A substance is said to be **volatile** if it has a low boiling point. So volatility **decreases** down the group.)

2) **Electronegativity decreases down the group**.
   Electronegativity, remember, is the tendency of an atom to **attract** a bonding pair of **electrons**. The halogens are all highly electronegative elements. But larger atoms attract electrons **less** than smaller ones. So, going down the group, as the atoms become **larger**, the electronegativity **decreases**.

   Fluorine is the most electronegative element.

Some Halogens Form *Coloured Solutions*

Halogens in their natural state exist as covalent diatomic molecules (e.g. Br_2, Cl_2).
Because they're covalent, they have **low solubility in water**.
But they do dissolve easily in **organic compounds** like hexane.

Some of these resulting solutions have distinctive colours that can be used to identify them $\longrightarrow$

	colour in water	colour in hexane
chlorine	virtually colourless	virtually colourless
bromine	yellow/orange	orange/red
iodine	brown	pink/violet

Halogens get *Less Reactive* Down the Group

1) Halogen atoms react by **gaining an electron** in their outer p sub-shell. This means they're **reduced**. As they're reduced, they **oxidise** another substance (it's a redox reaction) — so they're **oxidising agents**.

$$X + e^- \rightarrow X^-$$
ox. state: 0   -1

2) As you go down the group, the atoms become **larger** so the outer electrons are **further** from the nucleus. The outer electrons are also **shielded** more from the attraction of the positive nucleus, because there are more inner electrons. This makes it harder for larger atoms to attract the electron needed to form an ion, so larger atoms are less reactive.

3) Another way of saying that the halogens get **less reactive** down the group is to say that they become **less oxidising**. (See the next page for more on this.)

Daisy the cow *

You Can Use *Patterns* to *Predict Properties*

1) The smallest halogen, **fluorine**, is the **most reactive** non-metal element. Fluorine isn't used in schools and colleges because it's so dangerous, but you can **predict** its properties by looking at those of the other halogens. $\longrightarrow$

2) The **melting** and **boiling points** increase down the group, so you can predict that fluorine would be a gas at room temperature, like chlorine below it. Similarly, fluorine should be **coloured** as all the other halogens are. In fact, fluorine is a very pale yellow gas at room temperature.

3) Astatine (below iodine in the periodic table) is a solid. You'd expect it to be the **least reactive** halogen, but its properties haven't been studied because it's highly radioactive and decays quickly.

Halogen	Melting Point / °C	Boiling Point / °C
F		
Cl	−101	−34
Br	−7	58
I	114	183
At		

Increasing Reactivity

* She wanted to be in the book. I said OK.

Group 7 — The Halogens

Halogens *Displace* Less Reactive Halide Ions from Solution

1) The halogens' **relative oxidising strengths** can be seen in their **displacement reactions** with halide ions. For example, if you mix bromine water, $Br_{2(aq)}$, with potassium iodide solution, the bromine displaces the iodide ions (it oxidises them), giving iodine, $I_{2(aq)}$ and potassium bromide, $KBr_{(aq)}$. You can see what happens by following the **colour changes**.

	Potassium chloride solution $KCl_{(aq)}$ - colourless	Potassium bromide solution $KBr_{(aq)}$ - colourless	Potassium iodide solution $KI_{(aq)}$ - colourless
Chlorine water $Cl_{2(aq)}$ - colourless	no reaction	orange solution (Br_2) formed	brown solution (I_2) formed
Bromine water $Br_{2(aq)}$ - orange	no reaction	no reaction	brown solution (I_2) formed
Iodine solution $I_{2(aq)}$ - brown	no reaction	no reaction	no reaction

2) You can make the changes easier to see by shaking the reaction mixture with an **organic solvent** like hexane. The halogen that's present will dissolve readily in the organic solvent, which settles out as a distinct layer above the aqueous solution. This example shows the presence of **iodine**. *(The colours of the other solutions are on the previous page.)*

hexane layer
aqueous layer

3) These displacement reactions can be used to help **identify** which halogen (or halide) is present in a solution.

> A **halogen** will **displace a halide** from solution if the halide is **below it** in the periodic table, e.g.

Periodic table	Displacement reaction	Ionic equation
Cl	chlorine (Cl_2) will displace bromide (Br^-) and iodide (I^-)	$Cl_{2(aq)} + 2Br^-_{(aq)} \rightarrow 2Cl^-_{(aq)} + Br_{2(aq)}$ $Cl_{2(aq)} + 2I^-_{(aq)} \rightarrow 2Cl^-_{(aq)} + I_{2(aq)}$
Br	bromine (Br_2) will displace iodide (I^-)	$Br_{2(aq)} + 2I^-_{(aq)} \rightarrow 2Br^-_{(aq)} + I_{2(aq)}$
I	no reaction with F^-, Cl^-, Br^-	

> You can also say a halogen will oxidise a halide if the halide is below it in the periodic table.

$$Cl_{2(aq)} + 2Br^-_{(aq)} \rightarrow 2Cl^-_{(aq)} + Br_{2(aq)}$$

ox. state of Cl	0	$\rightarrow$ -1	reduction
ox. state of Br	-1	$\rightarrow$ 0	oxidation

Practice Questions

Q1 Place the halogens F, Cl, Br and I in order of increasing: (a) boiling point   (b) volatility   (c) electronegativity

Q2 What would be seen when chlorine water is added to potassium iodide solution?

Q3 What colour solution is formed when iodine dissolves in: (a) water   (b) hexane?

Exam Questions

Q1 a)   Write an ionic equation for the reaction between iodine solution and sodium astatide (NaAt).   [1 mark]

   b)   For the equation in (a), deduce which substance is oxidised.   [1 mark]

Q2 Iodide ions react with chlorate(I) ions and water to form iodine, chloride ions and hydroxide ions.

   a)   Write a balanced equation for this reaction.   [2 marks]
   b)   Show by use of oxidation states which substance has been oxidised and which has been reduced.   [2 marks]
   c)   Predict the colour change for the reaction.   [1 mark]

Q3 Write formulae for the following compounds (assume all the anions have a charge of -1).

   a)   magnesium fluoride   [1 mark]
   b)   potassium bromate(I)   [1 mark]
   c)   sodium chlorate(V)   [1 mark]

Don't skip this page — it could cost you £31 000...

Let me explain... the other night I was watching Who Wants to Be a Millionaire, and this question was on for £32 000:

Which of the these elements is a halogen?
A Argon   B Nitrogen
C Fluorine   D Sodium

Bet Mr Redmond from Wiltshire wishes he paid more attention in Chemistry now, eh. Ha sucker...

More on the Halogens

All good things must come to an end, but not straight away. Those halogens just love to react, so here's more...

Here's Some More Reactions of the Halogens to **Learn**... *Edexcel (Unit 2) only*

Remember, when halogens react they're reduced — and they oxidise other substances (see page 68).

They Oxidise Metals...

For example, **fluorine** and **chlorine** react with hot **iron** to form iron(III) halides. (Iron is taken to its highest oxidation state, +3, because these halogens are very **strong oxidising agents**.)

$$2Fe_{(s)} + 3Cl_{2(g)} \rightarrow 2FeCl_{3(s)}$$

The iron(III) chloride is produced as a vapour, which condenses to a solid.

Iron is oxidised: $2Fe \rightarrow 2Fe^{3+} + 6e^-$

Chlorine is reduced: $3Cl_2 + 6e^- \rightarrow 6Cl^-$

Bromine's a **weaker** oxidising agent so you get a mixture of iron(**II**) and iron(**III**) bromide. With **iodine**, you only get iron(**II**) iodide — no Fe^{3+} ions form.

...and Non-Metals

For example, chlorine reacts with **sulfur** to form sulfur(I) chloride. (Sulfur is oxidised to +1 and chlorine is reduced to –1.)

$$S_{8(s)} + 4Cl_{2(g)} \rightarrow 4S_2Cl_{2(l)}$$

...and Some Ions

Hallo Jen.

Go away Nigel.

For example, all the halogens except iodine (which is less oxidising than the others) will oxidise iron(II) ions to iron(III) ions in solution. The solution will change colour from **green** to **orange**.

For example: $Cl_2 + 2e^- \rightarrow 2Cl^-_{(aq)}$

$$2Fe^{2+}_{(aq)} \rightarrow 2Fe^{3+}_{(aq)} + 2e^-$$

green   orange

Most Halogens Can Be Extracted by **Electrolysis** of **Halide Solutions**

OCR B (Unit 2) only

1) When you **electrolyse** aqueous solutions containing **iodide** or **bromide** ions, the **halogen** element is released at the **anode** (the positive electrode).

2) The **halide ions lose electrons** to the electrode and are **oxidised** to atoms, which combine to form **molecules**.

For example, electrolysing sodium **bromide** solution produces **bromine** at the anode. $\longrightarrow$ $2Br^-_{(aq)} \rightarrow 2e^- + Br_{2(aq)}$

3) At the **cathode**, hydrogen ions (from the water) form hydrogen gas: $\longrightarrow$ $2H^+_{(aq)} + 2e^- \rightarrow H_{2(g)}$

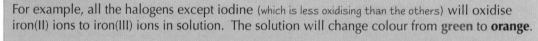

You can only extract **chlorine** from **concentrated sodium chloride** solution:

1) In sodium chloride solution, there are two cations present (Na^+ and H^+) and two anions (Cl^- and OH^-). Which anion is discharged depends on the **concentration** of the solution.

2) In very **dilute** solutions, the chloride ions (Cl^-) **aren't discharged** — they hang onto their extra electrons. The **OH**⁻ ions lose their extra electron instead and the products at the anode are **oxygen** and water. $\longrightarrow$ $4OH^-_{(aq)} \rightarrow 4e^- + 2H_2O_{(l)} + O_{2(g)}$

3) But if the solution is **concentrated**, chloride ions are discharged and **chlorine** is produced. $2Cl^-_{(aq)} \rightarrow 2e^- + Cl_{2(aq)}$

4) In both cases, **hydrogen** is released at the cathode (as it is with other halide solutions). Here's a summary. $\longrightarrow$

	anode	cathode
Dilute	O_2	H_2
Concentrated	Cl_2	H_2

Fluorine can't be produced by electrolysis of aqueous fluoride solutions — even with concentrated fluoride solutions the hydroxide ions are discharged instead (as above).

More on the Halogens

Storing and Transporting Halogens — It's a Risky Business... *OCR B (Unit 2) only*

The more reactive halogens can be quite dangerous. They must be kept away from **flammable materials** (being oxidising agents, they increase fire risks). And they're **toxic** and **corrosive**, so must be kept away from **skin** and **eyes**.

1) **Fluorine** is the most reactive halogen, and the most hazardous. Wherever possible, it's produced where it will be used — to **avoid** transporting or storing it. It reacts with most metals and non-metals and can only be stored in expensive containers lined with nickel or copper-nickel alloys — and these containers have to be **small**, so that if there's an accident the damage is limited.

2) **Chlorine** is used a lot in industry. It can be stored as a **liquid** under **pressure** in small cylinders. Like fluorine, it's only transported if no alternative is possible — usually it's produced on site or is made into less hazardous compounds before being transported.

3) **Bromine** is a **liquid** at room temperature, so it's easier to store, but it is volatile (evaporates readily). It can be transported in small quantities but more often it's converted into bromine compounds first.

4) **Iodine** is a solid at room temperature, and much less reactive, so is relatively easy to transport.

... But They are Very Useful *Edexcel (Unit 2) and OCR B (Unit 2)*

1) Although they're pretty hazardous, both **fluorine** and **chlorine** are widely used because they're needed to make many useful compounds.

   You're expected to know some of those compounds, and examples of their uses. ⟹

Halogen	is used to make:	which has these useful properties:	and is used for:
Fluorine	PTFE (polytetrafluoro-ethene)	inert, low-friction, thermally stable	non-stick coating on pans
	HCFCs (hydrochloro-fluorocarbons)	inert, gas at room temperature	refrigerant
	sodium fluoride	strengthens tooth enamel	toothpaste
Chlorine	PVC (polyvinyl chloride)	electrical insulator	electrical wires
	bleach	kills bacteria	water treatment

2) **Bromine** is used in **medicines**, and in many **agricultural** chemicals, e.g. pesticides. It's also an ingredient of **flame retardants** used in electronics, clothing and furniture.

3) **Iodine** is used in **medicines** too. It's also an essential **nutrient** — table salt often contains added potassium iodide.

Practice Questions

Q1 What is the orange-brown substance formed when iron is heated in chlorine?

Q2 What happens to the chlorine molecules when they react with iron?

Q3 What is the anode product if a dilute solution of sodium chloride is electrolysed?

Q4 Name a product made using fluorine.

Exam Questions

Q1 When copper foil is heated in a stream of dry chlorine, the copper is oxidised to its highest oxidation state and a white powder is formed as the only product.

   a) Name the powder produced. [1 mark]

   b) Write half-equations for the oxidation and reduction steps in this reaction. Indicate which equation shows oxidation and which shows reduction. [3 marks]

Q2 Chlorine is a very important industrial chemical.

   a) Explain why chlorine is normally produced on the same site where it is to be used. [4 marks]

   b) Name two important compounds made using chlorine, and give one example of how each is used. [2 marks]

   c) Write half-equations for the electrolysis of concentrated sodium chloride solution, showing the reaction: (i) at the anode   (ii) at the cathode [4 marks]

Just take a look at these pages... you know what you've got to do...

Never in all my years have I seen an AS Chemistry page so screaming out with the words — "learn me, learn me, learn ALL OF ME, up a bit, across a bit, oh yes that's it, learn me..." ahem, you get the idea. It's quite nice to learn about some real uses of chemicals after all of that theory stuff about periodic trends, don't you think? No? Just me then. Again.

Halide Ions

Halides are compounds containing the –1 halogen ion, e.g. Cl⁻. Their names all end in "-ide", e.g. sodium bromide.
This page is for AQA (Unit 2), OCR A (Unit 1) and Edexcel (Unit 2).

The **Reducing Power** of Halides **Increases** Down the Group...

To reduce something, the halide ion needs to lose an electron from its outer shell.
How easy this is depends on the **attraction** between the **nucleus** and the outer **electrons**.

As you go down the group, the attraction gets **weaker** because:

> 1) the ions get bigger, so the electrons are **further** away from the positive nucleus
> 2) there are extra inner electron shells, so there's a greater **shielding** effect.

An example of them doing this is the good old halogen / halide displacement reaction
(the one you learned on p69... yes, that one). And here comes some more examples to learn...

...which Explains their Reactions with **Sulfuric Acid**   *Not OCR A*

All the halides react with concentrated sulfuric acid to give a **hydrogen halide** as a
product to start with. But what happens next depends on which halide you've got...

Reaction of NaF or NaCl with H_2SO_4

$$NaF_{(s)} + H_2SO_{4(aq)} \rightarrow NaHSO_{4(s)} + HF_{(g)}$$
$$NaCl_{(s)} + H_2SO_{4(aq)} \rightarrow NaHSO_{4(s)} + HCl_{(g)}$$

It doesn't matter too much what metal ion you've got — potassium chloride would react in exactly the same way.

1) Hydrogen fluoride (HF) or hydrogen chloride gas (HCl) is formed. You'll see misty fumes as the gas comes into contact with moisture in the air.
2) But HF and HCl aren't strong enough reducing agents to reduce the sulfuric acid, so the reaction stops there.
3) It's not a redox reaction — the oxidation states of the halide and sulfur stay the same (–1 and +6).

Reaction of NaBr with H_2SO_4

$$NaBr_{(s)} + H_2SO_{4(aq)} \rightarrow NaHSO_{4(s)} + HBr_{(g)}$$

$$2HBr_{(aq)} + H_2SO_{4(aq)} \rightarrow Br_{2(g)} + SO_{2(g)} + 2H_2O_{(l)}$$

ox. state of S:	+6	→	+4	reduction
ox. state of Br:	-1	→	0	oxidation

1) The first reaction gives misty fumes of hydrogen bromide gas (HBr).
2) But the HBr is a stronger reducing agent than HCl and reacts with the H_2SO_4 in a redox reaction.
3) The reaction produces choking fumes of SO_2 and orange fumes of Br_2.

Again, the same sort of reactions would happen with potassium bromide or potassium iodide.

Reaction of NaI with H_2SO_4

$$NaI_{(s)} + H_2SO_{4(aq)} \rightarrow NaHSO_{4(s)} + HI_{(g)}$$

$$2HI_{(g)} + H_2SO_{4(aq)} \rightarrow I_{2(s)} + SO_{2(g)} + 2H_2O_{(l)}$$

ox. state of S:	+6	→	+4	reduction
ox. state of I:	-1	→	0	oxidation

1) Same initial reaction giving HI gas.
2) The HI then reduces H_2SO_4 like above.
3) But HI (being well 'ard as far as reducing agents go) keeps going and reduces the SO_2 to H_2S.

$$6HI_{(g)} + SO_{2(g)} \rightarrow H_2S_{(g)} + 3I_{2(s)} + 2H_2O_{(l)}$$

ox. state of S:	+4	→	–2	reduction
ox. state of I:	-1	→	0	oxidation

H_2S gas is toxic and smells of bad eggs. A bit like my mate Andy at times...

Halide Ions

This page is for AQA (Unit 2), OCR A (Unit 1), OCR B (Unit 2) and Edexcel (Unit 2).

Silver Nitrate Solution is used to **Test for Halides**

The test for halides is dead easy. First you add **dilute nitric acid** to remove ions which might interfere with the test. Then you just add **silver nitrate solution** ($AgNO_{3\ (aq)}$). A **precipitate** is formed (of the silver halide).

$$Ag^+_{(aq)} + X^-_{(aq)} \rightarrow AgX_{(s)} \text{ ...where X is F, Cl, Br or I}$$

1) The **colour** of the precipitate identifies the halide.
2) Then to be extra sure, you can test your results by adding **ammonia solution**. (Each silver halide has a different solubility in ammonia.)

SILVER NITRATE TEST FOR HALIDE IONS...

Fluoride F⁻: no precipitate

Chloride Cl⁻: white precipitate, dissolves in dilute $NH_{3(aq)}$

Bromide Br⁻: cream precipitate, dissolves in conc. $NH_{3(aq)}$

Iodide I⁻: yellow precipitate, insoluble in conc. $NH_{3(aq)}$

Silver Halides React with **Sunlight**   *Edexcel only*

Silver halides **decompose** when light shines on them, producing **silver** and the **halogen**. For example:

$$2AgBr \rightarrow 2Ag + Br_2$$

This reaction is used in film photography — the film contains silver bromide particles that turn to opaque silver when they're exposed to light.

Hydrogen Halides are **Acidic Gases**   *Edexcel only*

Before I go, a few final words about the **hydrogen halides**...
1) They're all **colourless gases**.
2) They're **very soluble**, dissolving in water to make **strong acids**. (They'll happily turn blue litmus paper red.)
$$HCl_{(g)} \rightarrow H^+_{(aq)} + Cl^-_{(aq)}$$
3) Hydrogen chloride forms **hydrochloric** acid, hydrogen bromide forms **hydrobromic** acid and hydrogen iodide gives **hydroiodic** acid. (You don't hear of this last one much — that's because its name is too silly.)
4) They react with **ammonia gas** to give **white fumes**. Hydrogen chloride gives ammonium chloride.
$$NH_{3(g)} + HCl_{(g)} \rightarrow NH_4Cl_{(s)}$$
(It's an acid-base reaction.)

Practice Questions

Q1 Give two reasons why a bromide ion is a more powerful reducing agent than a chloride ion.
Q2 Name the gaseous products formed when sodium bromide reacts with concentrated sulfuric acid.
Q3 What happens when potassium iodide reacts with concentrated sulfuric acid?
Q4 What type of substance is formed when a hydrogen halide is passed through water?
Q5 What test could you do to show that an aqueous solution contains chloride ions?

Exam Questions

Q1 Describe tests you could carry out in order to distinguish between solid samples of sodium chloride and sodium bromide using: a) silver nitrate solution and aqueous ammonia,
b) concentrated sulfuric acid.
For each test, state the observations you would expect and write equations for the reactions that occur. [12 marks]

Q2 The halogen below iodine in Group 7 is astatine (At). Predict, giving an explanation, whether or not:
a) hydrogen sulfide gas would be evolved when concentrated sulfuric acid is added to a solid sample of sodium astatide, [4 marks]
b) silver astatide will dissolve in concentrated ammonia solution. [3 marks]

[Sing along with me] "Why won't this section end... Why won't this section end..."

AS Chemistry. What a bummer, eh... No one ever said it was going to be easy. Not even your teacher would be that cruel. There are plenty more equations on this page to learn. As well as that, make sure you really understand everything... what exactly reducing agents do... how you work out oxidation states for reactions... And no, you can't swap to English. Sorry.

Disproportionation and Water Treatment

Here's comes another page jam-packed with golden nuggets of halogen fun. Oh yes, I kid you not.
This page is the Alton Towers of AS Chemistry... white-knuckle excitement all the way...

This page is for AQA (Unit 2), OCR A (Unit 1) **and** Edexcel (Unit 2).

Halogens undergo **Disproportionation** with Alkalis

The halogens react with hot and cold alkali solutions. In these reactions, the halogen is simultaneously oxidised and reduced (called **disproportionation**)...

	$X_2 + 2NaOH \rightarrow NaXO + NaX + H_2O$	$3X_2 + 6NaOH \rightarrow NaXO_3 + 5NaX + 3H_2O$
Ion equation:	$X_2 + 2OH^- \rightarrow XO^- + X^- + H_2O$	$3X_2 + 6OH^- \rightarrow XO_3^- + 5X^- + 3H_2O$
Ox. state of X:	$0 \qquad\qquad +1 \quad -1$	$0 \qquad\qquad +5 \quad -1$
	COLD	**HOT**

The halogens (except fluorine) can exist in a wide range of oxidation states e.g.

-1	0	+1	+1	+3	+5	+7
Cl^-	Cl_2	ClO^-	BrO^-	BrO_2^-	IO_3^-	IO_4^-
chloride	chlorine	chlorate(I)	bromate(I)	bromate(III)	iodate(V)	iodate(VII)

All the **halogen -ate ions** have a **single halogen atom** and a charge of **–1**
— so if you forget the formula you should be able to work it out from the **oxidation number**.

For Example — *Chlorine* and *Sodium Hydroxide* make **Bleach**   *Not Edexcel*

If you mix chlorine gas with sodium hydroxide (products of the electrolysis of brine – see p70) at **room temperature**, you get **sodium chlorate(I) solution**, $NaClO_{(aq)}$ — which is common household **bleach**.
This is an example of the 'cold' reaction above — the oxidation state of Cl goes up **and** down by one.

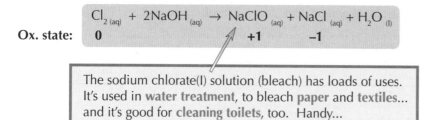

Ox. state: $Cl_{2\,(aq)} + 2NaOH_{(aq)} \rightarrow NaClO_{(aq)} + NaCl_{(aq)} + H_2O_{(l)}$
$\qquad\qquad\quad 0 \qquad\qquad\qquad\qquad +1 \qquad\quad -1$

The sodium chlorate(I) solution (bleach) has loads of uses. It's used in **water treatment**, to bleach **paper** and **textiles**... and it's good for **cleaning toilets**, too. Handy...

Brian gives Susie the water treatment

Chlorine is used to *Kill Bacteria in Water*   *Not Edexcel*

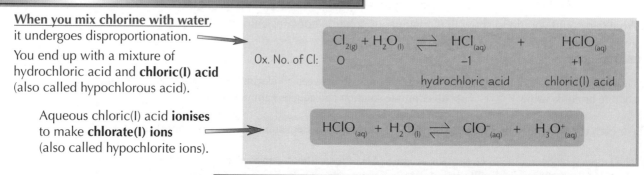

When you mix chlorine with water, it undergoes disproportionation.

You end up with a mixture of hydrochloric acid and **chloric(I) acid** (also called hypochlorous acid).

Ox. No. of Cl: $Cl_{2(g)} + H_2O_{(l)} \rightleftharpoons HCl_{(aq)} + HClO_{(aq)}$
$\qquad\qquad\qquad 0 \qquad\qquad\qquad\qquad -1 \qquad\quad +1$
$\qquad\qquad\qquad\qquad\qquad\qquad$ hydrochloric acid $\quad$ chloric(I) acid

Aqueous chloric(I) acid **ionises** to make **chlorate(I) ions** (also called hypochlorite ions).

$HClO_{(aq)} + H_2O_{(l)} \rightleftharpoons ClO^-_{(aq)} + H_3O^+_{(aq)}$

Chlorate(I) ions **kill bacteria**.

So, **adding chlorine** (or a compound containing chlorate(I) ions) to water can make it safe to **drink** or **swim** in.

Iodine tablets are used as a portable method of water purification (if you're camping in the mountains, for example). Iodine reacts with water in the same way as chlorine, and iodate(I) ions kill most harmful microorganisms.

$I_2 + H_2O \rightleftharpoons HI + HIO \longrightarrow HIO + H_2O \rightleftharpoons IO^- + H_3O^+$
$\qquad\qquad\qquad\qquad\qquad\qquad\qquad\qquad\qquad\qquad\qquad\qquad$ iodate(I) ions

Disproportionation and Water Treatment

This page is for AQA (Unit 2) and OCR A (Unit 1).

Chlorine in Water — There are Benefits, Risks and Ethical Implications

1) Clean drinking water is amazingly important — around the world almost **two million people die** every year from waterborne diseases like cholera, typhoid and dysentery because they have to drink dirty water.

2) In the UK, drinking water is **treated** to make it safe. **Chlorine** is an important part of water treatment:

   - It **kills disease-causing microorganisms** (see previous page).
   - If the correct amount is added, enough chlorine remains in the water to kill bacteria that might enter the supply **after** treatment, further down the pipes.
   - It prevents the growth of **algae**, gets rid of **bad tastes** and **smells**, and **removes discolouration** caused by organic compounds.

3) However, there are risks from using chlorine to treat water:

   - **Chlorine gas is very harmful** if it's breathed in — it irritates the **respiratory system**. **Liquid chlorine** on the skin or eyes causes severe **chemical burns**. Accidents involving chlorine could be really serious, or fatal.
   - Water contains a variety of organic compounds, e.g. from the decomposition of plants. Chlorine reacts with these compounds to form **chlorinated hydrocarbons**, e.g. chloromethane (CH_3Cl) — and many of these chlorinated hydrocarbons are carcinogenic (cancer-causing). However, this increased cancer risk is small compared to the risks from untreated water — a cholera epidemic, say, could kill thousands of people.

4) There are ethical considerations too. We don't get a **choice** about having our water chlorinated — some people object to this as forced 'mass medication'.

Some Areas Have Fluoridated Water

Some areas <u>don't</u> have fluoridated water. Deciding whether to fluoridate the water supply involves the use of scientific evidence to balance benefits against risks.

1) In some areas of the UK **fluoride ions** are also added to drinking water. Health officials recommend this because there's **loads** of good evidence that it helps to prevent **tooth decay**.

2) Over-fluoridation can cause fluorosis, which leads to **discoloured teeth**. There's also a **small** amount of evidence linking fluoridated water to conditions including weakening of bones and a slightly increased risk of **bone cancer**.

3) Most **toothpaste** is fluoridated, so some people think fluorine in water is unnecessary. And the **ethical argument** against 'mass medication' that applies to chlorinated water applies to fluorine too.

Practice Questions

Q1 What does disproportionation mean?

Q2 Write the equation for the reaction of chlorine with water. State underneath the oxidation number of the chlorine.

Q3 What are the health benefits of adding chlorine to drinking water?

Exam Questions

Q1 If chlorine gas and sodium hydroxide are allowed to mix at room temperature, sodium chlorate(I) is formed.

    a) This is a disproportionation reaction.
       Give the ionic equation for the reaction and use it to explain what is meant by disproportionation. [4 marks]

    b) Bromine reacts with water to form a mixture of two acids.
       Write the formulae of the two acids and give the oxidation state of bromine in each. [3 marks]

Q2 a) In most parts of the UK, the public water supply is chlorinated.
       Explain two possible hazards associated with the chlorination of drinking water. [2 marks]

    b) In some areas, fluorine is also added to drinking water to help prevent tooth decay.
       Suggest two possible reasons why people object to this practice. [2 marks]

Remain seated until the page comes to a halt. Please exit to the right...

Oooh, what a lovely page, if I do say so myself. I bet the question of how bleach is made has plagued your mind since childhood. Well now you know. Nowt too taxing here — you just need to learn all the equations, and make sure you can tell what's oxidised and what's reduced. Then there's the pros and cons of treating water with chlorine... it never ends.

Iodine-Sodium Thiosulfate Titration

Strictly speaking, these two pages are only for people doing Edexcel (Unit 1). But don't turn over just yet, even if that's not you... Everyone needs to do titration calculations sooner or later, and a wee bit more practice can only be a good thing.

Iodine-Sodium Thiosulfate Titrations are Dead Handy

Iodine-sodium thiosulfate titrations are a way of finding the concentration of an **oxidising agent**.
The **more concentrated** an oxidising agent is, the **more ions will be oxidised** by a certain volume of it.
So here's how you can find out the concentration of a solution of the oxidising agent **potassium iodate(V)**:

STAGE 1: Use a sample of oxidising agent to oxidise as much iodide as possible.

1) Measure out a certain volume of potassium iodate(V) (the oxidising agent) — say **25 cm³**.

2) Add this to an excess of acidic **potassium iodide** solution.
The iodate(V) ions in the potassium iodate(V) solution
oxidise some of the **iodide ions** to **iodine**.

$$IO_3^-{}_{(aq)} + 5I^-{}_{(aq)} + 6H^+{}_{(aq)} \rightarrow 3I_2{}_{(aq)} + 3H_2O$$

STAGE 2: Find out how many moles of iodine have been produced.

You do this by **titrating** the resulting solution with **sodium thiosulfate**.
(You need to know the concentration of the sodium thiosulfate solution.)

The iodine in the solution reacts
with **thiosulfate ions** like this:

$$I_2 + 2S_2O_3^{2-} \rightarrow 2I^- + S_4O_6^{2-}$$

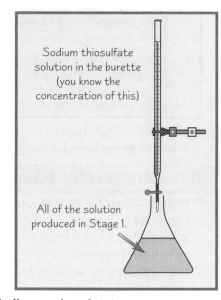

Sodium thiosulfate
solution in the burette
(you know the
concentration of this)

All of the solution
produced in Stage 1.

Titration of Iodine with Sodium Thiosulfate

1) Put all the solution produced in Stage 1 in a flask.

2) From the burette, add sodium thiosulfate solution to the solution in the flask.

3) It's dead hard to see the end point, so when the iodine colour fades to pale yellow, add 2 cm³ of starch solution (to detect the presence of iodine). The solution in the conical flask will go dark blue, showing there's still some iodine there.

4) Add sodium thiosulfate <u>one drop at a time</u> until the blue colour disappears.

5) When this happens, it means all the iodine has <u>just</u> been reacted.

6) Now you can <u>calculate</u> the number of moles of iodine in the solution.

Here's how you'd do the titration calculation to find the **number of moles of iodine** produced in Stage 1.

 The iodine in the solution produced in Stage 1 reacted fully with 11.1 cm³ of 0.12 mol dm⁻³ thiosulfate solution.

$$I_2 + 2S_2O_3^{2-} \rightarrow 2I^- + S_4O_6^{2-}$$
$$11.1 \text{ cm}^3$$
$$0.12 \text{ mol dm}^{-3}$$

Number of moles of thiosulfate $= \dfrac{\text{concentration} \times \text{volume (cm}^3)}{1000} = \dfrac{0.12 \times 11.1}{1000} = 1.332 \times 10^{-3}$ moles

1 mole of iodine reacts with **2 moles** of thiosulfate,

So number of **moles of iodine** in the solution $= 1.332 \times 10^{-3} \div 2 = 6.66 \times 10^{-4}$ **moles**

STAGE 3: Calculate the concentration of the oxidising agent.

1) Now you look back at your original equation: $\quad IO_3^-{}_{(aq)} + 5I^-{}_{(aq)} + 6H^+{}_{(aq)} \rightarrow 3I_2{}_{(aq)} + 3H_2O$

2) The equation shows that **one mole** of iodate(V) ions produces **three moles** of iodine.
25 cm³ of potassium iodate(V) solution produced **6.66 × 10⁻⁴ moles of iodine**.
So there must have been **6.66 × 10⁻⁴ ÷ 3 = 2.22 × 10⁻⁴ moles of iodate(V) ions**.
There would be the same number of moles of potassium iodate(V) in the solution. So now it's straightforward to find the **concentration** of the potassium iodate(V) solution, which is what you're after:

$$\text{number of moles} = \dfrac{\text{concentration} \times \text{volume (cm}^3)}{1000} \implies 2.22 \times 10^{-4} = \dfrac{\text{concentration} \times 25}{1000}$$

$$\implies \textbf{concentration of potassium iodate(V) solution} = \textbf{0.00888 mol dm}^{-3}$$

Iodine-Sodium Thiosulfate Titration

You Have to Be Able to *Evaluate* the Titration Procedure

Titrations like the one on the previous page can give very accurate results, but there are a few ways things could go pear-shaped:

1) Using contaminated apparatus could make your results inaccurate — so make sure the burette is very **clean**, and **rinse** it out with sodium thiosulfate before you start (because traces of water will dilute the solution).

2) It's important to **read the burette correctly** (from the bottom of the meniscus, with your eyes level with the liquid).

3) To reduce the effect of random errors, **repeat** the experiment and take an average.

4) But remember to **wash** the flask between experiments or use a new, clean one.

Choppy seas made it difficult for Captain Blackbird to read the burette accurately.

This particular experiment can also have some specific problems:

- The solutions you're using will react very slowly with the air, so they should be made up as freshly as possible.
- If you add the **starch** solution **too soon** during the titration, the iodine will 'stick' to the starch and won't react as expected with the thiosulfate, making the result unreliable. Only add the starch when the solution is **pale yellow**.

Practice Questions

Q1 What is added during an iodine-sodium thiosulfate titration to make the end point easier to see?

Q2 How can an iodine-sodium thiosulfate titration help you to work out the concentration of an oxidising agent?

Q3 How many moles of thiosulfate ions react with one mole of iodine molecules?

Q4 Describe the colour change at the end point of the titration.

Exam Question

Q1 10 cm³ of potassium iodate(V) solution was reacted with excess acidified potassium iodide solution. All of the resulting solution was titrated with 0.15 mol dm⁻³ sodium thiosulfate solution. It fully reacted with 24.0 cm³ of the sodium thiosulfate solution.

a) Write an equation showing how iodine is formed in the reaction between iodate(V) ions and iodide ions in acidic solution. [2 marks]

b) How many moles of thiosulfate ions were there in 24.0 cm³ of the sodium thiosulfate solution? [1 mark]

c) In the titration, iodine reacted with sodium thiosulfate according to this equation:

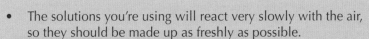

$$I_{2(aq)} + 2Na_2S_2O_{3(aq)} \rightarrow 2NaI_{(aq)} + Na_2S_4O_{6(aq)}$$

Calculate the number of moles of iodine that reacted with the sodium thiosulfate solution. [1 mark]

d) How many moles of iodate(V) ions produce 1 mole of iodine from potassium iodide? [1 mark]

e) What was the concentration of the potassium iodate(V) solution? [2 marks]

Two vowels went out for dinner — they had an iodate...

This might seem like quite a faff — you do a redox reaction to release iodine, titrate the iodine solution, do a sum to find the iodine concentration, write an equation, then do another sum to work out the concentration of something else. The thing is though, it does work, and you do have to know how. If you're rusty on the calculations, look back to p30-31.

Basic Stuff

Organic chemistry is all about carbon compounds. There are loads of them, and you're mainly made up of them, so they're fairly important. Chemists have organised them into families, which makes them a tad easier to cope with.
These three pages are for AQA (Unit 1), OCR A (Unit 2), OCR B (Unit 1 and 2) and Edexcel (Unit 1).

There are **Loads of Ways** of **Representing** Organic Compounds

TYPE OF FORMULA	WHAT IT SHOWS YOU	FORMULA FOR BUTAN-1-OL
General formula	An algebraic formula that can describe **any member** of a family of compounds.	$C_nH_{2n+1}OH$ (for all alcohols)
Empirical formula	The **simplest ratio** of atoms of each element in a compound (cancel the numbers down if possible). (So ethane, C_2H_6, has the empirical formula CH_3.)	$C_4H_{10}O$
Molecular formula	The **actual** number of atoms of each element in a molecule, with any **functional groups** indicated.	C_4H_9OH
Structural formula	Shows the atoms **carbon by carbon**, with the attached hydrogens and functional groups.	$CH_3CH_2CH_2CH_2OH$
Displayed formula	Shows how all the atoms are **arranged**, and all the bonds between them.	H H H H H–C–C–C–C–OH H H H H
Skeletal formula	Shows the **bonds** of the carbon skeleton **only**, with any functional groups. The hydrogen and carbon atoms aren't shown. This is handy for drawing large complicated structures, like cyclic hydrocarbons.	OH

A functional group is a reactive part of a molecule — it gives it most of its chemical properties.

Homologous Compounds have the Same **General Formulas**

1) A **homologous series** is a group of compounds that can all be represented by the same **general formula**.

2) You can use a general formula to work out the **molecular formula** of any member of a homologous series.

> **Example:** The alkanes have the general formula C_nH_{2n+2}. What's the formula of the alkane with six carbons?
>
> $$n = 6, \text{ so the formula is } C_6H_{(2\times6)+2} = C_6H_{14}$$

3) Each **successive member** of a homologous series differs by a '**CH_2**' group.

> E.g. **Alcohols** have the general formula $C_nH_{2n+1}OH$. Here are the first six in the homologous series.
>
> | Methanol | Ethanol | Propanol | Butanol | Pentanol | Hexanol |
> |---|---|---|---|---|---|
> | CH_3OH | C_2H_5OH | C_3H_7OH | C_4H_9OH | $C_5H_{11}OH$ | $C_6H_{13}OH$ |
>
> You can see how each alcohol has one more **CH_2 group** than the one before.

4) Here are the **homologous series** that you might need to know about:

Homologous series	Prefix or Suffix	Example
alkanes	-ane	Propane $CH_3CH_2CH_3$
branched alkanes	alkyl- (-yl)	methylpropane $CH_3CH(CH_3)CH_3$
alkenes	-ene	propene $CH_3CH=CH_2$
haloalkanes/ halogenoalkanes	chloro- bromo- iodo-	chlorethane CH_3CH_2Cl
alcohols	-ol	ethanol CH_3CH_2OH
aldehydes	-al	ethanal CH_3CHO

Homologous series	Prefix or Suffix	Example
ketones	-one	propanone CH_3COCH_3
cycloalkanes	cyclo- -ane	cyclohexane C_6H_{12}
arenes	benzene	ethylbenzene $C_6H_5C_2H_5$
esters	alkyl -oate	propyl ethanoate $CH_3COOCH_2CH_2CH_3$
carboxylic acids	-oic acid	ethanoic acid CH_3COOH
ethers	alkoxy-	methoxypropane $CH_3OCH_2CH_2CH_3$

Basic Stuff

Nomenclature *is a Fancy Word for the* Naming *of Organic Compounds*

You can name any organic compound using these **rules** of nomenclature.

1) Count the carbon atoms in the **longest continuous chain** — this gives you the stem:

Number of carbons	1	2	3	4	5	6	7	8	9	10
Stem	meth-	eth-	prop-	but-	pent-	hex-	hept-	oct-	non-	dec-

2) The **main functional group** of the molecule usually gives you the
   end of the name (the **suffix**) — see the table on the previous page.

   The longest chain is 5 carbons, so the stem is **pent-**

   The main functional group is **-OH**, so the
   compound's name is going to be based on
   "**pentanol**".

   Don't forget — the longest carbon chain may be bent.

3) Number the carbons in the **longest** carbon chain so that the carbon with the
   main functional group attached has the lowest possible number.

   If there's more than one longest chain, pick the one with the **most side-chains**.

4) Write the carbon number that the functional group is on **before the suffix**.

   Longest chain with
   most side-chains

   -OH has lowest
   possible number.

   –OH is on carbon-2,
   so it's some sort of
   "pentan-2-ol".

5) Any side-chains or less important functional groups are added as prefixes at the start of the name.
   Put them in **alphabetical** order, with the **number** of the carbon atom each is attached to.

6) If there's more than one **identical** side-chain or functional group, use **di-** (2), **tri-** (3) or **tetra-** (4)
   before that part of the name — but ignore this when working out the alphabetical order.

   There's an ethyl group on carbon-3, and methyl groups on carbon-2 and carbon-4,
   so it's **3-ethyl-2,4-dimethylpentan-2-ol**

IUPAC Rules Help Avoid Confusion

The **IUPAC system** for naming organic compounds is the agreed
international language of chemistry. Years ago, organic compounds were
given whatever names people fancied, such as acetic acid and ethylene.
But these names caused **confusion** between different countries.

The IUPAC system means scientific ideas can be communicated **across the
globe** more effectively. So it's easier for scientists to get on with testing
each other's work, and either confirm or dispute new theories.

*Fancy a cup of tea?
Tea, you know... Brown stuff.
Oh come on, don't just sit
there looking confused...*

Basic Stuff

Structural Isomers have different Structural Arrangements of Atoms

In structural isomers the atoms are **connected** in different ways. But they still have the **same molecular formula**. There are **three types** of structural isomers that you need to know about:

CHAIN ISOMERS

Chain isomers have different arrangements of the **carbon skeleton**. Some are **straight chains** and others **branched**.

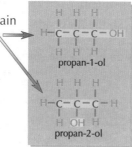

butane

methylpropane

POSITIONAL ISOMERS

Positional isomers have the **same skeleton** and the **same functional group**. The difference is that the group is attached to a **different carbon atom**.

butan-1-ol

butan-2-ol

FUNCTIONAL GROUP ISOMERS

Functional group isomers have the same atoms arranged into **different functional groups**.

butan-1-ol

ethoxyethane

Don't be Fooled — What Looks Like an Isomer Might Not Be

Atoms can rotate as much as they like around single **C–C bonds**. Remember this when you work out structural isomers — sometimes what looks like an isomer, isn't.

For example, there are only **two** chain or positional isomers of **C_3H_7OH**.

propan-1-ol

propan-1-ol again...

... and again propan-1-ol

... and again propan-1-ol

propan-2-ol

propan-2-ol again...

Practice Questions

Q1 What is the general formula for alkanes? Give the molecular formula of an alkane with three carbons.

Q2 Explain the difference between molecular formulas and structural formulas.

Q3 What are isomers? What is a positional isomer?

Exam Questions

Q1 1-bromobutane is prepared from butan-1-ol in this reaction: $C_4H_9OH + NaBr + H_2SO_4 \rightarrow C_4H_9Br + NaHSO_4 + H_2O$
   a) Draw the displayed formulae for butan-1-ol and 1-bromobutane. [2 marks]

   b) What is the functional group in butan-1-ol and why is it necessary to state its position on the carbon chain? [2 marks]

Q2 There are five chain isomers of the alkane C_6H_{14}.
   a) Draw and name all five isomers of C_6H_{14}. [10 marks]
   b) Alkanes are an example of a homologous series. What is a homologous series? [2 marks]
   c) (i) Write down the molecular formula for the alkane molecule that has four carbon atoms. [1 mark]
      (ii) Write out the full structural formula for the straight-chain isomer of the alkane in part c)(i). [1 mark]

Q3 The alkane with the molecular formula C_5H_{12} has these chain isomers.
   a) Name these isomers. [3 marks]
   b) Explain what chain isomers are. [2 marks]

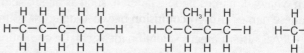

Human structural isomers...

Alkanes and Petroleum

I'm an alkane and I'm OK — I sleep all night and I work all day...
These three pages are for AQA (Unit 1), OCR A (Unit 2), OCR B (Unit 1) and Edexcel (Units 1 and 2).

Alkanes are **Saturated Hydrocarbons**

1) Alkanes have the **general formula** C_nH_{2n+2}. They only contain **carbon** and **hydrogen** atoms, so they're **hydrocarbons**.

2) Every carbon atom in an alkane has **four single bonds** with other atoms. It's **impossible** for carbon to make more than four bonds, so alkanes are **saturated**. Here are a few examples of alkanes —

3) You get **cycloalkanes** too. They have a ring of carbon atoms with two hydrogens attached to each carbon.

4) Cycloalkanes have a **different general formula** from that of normal alkanes (C_nH_{2n}, assuming they have only one ring), but they are still **saturated**.

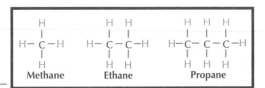

Cyclohexane C_6H_{12} — cycloalkanes have two fewer hydrogens than normal alkanes

Boiling Points of Alkanes Depend on **Size and Shape** — OCR A and Edexcel (Unit 2)

The smallest alkanes, like methane, are **gases** at room temperature and pressure — they've got very low boiling points. Larger alkanes are **liquids** — they have higher boiling points.

1) Alkanes have **covalent bonds** inside the molecules. **Between** the molecules, there are **van der Waals** forces (see page 50) which hold them all together.

2) The **longer** the carbon chain, the **stronger** the van der Waals forces. This is because there's **more molecular surface area** and more electrons to interact.

3) So as the molecules get longer, it takes **more energy** to overcome the van der Waals forces and separate them, and the boiling point **rises**.

4) A **branched-chain** alkane has a **lower** boiling point than its straight-chain isomer. Branched-chain alkanes can't **pack closely** together and they have smaller **molecular surface areas** — so the van der Waals forces are reduced.

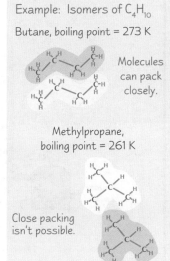

Example: Isomers of C_4H_{10}
Butane, boiling point = 273 K
Molecules can pack closely.
Methylpropane, boiling point = 261 K
Close packing isn't possible.

- **Long-chain alkanes have higher boiling points than short-chain alkanes.**
- **Straight-chain alkanes have higher boiling points than branched alkanes.**

5) The **melting temperatures** of alkanes vary in a similar way, for the same reasons.

Alkanes Have a **Tetrahedral Shape** Around Each Carbon

Alkanes aren't flat — the atoms around each carbon form **3-D tetrahedral shapes**. The angle between any two of the covalent bonds is **109.5°**. The electron pairs in the bonds **repel** each other so the bonds arrange themselves as **far apart** from each other as possible.

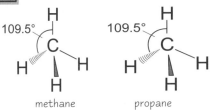

methane   propane

Alkanes Burn **Completely** in Oxygen

1) If you burn (**oxidise**) alkanes with **oxygen**, you'll get **carbon dioxide** and water — this is a **combustion reaction**.

Here's the equation for the combustion of propane — $C_3H_{8(g)} + 5O_{2(g)} \rightarrow 3CO_{2(g)} + 4H_2O_{(g)}$

2) Combustion reactions happen between **gases**, so liquid alkanes have to be **vaporised** first. Smaller alkanes turn into **gases** more easily (they're more **volatile**), so they'll **burn** more easily too.

3) Larger alkanes release heaps more **energy** per mole because they have more bonds to react. For every extra $-CH_2-$ unit, the **enthalpy change of combustion**, ΔH_c, increases on average by a whopping **654 kJ mol⁻¹**. (See page 88 for more on enthalpy changes.)

Alkanes and Petroleum

Crude Oil is a Mixture of Hydrocarbons

1) **Petroleum** is just a **poncy word** for crude oil — the black, yukky stuff they get out of the ground with huge oil wells. It's mostly **alkanes**. They range from **smallish alkanes**, like pentane, to **massive alkanes** with more than 50 carbons.

2) Crude oil isn't very useful as it is, but you can **separate** it into more useful bits (or **fractions**) by **fractional distillation**.

Here's how fractional distillation works — don't try this at home.

1) First, the crude oil is **vaporised** at about 350 °C.

2) The vaporised crude oil goes into the **fractionating column** and rises up through the trays. The largest hydrocarbons don't **vaporise** at all, because their boiling points are too high — they just run to the bottom and form a gooey **residue**.

3) As the crude oil vapour goes up the fractionating column, it gets **cooler**. Because of the different chain lengths, each fraction **condenses** at a different temperature. The fractions are **drawn off** at different levels in the column.

4) The hydrocarbons with the **lowest boiling points** don't condense. They're drawn off as **gases** at the top of the column.

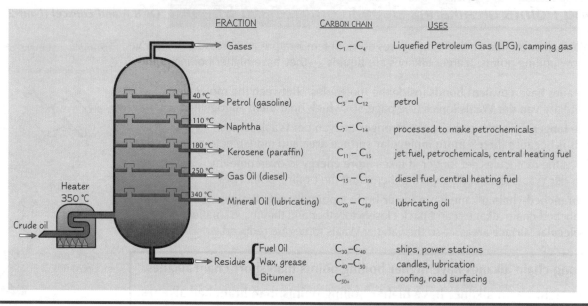

FRACTION	CARBON CHAIN	USES
Gases	$C_1 - C_4$	Liquefied Petroleum Gas (LPG), camping gas
Petrol (gasoline) 40 °C	$C_5 - C_{12}$	petrol
Naphtha 110 °C	$C_7 - C_{14}$	processed to make petrochemicals
Kerosene (paraffin) 180 °C	$C_{11} - C_{15}$	jet fuel, petrochemicals, central heating fuel
Gas Oil (diesel) 250 °C	$C_{15} - C_{19}$	diesel fuel, central heating fuel
Mineral Oil (lubricating) 340 °C	$C_{20} - C_{30}$	lubricating oil
Residue — Fuel Oil	$C_{30} - C_{40}$	ships, power stations
Wax, grease	$C_{40} - C_{50}$	candles, lubrication
Bitumen	C_{50+}	roofing, road surfacing

Heater 350 °C — Crude oil

Heavy Fractions can be 'Cracked' to Make Smaller Molecules

1) People want loads of the **light** fractions like petrol and naphtha. They don't want so much of the **heavier** stuff like bitumen though.

2) To meet this demand, the less popular heavier fractions are **cracked**. Cracking involves **breaking** long-chain alkanes into **smaller** hydrocarbons (which can include alkenes). It involves breaking the **C–C bonds**. You could crack **decane** like this —

$$C_{10}H_{22} \rightarrow C_2H_4 + C_8H_{18}$$
decane   ethene   octane

There are **two types** of **cracking** you need to know about:

THERMAL CRACKING

- It takes place at **high temperature** (up to 1000 °C) and **high pressure** (up to 70 atm).
- It produces a lot of **alkenes**.
- These **alkenes** are used to make heaps of valuable products, like **polymers**. A good example is **poly(ethene)**, which is made from ethene (have a squiz at page 124 for more on polymers).

CATALYTIC CRACKING

- This makes mostly **motor fuels** and **aromatic** hydrocarbons (see page 118).
- It uses something called a **zeolite catalyst**, at a **slight pressure** and **high temperature** (about 450 °C).
- Using a catalyst **cuts costs**, because the reaction can be done at a **lower** temperature and pressure. The catalyst also **speeds** up the reaction, and time is money and all that.

Alkanes and Petroleum

Hydrocarbons with a **High Octane Rating** Burn More **Smoothly**   *OCR B (Unit 1) only*

1) Here's a super-quick whizz through how a **petrol engine** works:
   The **fuel/air** mixture is squashed by a **piston** and **ignited** with a spark, creating an **explosion**. This drives the piston up again, turning the **crankshaft**. Four pistons work **one after the other**, so that the engine runs smoothly.

2) The problem is, **straight-chain alkanes** in petrol tend to **auto-ignite** — when the fuel/air mixture is compressed they explode without being ignited by the spark. This extra explosion causes '**knocking**' in the engine.

3) To get rid of knocking and make combustion more efficient, **shorter branched-chain alkanes**, **cycloalkanes** and **arenes** are included in petrols, creating a **high octane rating**.

The octane rating of a petrol tells you how likely it is to auto-ignite. The higher the number, the less likely it is to auto-ignite. It's based on a scale where 100% heptane has a rating of 0, and 100% 2,2,4-trimethylpentane has a rating of 100.

Heptane C_7H_{16} (a straight-chain alkane)

2,2,4–trimethylpentane $C(CH_3)_3CH_2CH(CH_3)_2$ (a branched-chain alkane)

Isomerisation creates *Branched-Chain Isomers*   *OCR A (Unit 2) and OCR B (Unit 1)*

Isomerisation is often carried out by heating a **straight-chain** alkane with a **platinum catalyst** stuck on inert aluminium oxide. The molecule is broken up and put back together as a **branched-chain isomer**.

A form of **zeolite** (a mineral with minute tunnels and cavities) is used as a **molecular sieve** to separate the isomers. The molecules which still have **straight chains** go through the zeolite 'sieve' and are **recycled**.

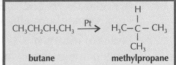

$$CH_3CH_2CH_2CH_3 \xrightarrow{Pt} H_3C-\overset{H}{\underset{CH_3}{C}}-CH_3$$

butane → methylpropane

Alkanes can be *Reformed* into *Cycloalkanes and Arenes*   *OCR A (Unit 2), OCR B (Unit 1) and Edexcel (Unit 1)*

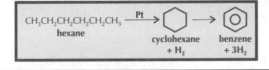

$$CH_3CH_2CH_2CH_2CH_2CH_3 \xrightarrow{Pt}$$
hexane → cyclohexane $+ H_2$ → benzene $+ 3H_2$

Reforming converts **alkanes** into **arenes** (aromatic hydrocarbons — see page 118) using a catalyst (e.g. platinum stuck on aluminium oxide again).

Practice Questions

Q1 What shape is a methane molecule?

Q2 What is the naphtha fraction of crude oil used for?

Q3 What is cracking?

Q4 What is the purpose of zeolite in isomerisation?

Exam Questions

Q1 Here are three isomers of pentane.
   a) Which isomer has the highest boiling point?
      Explain your answer as fully as possible.   [3 marks]
   b) Decane has a higher boiling point than the isomers shown in part a). Explain this difference.   [3 marks]
   c) Write a balanced chemical equation for the complete combustion of molecule **A**, above.   [2 marks]

Q2 Crude oil is a source of fuels and petrochemicals. It's vaporised and separated into fractions using fractional distillation.
   a) Some heavier fractions are processed using cracking.
      i) Give one reason why cracking is carried out.   [2 marks]
      ii) Write a possible equation for the cracking of dodecane, $C_{12}H_{26}$.   [1 mark]
   b) Some hydrocarbons are processed using isomerisation or reforming, producing a petrol with a high octane rating.
      i)   What is meant by a petrol's octane rating?   [3 marks]
      ii) What kinds of compounds are found in a petrol with a high octane rating? What effect do they have on the petrol's performance?   [4 marks]
      iii) Draw and name two isomers formed from pentane by isomerisation. Which isomer would increase the octane rating of a petrol the most?   [5 marks]

Crude oil — not the kind of oil you could take home to meet your mother...

This ain't the most exciting page in the history of the known universe. Although in a galaxy far, far away there may be lots of pages on even more boring topics. But, that's neither here nor there, cos you've got to learn the stuff anyway. Get fractional distillation and cracking straight in your brain and make sure you know why people bother to do it.

Alkanes as Fuels

Alkanes are absolutely fantastic as fuels. Except for the fact that they produce loads of nasty pollutant gases.
These pages are for AQA (Unit 1), OCR A (Unit 2), OCR B (Unit 1) and Edexcel (Unit 1).

Alkanes are Useful Fuels

When you **burn** an alkane in plenty of air, you end up with **carbon dioxide** and **water** (see page 81). It's an **exothermic** reaction. Alkanes make great fuels — burning just **one mole** of **methane** releases a humungous amount of **energy**.

Carbon dioxide isn't poisonous, but it is a **greenhouse gas** and is thought to be causing climate change (see p146-147).

Carbon Monoxide is Formed if Alkanes Burn Incompletely

If there's not enough oxygen, hydrocarbons **combust incompletely**, and you get carbon monoxide gas instead of carbon dioxide. E.g.

$$CH_{4(g)} + 1\tfrac{1}{2}O_{2(g)} \rightarrow CO_{(g)} + 2H_2O_{(g)} \qquad C_8H_{18(g)} + 8\tfrac{1}{2}O_{2(g)} \rightarrow 8CO_{(g)} + 9H_2O_{(g)}$$

This is bad news because carbon monoxide gas is **poisonous**. Carbon monoxide molecules bind to the same sites on **haemoglobin molecules** in red blood cells as oxygen molecules. So **oxygen** can't be carried around the body.

Luckily, carbon monoxide can be removed from exhaust gases by **catalytic converters** on cars. Also, **oxygenates** are added to petrol to reduce carbon monoxide emissions. They help the fuel to **combust fully**.

And if that's Not Bad Enough... Burning Fuels Produces Other Pollutants Too

UNBURNT HYDROCARBONS AND OXIDES OF NITROGEN (NO$_x$) CONTRIBUTE TO SMOG

1) Engines **don't burn** all the fuel molecules. Some of these come out as **unburnt hydrocarbons**.

2) **Oxides of nitrogen** (NO$_x$) are produced when the high pressure and temperature in a car engine cause the nitrogen and oxygen atoms in the air to react together.

3) The hydrocarbons and nitrogen oxides react in the presence of sunlight to form **ground-level ozone** (O$_3$), which is a major component of **smog**. **Low level ozone** irritates eyes, aggravates respiratory problems and even causes lung damage (ozone isn't nice stuff, unless it is high up in the atmosphere as part of the ozone layer — see p. 144).

4) **Catalytic converters** on cars remove unburnt hydrocarbons and oxides of nitrogen from the exhaust.

SULFUR DIOXIDE

1) **Acid rain** is caused by burning fossil fuels that contain **sulfur**. The sulfur burns to produce **sulfur dioxide** gas which then enters the atmosphere, dissolves in the moisture, and is converted into **sulfuric acid**.
   The same process occurs when nitrogen dioxide (NO$_2$) escapes into the atmosphere — nitric acid is produced.

2) Acid rain destroys trees and vegetation, as well as corroding buildings and statues and killing fish in lakes. Luckily, sulfur dioxide can be removed from power station flue gases using **calcium oxide**.

Fossil Fuels are Non-Renewable

The three fossil fuels **coal**, **oil** and **natural gas** are major fuels. But, there's a finite amount of them and they're running out. Oil will be the first to go — and as it gets really scarce, it'll become more **expensive**. It's not **sustainable** to keep using them willy-nilly (see page 149 for more on sustainability).

One solution is to produce more renewable vegetable-based fuels, like **biodiesel**. Biodiesel is made by refining renewable fats and oils, such as vegetable oils (biodiesel can even be made from used restaurant frying oil). **Alcohols** (such as **bioethanol** — see the next page) are also alternatives.

Learn What Carbon Footprint and Carbon Neutral Mean

A **carbon footprint** tells you how much effect something has on the environment. The more carbon dioxide an activity causes to be released, the bigger its carbon footprint.

A couple of overturned bins make a great alternative to motor transport

Carbon neutral activities have **no overall carbon emission** into the atmosphere.

1) All **products** have a **carbon footprint**. It takes **energy** to extract the raw materials, make the thing and then transport it. The energy more than likely comes from **burning fossil fuels**.

2) **Everyone** has a carbon footprint. Most of the things you do involve carbon being emitted somehow — e.g. **watching TV** and **travelling in cars or buses** involves energy from burning fossil fuels. And then everything you **buy**, including food, adds to your carbon footprint.

3) **Trees** remove CO$_2$ during photosynthesis. So you can make an activity or product **carbon neutral** by planting enough trees to remove all of the CO$_2$ that's emitted in doing the activity or making and transporting the product.

Alkanes as Fuels

Burning Most Fuels has a Carbon Footprint

You need to be able to say whether fuels are **carbon neutral** and why.

PETROL IS DEFINITELY NOT CARBON NEUTRAL

Burning petrol releases CO_2 into the atmosphere that was trapped in the earth millions of years ago.

BIOETHANOL IS CARBON NEUTRAL (MORE OR LESS)

Bioethanol is a possible substitute for petrol. It's produced by the **fermentation of sugar** from crops such as maize. It's thought of as being **carbon neutral**, because all the CO_2 released when the fuel is burned was removed by the crop as it grew. **BUT** — there are still carbon emissions if you consider the **whole** process. Making the fertilisers and powering agricultural machinery will probably involve burning fossil fuels.

A potential problem with using crops to make fuels is that developed countries (like us) will create a huge demand as they try and find fossil fuel alternatives. Poorer developing countries (in South America, say) will use this as a way of earning money and rush to convert their farming land to produce these 'crops for fuels', which may mean they won't grow enough food to eat.

HYDROGEN GAS CAN BE PRETTY MUCH CARBON NEUTRAL

Hydrogen gas can either be **burned in a modified engine**, or used in a **fuel cell**. A fuel cell converts hydrogen and oxygen into **water**, and this chemical process produces **electricity** to power the vehicle. Either way, the big advantage is that **water** is the **only** waste product. Hydrogen can be extracted from **water** — you need energy to extract it though. If this energy comes from a **renewable source**, say wind or solar, it will be pretty much **carbon neutral** (but there'll be some carbon emitted when making the solar panels or wind turbines).

The trouble is, people are worried about using such a flammable gas — an airship, called the 'Hindenburg', which contained hydrogen gas exploded in 1937. But with new technology, fuel cells are very safe. Petrol is also very flammable, but people are accustomed to using it in their daily lives. On top of this, hydrogen cars cost lots more than petrol cars at the moment. Another technical problem is safely storing large quantities of hydrogen gas at refuelling stations.

NUCLEAR REACTORS DON'T PRODUCE CO_2 — BUT THE WHOLE NUCLEAR CYCLE DOES

Nuclear reactors **don't** cause air pollution, but mining the uranium ore, building and finally decommissioning nuclear plants **isn't** carbon neutral. Nuclear power may help us eke out our remaining fossil fuel supplies, but then there's the **radioactive waste** to deal with. Not to mention the public's fears about the possibility of a nuclear **disaster**...

Practice Questions

Q1 Write a chemical equation for the incomplete combustion of methane gas in air.

Q2 Which exhaust gases contribute to smog?

Q3 What is a 'carbon footprint'?

Q4 What is a raw material for the production of bioethanol?

Exam Questions

Q1 Nitrogen monoxide gas is a pollutant formed when internal combustion engines burn fuels.

   (a) Write a balanced chemical equation for the formation of nitrogen monoxide from oxygen and nitrogen. [2 marks]

   (b) Nitrogen monoxide is converted into NO_2 by reaction with oxygen.
      Write a balanced chemical equation for this reaction. [2 marks]

   (c) Name an environmental problem resulting from NO_2 gas being released into the atmosphere. [1 mark]

Q2 (a) Describe why using petrol as a fuel is not carbon neutral. [1 mark]

   (b) Crude oil, from which petrol is obtained, is called a 'finite' resource. Explain the term 'finite'. [1 mark]

   (c) Bioethanol is a renewable fuel that is a viable alternative to petrol. It can be made from sugar cane.
      (i) What process converts the sugar from the sugar cane into ethanol? [1 mark]
      (ii) Explain why the use of bioethanol is considered to be carbon neutral. [2 marks]

Hay up — this page has horsepower...

We rely on fuels to provide the energy for our 21st century lifestyles — cars-a-plenty, power on tap, and so on. It's certainly convenient, but there are problems too — like the greenhouse effect, and the fact that we're going to run out of fossil fuels fairly soon-ish. Learn all the stuff on these pages. Even the fiddly details about what's carbon neutral and what's not.

Alkanes — Substitution Reactions

Oooh, eh... mechanisms. You might like them. You might not. But you've gotta learn 'em.
Reactions don't happen instantaneously — there are often a few steps. And mechanisms show you what they are.
***These pages are for** AQA (Unit 2), OCR A (Unit 2), OCR B (Unit 2) **and** Edexcel (Unit 1).*

There are **Two Types** of Bond Fission — **Homolytic** and **Heterolytic**

Breaking a covalent bond is called **bond fission**. A single covalent bond is a shared pair of electrons between two atoms. It can break in two ways:

Heterolytic Fission:
In heterolytic fission **two different** substances are formed — a positively charged **cation** (X^+), and a negatively charged **anion** (Y^-).

$$X \colon Y \rightarrow X^+ + Y^-$$

('hetero' means 'different')

Homolytic Fission:
In homolytic fission two electrically uncharged **'radicals'** are formed. Radicals are particles that have an unpaired electron.

$$X \colon Y \rightarrow X\bullet + Y\bullet$$

Because of the unpaired electron, these radicals are very reactive.

A double-headed arrow shows that a pair of electrons move. A single-headed arrow shows the movement of a single electron. Makes sense.

Halogens React with **Alkanes**, Forming **Haloalkanes**

1) Halogens react with alkanes in **photochemical** reactions. Photochemical reactions are started by **ultraviolet** light.

2) A hydrogen atom is **substituted** (replaced) by chlorine or bromine. This is a **free radical substitution reaction**.

Chlorine and **methane** react with a bit of a bang to form **chloromethane**:

$$CH_4 + Cl_2 \xrightarrow{UV} CH_3Cl + HCl$$

The **reaction mechanism** has three stages:

Initiation reactions — free radicals are produced.

1) Sunlight provides enough energy to break the Cl-Cl bond — this is **photodissociation**.
$$Cl_2 \xrightarrow{UV} 2Cl\bullet$$

2) The bond splits **equally** and each atom gets to keep one electron — **homolytic fission**. The atom becomes a highly reactive **free radical**, $Cl\bullet$, because of its **unpaired electron**.

Propagation reactions — free radicals are used up and created in a chain reaction.

1) $Cl\bullet$ attacks a **methane** molecule: $Cl\bullet + CH_4 \rightarrow CH_3\bullet + HCl$

2) The new **methyl free radical**, $CH_3\bullet$, can attack another Cl_2 molecule: $CH_3\bullet + Cl_2 \rightarrow CH_3Cl + Cl\bullet$

3) The new $Cl\bullet$ can attack **another** CH_4 molecule, and so on, until all the Cl_2 or CH_4 molecules are wiped out.

Termination reactions — free radicals are mopped up.
1) If two free radicals join together, they make a **stable molecule**.
2) There are **heaps** of possible termination reactions.
Here's a couple of them to give you the idea: $Cl\bullet + CH_3\bullet \rightarrow CH_3Cl$
$$CH_3\bullet + CH_3\bullet \rightarrow C_2H_6$$

Some products formed will be trace impurities in the final sample.

The reaction between bromine and methane works in exactly the same way.
$$CH_4 + Br_2 \xrightarrow{UV} CH_3Br + HBr$$

Alkanes — Substitution Reactions

The Problem is — You End Up With a **Mixture of Products**

1) The big problem with free-radical substitution is that you **don't only get chloromethane**, but a **mixture of products**.

2) If there's **too much chlorine** in the reaction mixture, some of the remaining **hydrogen atoms** on the **chloromethane molecule** will be swapped for chlorine atoms.

The propagation reactions happen again, this time to make **dichloromethane**.

$$Cl^\bullet + CH_3Cl \rightarrow CH_2Cl^\bullet + HCl$$

$$CH_2Cl^\bullet + Cl_2 \rightarrow \mathbf{CH_2Cl_2} + Cl^\bullet$$
dichloromethane

3) It doesn't stop there. Another substitution reaction can take place to form **trichloromethane**.

$$Cl^\bullet + CH_2Cl_2 \rightarrow CHCl_2^\bullet + HCl$$

$$CHCl_2^\bullet + Cl_2 \rightarrow \mathbf{CHCl_3} + Cl^\bullet$$
trichloromethane

4) **Tetrachloromethane** (CCl_4) is formed in the last possible substitution. There are no more hydrogens attached to the carbon atom, so the substitution process has to stop.

5) So the end product is a mixture of CH_3Cl, CH_2Cl_2, $CHCl_3$ and CCl_4. This is a nuisance, because you have to separate the **chloromethane** from the other three unwanted by-products.

6) The best way of reducing the chance of these by-products forming is to have an **excess of methane**. This means there's a greater chance of a chlorine radical colliding only with a **methane molecule** and not a **chloromethane molecule**.

Practice Questions

Q1 What's a free radical?

Q2 What's homolytic fission?

Q3 What's photodissociation?

Q4 Complete this equation: $CH_4 + Cl_2 \xrightarrow{\text{UV}}$

Q5 Write down three possible products, other than chloromethane, from the photochemical reaction between CH_4 and Cl_2.

Exam Questions

Q1 When irradiated with UV light, methane gas will react with bromine to form a mixture of several organic compounds.

   (a) Name the type of mechanism involved in this reaction.   [1 mark]

   (b) Write an overall equation to show the formation of bromomethane from methane and bromine.   [1 mark]

   (c) Write down the two equations in the propagation step for the formation of CH_3Br.   [2 marks]

   (d) (i) A small amount of ethane is found in the product mixture.
       Write the chemical equation for the formation of ethane in this reaction.   [1 mark]

     (ii) Name the mechanistic step that leads to the formation of ethane.   [1 mark]

   (e) Name the major product formed when a large excess of bromine reacts with methane in the presence of UV light.   [1 mark]

Q2 The alkane ethane is a saturated hydrocarbon. It is mostly unreactive, but will react with bromine in a photochemical reaction.

Write an equation and outline the mechanism for the photochemical reaction of bromine with ethane. You should assume ethane is in excess.   [6 marks]

This page is like...totally radical, man...

Mechanisms can be an absolute pain in the bum to learn, but unfortunately reactions are what Chemistry's all about. If you don't like it, you should have taken art — no mechanisms in that, just pretty pictures. Ah well, there's no going back now. You've just got to sit down and learn the stuff. Keep hacking away at it, till you know it all off by heart.

Enthalpy Changes

A whole new section to enjoy — but don't forget, Big Brother is watching...
These pages are for AQA (Unit 2), OCR A (Unit 2), OCR B (Unit 1) and Edexcel (Unit 1).

Chemical Reactions Often Have Enthalpy Changes

When chemical reactions happen, some bonds are **broken** and some bonds are **made**. More often than not, this'll cause a **change in energy**. The souped-up chemistry term for this is **enthalpy change** —

> **Enthalpy change**, ΔH (delta H), is the heat energy transferred in a reaction at **constant pressure**. The units of ΔH are **kJ mol^{-1}**.

You write $\Delta H^{\ominus}$ to show that the elements were in their **standard states** (i.e. their states at a pressure of 100 kPa), and that the measurements were made under **standard conditions**. Standard conditions are **100 kPa (about 1 atm) pressure** and a **temperature of 298 K (25 °C)**. The next page explains why this is necessary.

Reactions can be either Exothermic or Endothermic

> **Exothermic** reactions **give out** energy. ΔH is **negative**.

In exothermic reactions, the temperature often goes **up**.

> **Oxidation** is exothermic. Here are two examples:
>
> • The **combustion** of a fuel like methane $\longrightarrow$ $CH_{4(g)} + 2O_{2(g)} \longrightarrow CO_{2(g)} + 2H_2O_{(l)}$ $\Delta H_c^{\ominus} = -890$ kJ mol^{-1} **exothermic**
>
> • The oxidation of **carbohydrates**, such as glucose, $C_6H_{12}O_6$, in respiration.

The symbols $\Delta H_c^{\ominus}$ and $\Delta H_r^{\ominus}$ (below) are explained on the next page.

> **Endothermic** reactions **absorb** energy. ΔH is **positive**.

In these reactions, the temperature often **falls**.

> The **thermal decomposition** of calcium carbonate is endothermic.
>
> $CaCO_{3(s)} \longrightarrow CaO_{(s)} + CO_{2(g)}$ $\Delta H_r^{\ominus} = +178$ kJ mol^{-1} **endothermic**
>
> The main reactions of **photosynthesis** are also endothermic — sunlight supplies the energy.

Enthalpy Profile Diagrams Show Energy Change in Reactions

1) **Enthalpy Profile Diagrams** show you how the enthalpy (energy) changes during reactions.
2) The **activation energy**, E_a, is the minimum amount of energy needed to begin breaking reactant bonds and start a chemical reaction.

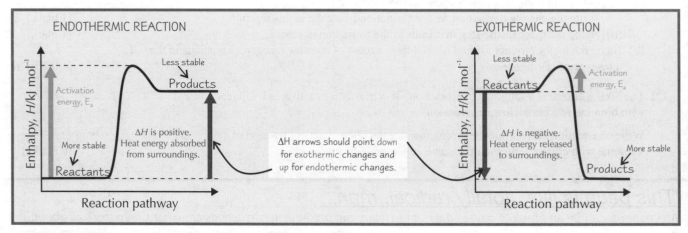

3) The **less enthalpy** a substance has, the **more stable** it is.

Enthalpy Changes

You Need to Specify the Conditions for Enthalpy Changes

1) You can't directly measure the **actual** enthalpy of a system. In practice, that doesn't matter, because it's only ever enthalpy **change** that matters. You can find enthalpy changes either by **experiment** or in **textbooks**.

2) Enthalpy changes you find in textbooks are usually **standard** enthalpy changes — enthalpy changes under **standard conditions** (**298 K** and **100 kPa**).

3) This is important because changes in enthalpy are affected by **temperature** and **pressure** — using standard conditions means that everyone can know **exactly** what the enthalpy change is describing.

There are Different Types of ΔH Depending On the Reaction

1) **Standard enthalpy change of reaction**, $\Delta H_r^\ominus$, is the enthalpy change when the reaction occurs in the **molar quantities** shown in the **chemical equation**, under standard conditions in their standard states.

2) **Standard enthalpy change of formation**, $\Delta H_f^\ominus$, is the enthalpy change when **1 mole** of a **compound** is formed from its **elements** in their standard states under standard conditions, e.g. $2C_{(s)} + 3H_{2(g)} + \frac{1}{2}O_{2(g)} \longrightarrow C_2H_5OH_{(l)}$

3) **Standard enthalpy change of combustion**, $\Delta H_c^\ominus$, is the enthalpy change when **1 mole** of a substance is completely **burned in oxygen** under standard conditions.

4) **Standard enthalpy of neutralisation**, $\Delta H_{neut}^\ominus$, is the enthalpy change when **1 mole** of **water** is formed from the neutralisation of **hydrogen ions** by **hydroxide ions** under standard conditions, e.g. $H^+_{(aq)} + OH^-_{(aq)} \longrightarrow H_2O_{(l)}$

5) **Standard enthalpy change of atomisation**, $\Delta H_{at}^\ominus$, is the enthalpy change when **1 mole** of **gaseous atoms** is formed from the element in its **standard state**, e.g. $\frac{1}{2}Cl_{2(g)} \longrightarrow Cl_{(g)}$

Practice Questions

Q1 Explain the terms exothermic and endothermic, giving an example in each case.

Q2 Draw and label enthalpy profile diagrams for an exothermic and an endothermic reaction.

Q3 Define standard enthalpy of formation and standard enthalpy of combustion.

Exam Questions

Q1 Hydrogen peroxide, H_2O_2, can decompose into water and oxygen. $2H_2O_{2(l)} \longrightarrow 2H_2O_{(l)} + O_{2(g)}$ $\Delta H_r^\ominus = -98$ kJ mol^{-1}

Draw an enthalpy profile diagram for this reaction. Mark the activation energy and ΔH on the diagram. [3 marks]

Q2 Methanol, CH_3OH, when blended with petrol, can be used as a fuel. $\Delta H_c^\ominus[CH_3OH] = -726$ kJ mol^{-1}.
a) Write an equation, including state symbols, for the standard enthalpy change of combustion of methanol. [2 marks]

b) Write an equation, including state symbols, for the standard enthalpy change of formation of methanol. [2 marks]

c) Liquid petroleum gas is a fuel that contains propane, C_3H_8.
Give <u>two</u> reasons why the following equation does not represent a standard enthalpy change of combustion. [2 marks]

$$2C_3H_{8(g)} + 10O_{2(g)} \longrightarrow 8H_2O_{(g)} + 6CO_{2(g)} \quad \Delta H_r = -4113 \text{ kJ mol}^{-1}$$

It's getting hot in here, so take off all your bonds...

Quite a few definitions here. And you need to know them all. If you're going to bother learning them, you might as well do it properly and learn all the pernickety details. They probably seem about as useful as a dead fly in your custard right now, but all will be revealed over the next few pages. Learn them now, so you've got a bit of a head start.

Measuring Enthalpy Changes Directly

You can find some enthalpy changes by doing an experiment and then a calculation...
These pages are for AQA (Unit 2), OCR A (Unit 2), OCR B (Unit 1) and Edexcel (Unit 1).

You can find out Enthalpy Changes using Calorimetry

In **calorimetry** you find how much heat is given out by a reaction by measuring the **temperature change** of some water.

1) To find the enthalpy of **combustion** of a **flammable liquid**, you burn it — using apparatus like this...

2) As the fuel burns, it heats the water. You can work out the **heat absorbed** by the water if you know the **mass of water**, the **temperature change of the water** (ΔT), and the **specific heat capacity of water** (= 4.18 J g^{-1} K^{-1}) — see below for the details.

3) Ideally, all the heat given out by the fuel as it burns would be **absorbed** by the water — allowing you to work out the enthalpy change of combustion (see below). In practice, you **always** lose some heat (as you heat the apparatus and the surroundings).

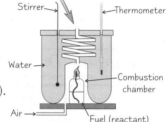

Calorimetry can also be used to calculate the enthalpy change for a reaction that happens **in solution**, such as **neutralisation** or **displacement**.

The specific heat capacity of water is the amount of heat energy it takes to raise the temperature of 1 g of water by 1 K.

1) To find the enthalpy change in a neutralisation reaction, add a **known volume** of acid to an **insulated container** and measure the **temperature**.

2) Then add a **known volume** of alkali, and record the **temperature rise**. (Stir the solution to make sure the solution is evenly heated.)

3) You can work out the heat needed to **raise the temperature** of the solution formed using the formula below — this **equals** the **heat given out** by the **reaction**.

4) You can usually assume that all solutions (reactants and product) have the **same density as water**. This means you can use **volume** (rather than mass) in your calculations (as 1 cm³ of water has a mass of 1 g).

Calculate Enthalpy Changes Using the Equation q = mcΔT

It seems there's a snazzy equation for everything these days, and enthalpy change is no exception:

$q = mc\Delta T$ where, q = heat lost or gained (in joules). This is the same as the enthalpy change if the pressure is constant.

m = mass of water in the calorimeter, or solution in the insulated container (in grams)

c = specific heat capacity of water (4.18 J g^{-1}K^{-1})

ΔT = the change in temperature of the water or solution

Example:

In a laboratory experiment, 1.16 g of an organic liquid fuel was completely burned in oxygen.

The heat formed during this combustion raised the temperature of 100 g of water from 295.3 K to 357.8 K.

Calculate the standard enthalpy of combustion, $\Delta H_c^{\ominus}$, of the fuel. Its M_r is 58.

1 First off, you need to calculate the **amount of heat** given out by the fuel using $q = mc\Delta T$.

$q = mc\Delta T$

$q = 100 \times 4.18 \times (357.8 - 295.3) = 26\ 125\ \text{J} = 26.125\ \text{kJ}$ ⟵ *Change the amount of heat from J to kJ.*

Remember — m is the mass of water, NOT the mass of fuel.

2 The standard enthalpy of combustion involves 1 mole of fuel. So next you need to find out **how many moles** of fuel produced this heat. It's back to the old $n = \dfrac{mass}{M}$ equation.

$$n = \frac{1.16}{58} = 0.02 \text{ moles of fuel}$$

3 So, the heat produced by 1 mole of fuel = $\dfrac{-26.125}{0.02}$

It's negative because combustion is an exothermic reaction.

$\approx$ **-1306 kJ mol^{-1}**. This is the standard enthalpy change of combustion.

As it turns out, this result isn't very accurate — loads of heat has been **lost** and not measured. This is explained on the next page. ⟵ 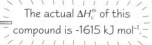 *The actual $\Delta H_c^{\ominus}$ of this compound is -1615 kJ mol^{-1}.*

Measuring Enthalpy Changes Directly

Experimental Results *Always* Include *Errors*

You need to know about **errors** in experiments — there are **two kinds**, and you always get **both** when you do an experiment.

1) **Systematic errors** are repeated **every time** you carry out the experiment, and always affect your result in the **same way** (e.g. they always make your answer bigger than it should be, or always make it smaller than it should be). They're due to the **experimental set-up**, or **limitations of the equipment**. For example, a balance that always reads 0.2 g less than the true value will result in systematic errors.

2) Here are some examples of **systematic errors** in calorimetry experiments...

Experimental problems with calorimetry generally...
- Some heat will be **absorbed** by the **container**, rather than going towards heating up the **water**.
- Some heat is always **lost to the surroundings** during the experiment (however well you **insulate** the container).

Experimental problems with flammable-liquid calorimetry...
- Some combustion may be **incomplete** — which will mean **less energy** will be given out.
- Some of the flammable liquid may escape by **evaporation** (they're usually quite **volatile**).

3) **Random errors** are... random — there's no pattern to them. And they **always** happen. The best way to deal with these is to **repeat** your experiment, and take the **average** of all your readings (see below).

Accuracy and *Reliability* are *NOT* the Same

Ideally you want both of these.

1) **Accuracy** and **reliability** are not the same thing. **Accuracy** means 'how close to the true value' your results are. **Reliability** means 'how reproducible' your results are.

2) **Repeating** an experiment shows whether your results are **reliable**. If you repeat an experiment and find the average (the mean), the effect of **random errors** is reduced — **positive** random errors and **negative** random errors should mostly **cancel out**. The more times you repeat an experiment, the more reliable your mean is.

3) But reliable results **aren't** necessarily more **accurate**. Repeating an experiment doesn't do anything to eliminate **systematic** errors.

average

Accurate but not reliable — large random errors, but centred around the bullseye. The average is spot on.

Reliable but not accurate — large systematic errors, but very precise.

Practice Questions

Q1 Briefly describe an experiment that could be carried out to find the enthalpy change of a reaction.

Q2 Why is the enthalpy change determined in a laboratory likely to be lower than the value shown in a data book?

Q3 What equation is used to calculate the heat change in a chemical reaction?

Exam Questions

Q1 The initial temperature of 25 cm^3 of 1.0 mol dm^{-3} hydrochloric acid in a polystyrene cup was measured as 19 °C. This acid was exactly neutralised by 25 cm^3 of 1.0 mol dm^{-3} sodium hydroxide solution. The maximum temperature of the resulting solution was measured as 25.5 °C.

Calculate the molar enthalpy change of neutralisation for the hydrochloric acid. (You may assume the neutral solution formed has a specific heat capacity of 4.18 J K^{-1} g^{-1}, and a density of 1.0 g cm^{-3}.) [7 marks]

Q2 A 50 cm^3 sample of 0.2 M copper(II) sulfate solution placed in a polystyrene beaker gave a temperature increase of 2.6 K when excess zinc powder was added and stirred. (Ignore the increase in volume due to the zinc.)

a) Calculate the enthalpy change when 1 mole of zinc reacts. Assume the solution's specific heat capacity is 4.18 J g^{-1}K^{-1}. The equation for the reaction is: $Zn_{(s)} + CuSO_{4(aq)} \rightarrow Cu_{(s)} + ZnSO_{4(aq)}$ [6 marks]

b) Describe one source of systematic error, and the effect this will have on the experimental results. [2 marks]

It can bz hard to noticz whzn you'rz making systzmatic zrrors...

Errors always happen — that's a fact of life. But that doesn't mean you can just turn your mind off to them. Sometimes you might be able to see what your systematic errors are, and do something about them. As for random errors... well, not being slapdash about things, plus repeating your experiments, can help reduce those. It's all quite "How Science Works-y", this.

Hess's Law

Sometimes you can't work out an enthalpy change by measuring a single temperature change. But there's still a way.
These pages are for AQA (Unit 2), OCR A (Unit 2), OCR B (Unit 1) and Edexcel (Unit 1).

Hess's Law — the Total Enthalpy Change is Independent of the Route Taken

Hess's Law says that:

> The **total enthalpy change** of a reaction is always **the same**, no matter **which route** is taken.

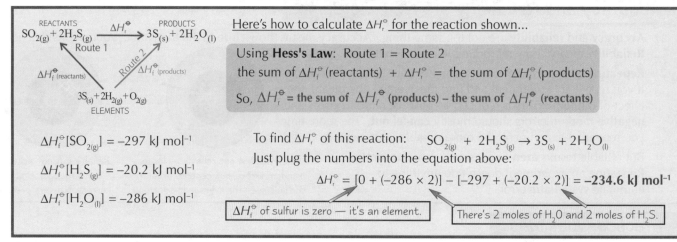

$$2NO_{2(g)} \xrightarrow[\text{Route 1}]{\Delta H_r} N_{2(g)} + 2O_{2(g)}$$

+114.4 kJ Route 2 −180.8 kJ

$$2NO_{(g)} + O_{2(g)}$$

This law is handy for working out enthalpy changes that you **can't find directly** by doing an experiment.

Here's an example:
The **total enthalpy change** for route 1 is the **same as for route 2**.
So, $\Delta H_r = +114.4 + (-180.8) = -66.4$ kJ mol^{-1}.

Enthalpy Changes Can be Worked Out From Enthalpies of Formation

You can find **enthalpy changes of formation** for hundreds of various compounds listed in textbooks.
They're handy because you can use them (along with Hess's Law) to find enthalpy changes for all kinds of **reactions**.

You need to know $\Delta H_f^\ominus$ for **all** the reactants and products that are **compounds**. The value of $\Delta H_f^\ominus$ for elements is **zero**.

REACTANTS
$$SO_{2(g)} + 2H_2S_{(g)} \xrightarrow{\Delta H_r^\ominus} 3S_{(s)} + 2H_2O_{(l)}$$ PRODUCTS
Route 1 / Route 2
$\Delta H_f^\ominus$ (reactants) / $\Delta H_f^\ominus$ (products)
$$3S_{(s)} + 2H_{2(g)} + O_{2(g)}$$
ELEMENTS

Here's how to calculate $\Delta H_r^\ominus$ for the reaction shown...

Using **Hess's Law**: Route 1 = Route 2
the sum of $\Delta H_f^\ominus$ (reactants) + $\Delta H_r^\ominus$ = the sum of $\Delta H_f^\ominus$ (products)

So, $\Delta H_r^\ominus$ = **the sum of** $\Delta H_f^\ominus$ **(products) – the sum of** $\Delta H_f^\ominus$ **(reactants)**

$\Delta H_f^\ominus[SO_{2(g)}] = -297$ kJ mol^{-1}

$\Delta H_f^\ominus[H_2S_{(g)}] = -20.2$ kJ mol^{-1}

$\Delta H_f^\ominus[H_2O_{(l)}] = -286$ kJ mol^{-1}

To find $\Delta H_r^\ominus$ of this reaction: $SO_{2(g)} + 2H_2S_{(g)} \rightarrow 3S_{(s)} + 2H_2O_{(l)}$
Just plug the numbers into the equation above:

$$\Delta H_r^\ominus = [0 + (-286 \times 2)] - [-297 + (-20.2 \times 2)] = \textbf{-234.6 kJ mol}^{-1}$$

$\Delta H_f^\ominus$ of sulfur is zero — it's an element.   There's 2 moles of H_2O and 2 moles of H_2S.

It **always** works, no matter how complicated the reaction — e.g. $2NH_4NO_{3(s)} + C_{(s)} \rightarrow 2N_{2(g)} + CO_{2(g)} + 4H_2O_{(l)}$

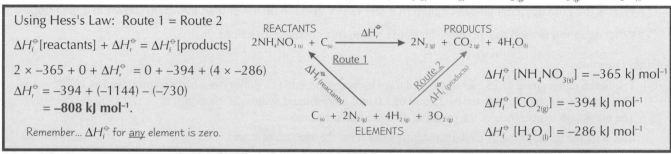

Using **Hess's Law**: Route 1 = Route 2
$\Delta H_f^\ominus$[reactants] + $\Delta H_r^\ominus$ = $\Delta H_f^\ominus$[products]
$2 \times -365 + 0 + \Delta H_r^\ominus = 0 + -394 + (4 \times -286)$
$\Delta H_r^\ominus = -394 + (-1144) - (-730)$
      $= \textbf{-808 kJ mol}^{-1}$.

Remember... $\Delta H_f^\ominus$ for <u>any</u> element is zero.

REACTANTS
$$2NH_4NO_{3(s)} + C_{(s)} \xrightarrow{\Delta H_r^\ominus} 2N_{2(g)} + CO_{2(g)} + 4H_2O_{(l)}$$ PRODUCTS
Route 1 / Route 2
ΔH_f (reactants) / ΔH_f (products)
$$C_{(s)} + 2N_{2(g)} + 4H_{2(g)} + 3O_{2(g)}$$
ELEMENTS

$\Delta H_f^\ominus[NH_4NO_{3(s)}] = -365$ kJ mol^{-1}

$\Delta H_f^\ominus[CO_{2(g)}] = -394$ kJ mol^{-1}

$\Delta H_f^\ominus[H_2O_{(l)}] = -286$ kJ mol^{-1}

Enthalpy Changes Can Also be Found From Enthalpies of Combustion

You can use a similar method to find **enthalpy changes of formation** from enthalpy changes of combustion.

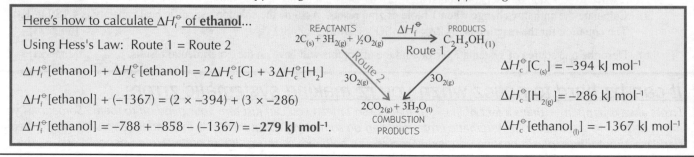

<u>Here's how to calculate $\Delta H_f^\ominus$ of **ethanol**...</u>

Using **Hess's Law**: Route 1 = Route 2

$\Delta H_f^\ominus$[ethanol] + $\Delta H_c^\ominus$[ethanol] = $2\Delta H_c^\ominus$[C] + $3\Delta H_c^\ominus$[H$_2$]

$\Delta H_f^\ominus$[ethanol] + $(-1367) = (2 \times -394) + (3 \times -286)$

$\Delta H_f^\ominus$[ethanol] $= -788 + -858 - (-1367) = \textbf{-279 kJ mol}^{-1}$.

REACTANTS
$$2C_{(s)} + 3H_{2(g)} + \tfrac{1}{2}O_{2(g)} \xrightarrow{\Delta H_f^\ominus} C_2H_5OH_{(l)}$$ PRODUCTS
Route 1 / Route 2
$3O_{2(g)}$ / $3O_{2(g)}$
$$2CO_{2(g)} + 3H_2O_{(l)}$$
COMBUSTION PRODUCTS

$\Delta H_c^\ominus[C_{(s)}] = -394$ kJ mol^{-1}

$\Delta H_c^\ominus[H_{2(g)}] = -286$ kJ mol^{-1}

$\Delta H_c^\ominus[\text{ethanol}_{(l)}] = -1367$ kJ mol^{-1}

Hess's Law

On p90 you saw how you could find the enthalpy change of a reaction using calorimetry. Sometimes you can **combine** the enthalpy change results from these experiments (neutralisations, for example) to work out an enthalpy change that you **can't find directly**. It's clever stuff... read on.

Hess's Law Lets You Find Enthalpy Changes Indirectly From Experiments

You **can't** find the enthalpy change of the thermal decomposition of calcium carbonate by measuring a temperature change.

$$CaCO_{3(s)} \rightarrow CaO_{(s)} + CO_{2(g)} \qquad \text{Enthalpy change} = ?$$

(It's an **endothermic reaction**, so you'd expect the temperature to fall. But you need to **heat it up** for the reaction to happen at all.)

But you can find it in an **indirect** way.
The aim is to make one of those **Hess cycles** (the technical name for a "Hess's Law triangle diagram thing").

1. As always, start by drawing the top of the triangle — include your **reactants** and **products**:

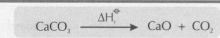

2. Next, you're going to carry out two **neutralisation** reactions involving **hydrochloric acid**, and use the results to complete your Hess cycle.
   You **can** find the enthalpy changes of these reactions (using calorimetry — see p90). Call them ΔH_1 and ΔH_2.

   Reaction 1: $CaCO_3 + 2HCl \rightarrow CaCl_2 + CO_2 + H_2O \qquad \Delta H_1$
   Reaction 2: $CaO + 2HCl \rightarrow CaCl_2 + H_2O \qquad \Delta H_2$

3. Now you can build the other two sides of your Hess cycle.
   Add **2 moles of HCl** to both sides of your triangle's top (representing the 2 moles of HCl in the above equations).

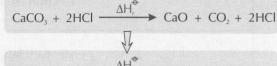

   And add the **products** of the neutralisations to the bottom of the triangle. Notice how all three corners 'balance'.

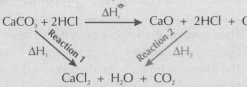

4. Mark the enthalpy changes you found on your diagram.

5. And do the maths... the enthalpy change you want to find is just: $\boxed{\Delta H_1 - \Delta H_2}$

Practice Questions

Q1 What is Hess's Law?

Q2 What is the standard enthalpy change of formation of any element?

Q3 Describe how you can make a "Hess cycle" to find the standard enthalpy change of a reaction using standard enthalpy changes of formation.

Exam Questions

Q1 Using the facts that the standard enthalpy change of formation of $Al_2O_{3(s)}$ is -1676 kJ mol^{-1} and the standard enthalpy change of formation of $MgO_{(s)}$ is -602 kJ mol^{-1}, calculate the enthalpy change of the following reaction.

$$Al_2O_{3(s)} + 3Mg_{(s)} \rightarrow 2Al_{(s)} + 3MgO_{(s)}$$

[3 marks]

Q2 Calculate the enthalpy change for the reaction below (the fermentation of glucose).

$$C_6H_{12}O_{6(s)} \rightarrow 2C_2H_5OH_{(l)} + 2CO_{2(g)}$$

Use the following standard enthalpies of combustion in your calculations:

$\Delta H_c^\ominus(\text{glucose}) = -2820$ kJ mol^{-1}, $\Delta H_c^\ominus(\text{ethanol}) = -1367$ kJ mol^{-1}

[3 marks]

To understand this lot, you're gonna need a bar of chocolate. Or two...

To get your head around those Hess diagrams, you're going to have to do more than skim them. It'll also help if you know the definitions for those standard enthalpy thingumabobs on page 89. If you didn't bother learning them, have a quick flick back and remind yourself about them — especially the standard enthalpy changes of combustion and formation.

Ions and Born-Haber Cycles

Born-Haber cycles can seem a bit much at first, but stick with them and practise lots— the fog will clear. Promise.
These three pages are for Edexcel (Unit 1) only.

Born-Haber Cycles Can Be Used to Calculate Lattice Energies

1) **Born-Haber cycles** show enthalpy changes when a **solid ionic compound** is formed from its **elements** in their standard states. They show two 'routes' — one direct and one indirect. From Hess's Law, both routes have the **same** total enthalpy change.

2) The main use of Born-Haber cycles is to calculate **lattice energies** (the energy change when <u>gaseous ions</u> form 1 mole of an <u>ionic solid</u> under standard conditions) — because lattice energies can't be found directly from experiments.

3) For example, take the Born-Haber cycle for the formation of **sodium chloride**. The **direct** way to form sodium chloride from its elements is the **standard enthalpy of formation**. The **indirect** route involves adding up all these enthalpy changes:

$Na_{(s)} \rightarrow Na_{(g)}$	standard enthalpy of atomisation of sodium metal, $\Delta H^{\ominus}_{at} [Na_{(s)}]$	109 kJ mol^{-1}
$Na_{(g)} \rightarrow Na^+_{(g)} + e^-$	first ionisation energy of sodium, $\Delta H_{m1} [Na_{(g)}]$ or $E_{m1} [Na_{(g)}]$	500 kJ mol^{-1}
$\frac{1}{2} Cl_{2(g)} \rightarrow Cl_{(g)}$	standard enthalpy of atomisation of chlorine gas, $\Delta H^{\ominus}_{at} [Cl_{(g)}]$	121 kJ mol^{-1}
$Cl_{(g)} + e^- \rightarrow Cl^-_{(g)}$	**electron affinity** of chlorine, $\Delta H_{m1} [Cl_{(g)}]$ or $E_{aff} [Cl_{(g)}]$ (The energy change when one mole of ions is formed from one mole of atoms.)	−370 kJ mol^{-1}
$Na^+_{(g)} + Cl^-_{(g)} \rightarrow NaCl_{(s)}$	standard lattice energy of sodium chloride, $\Delta H^{\ominus}_{latt} [Na^+Cl^-_{(s)}]$	You're probably trying to <u>find</u> this.

State symbols are important in Born-Haber cycles — elements must be in their **standard states** at the beginning. (Remember, 'standard states' means their states at 298 K, 100 kPa pressure.)
The elements (in their standard states) that make up sodium chloride are sodium metal, $Na_{(s)}$, and chlorine gas $Cl_{2(g)}$.
So, here's the Born-Haber cycle for sodium chloride — you start reading it from the bottom:

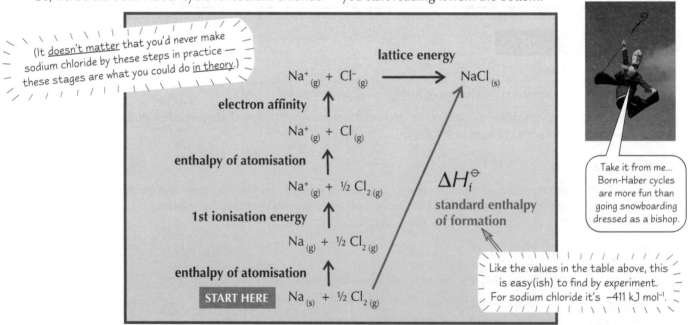

(It <u>doesn't matter</u> that you'd never make sodium chloride by these steps in practice — these stages are what you could do <u>in theory</u>.)

Take it from me... Born-Haber cycles are more fun than going snowboarding dressed as a bishop.

Like the values in the table above, this is easy(ish) to find by experiment. For sodium chloride it's −411 kJ mol^{-1}.

6) Using **Hess's Law**, the **direct route** (the **green arrow**) = the **indirect route** (the **purple** arrows). So to find the **lattice energy** from the Born-Haber cycle:

$$\Delta H^{\ominus}_f [NaCl_{(s)}] = \Delta H^{\ominus}_{at} [Na_{(s)}] + E_{m1} [Na_{(g)}] + \Delta H^{\ominus}_{at} [Cl_{(g)}] + E_{aff} [Cl_{(g)}] + \Delta H^{\ominus}_{latt} [Na^+Cl^-_{(s)}]$$

$−411 = 109 + 500 + 121 + (−370) + \Delta H^{\ominus}_{latt} [Na^+Cl^-_{(s)}]$

Now rearrange it — making sure you get the **signs** correct:
$\Delta H^{\ominus}_{latt} [Na^+Cl^-_{(s)}] = −411 − 109 − 500 − 121 − (−370) = \underline{\textbf{−771 kJ mol}^{-1}}$

Ions and Born-Haber Cycles

Theoretical Lattice Energies are Based on the Ionic Model

1) There are **two ways** to work out a lattice energy:
   - the **experimental** way — using **experimental enthalpy values** in a Born-Haber cycle (as on the previous page)
   - the **theoretical** way — doing some calculations based on the **purely ionic model** of a lattice (electrostatic theory)
2) To work out a 'theoretical' lattice energy, you assume that all the ions are **spherical** and have their charge **evenly distributed** around them — a **purely ionic** lattice. Then you work out how strongly the ions are **attracted** to one another based on their charges, the distance between them and so on (you don't need to know the details of these calculations, fortunately — just what they're based on). That gives you a value for the energy change when the ions form the lattice.

Comparing Lattice Energies Can Tell You 'How Ionic' an Ionic Lattice Is

For any one compound, the experimental and theoretical lattice energies are usually **different**.

How different they are tells you **how different** the lattice is from the 'purely ionic' model used for the theoretical calculations. For example, here are both lattice energy values for some **sodium halides**.

Compound	Lattice Energy (kJ mol⁻¹)	
	From experimental values in Born-Haber cycle	From theory
Sodium chloride	−771	−766
Sodium bromide	−742	−731
Sodium iodide	−698	−686

1) The experimental and theoretical values are a **pretty close match** — so you can say that these compounds fit the 'purely ionic' model (spherical ions with evenly distributed charge, etc.) very well.
2) This indicates that the structure of the lattice for these compounds is quite close to being **purely ionic**.

Right then, so far so good. Here are some more lattice energies, for **magnesium halides** this time:

1) The **experimental** lattice energies are **bigger** than the theoretical values by a fair bit — 10% or so.
2) This tells you that the **bonding** is, in practice, **stronger** than the calculations from the ionic model predict.
3) The difference shows that the bonding in the magnesium halides **isn't** as close to 'purely ionic' as it is with sodium halides.

Compound	Lattice Energy (kJ mol⁻¹)	
	From experimental values in Born-Haber cycle	From theory
Magnesium chloride	−2526	−2326
Magnesium bromide	−2440	−2097
Magnesium iodide	−2327	−1944

4) The ionic bonds in the magnesium halides are more **polarised** — they have **some covalent character** — whereas the bonds in sodium halides have almost no polarisation and very little covalent character.

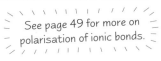
See page 49 for more on polarisation of ionic bonds.

Polarisation of Ionic Bonds Leads to Covalent Character in Ionic Lattices

So, **magnesium** halides have more covalent character in their ionic bonds than sodium halides. Here's why...

1) In a sodium halide, e.g. NaCl, the **cation**, Na^+, has only a **small charge** (+1) so it can't really pull electrons towards itself — so the charge is distributed evenly around the ions (there's almost **no polarisation**).
2) This is pretty much what the simple **ionic model** looks like — that's why the theoretical calculations of lattice energy match the experimental ones so well for sodium halides.
3) However, the magnesium halides don't fit the ionic model quite so well, because charge isn't evenly distributed around the ions — the cation, Mg^{2+}, has a **bigger charge** (+2), so it can pull electrons towards itself a bit, polarising the bond.
4) In general, the greater the **charge density** of a **cation** (its charge compared to its volume) the **more** it will polarise an ionic bond, and the poorer the match will be between experimental and theoretical values for lattice energy.

Ions and Born-Haber Cycles

Born-Haber Cycles Can Show Why Some Compounds Don't Exist

1) If lots of energy is **released** during the formation of a compound, the compound you get is nice and **stable** — it doesn't 'want' to break up again. (It's a bit like when things roll down a hill — they stay at the bottom and don't go uphill again.)

2) Some compounds either **don't form** in the first place, or else they **break up** very quickly to form more stable elements and compounds. For example, **NaCl** is found all over the place, but you never get **NaCl$_2$**. Here's why:

> 1) The Born-Haber cycle for NaCl (see page 94) gives a **negative** enthalpy of formation — the formation of NaCl from its elements is an **exothermic** process — energy is released overall. So NaCl is **stable**.
>
> 2) However, NaCl$_2$ is a completely different matter. To make it, you need **Na^{2+}** ions....
>
> 3) So the Born-Haber cycle for NaCl$_2$ would include the **second ionisation energy** for sodium — a whopping **+4560 kJ mol^{-1}** (it needs so much energy because you're trying to take an electron from Na$^+$'s now full outer shell).
>
> 4) When you add everything up, the enthalpy of formation of **NaCl$_2$** is positive. So forming NaCl$_2$ is an **endothermic** process — you need to put loads of energy in. It just **doesn't happen** because it's **energetically unfavourable** — the compound wouldn't be stable.

3) Similarly, MgCl$_2$ is much more stable than either MgCl$_3$ or MgCl:

- MgCl$_3$ can't exist because the huge third ionisation energy of Mg makes $\Delta H_f^\ominus$ **positive**.
- MgCl and MgCl$_2$ both have negative enthalpies of formation, so both compounds **can** form. But MgCl$_2$ has $\Delta H_f^\ominus = -673$ kJ mol^{-1}, whereas MgCl has $\Delta H_f^\ominus = -111$ kJ mol^{-1}. This means that **more energy** is released by forming MgCl$_2$, so MgCl$_2$ is **more stable**. So if any MgCl forms in a chemical reaction, it immediately **disproportionates** (see p74) to form MgCl$_2$ and Mg. $\Longrightarrow$ 2MgCl $\rightarrow$ MgCl$_2$ + Mg

Practice Questions

Q1 What enthalpy change is a Born-Haber cycle usually used to calculate? Give the definition of this enthalpy change.

Q2 Give chemical equations for the following, including the state symbols of all the species present:

a) $\Delta H_{at}^\ominus$ [K$_{(s)}$]   b) E_{m1} [K$_{(s)}$]   c) E_{aff} [I$_{(g)}$]   d) $\Delta H_{latt}^\ominus$ [KI$_{(s)}$]   b) $\Delta H_f^\ominus$ [MgO$_{(s)}$]

Exam Questions

Q1 The enthalpy changes involved in the formation of calcium oxide are shown below.

Enthalpy of atomisation of calcium = +177 kJ mol^{-1}	First ionisation energy of calcium = +590 kJ mol^{-1}
Second ionisation energy of calcium = +1100 kJ mol^{-1}	Enthalpy of atomisation of oxygen = +249 kJ mol^{-1}
Electron affinity of an oxygen atom = –141 kJ mol^{-1}	Electron affinity of O$^-$ = +790 kJ mol^{-1}
Lattice energy of calcium oxide = –3401 kJ mol^{-1}	

a) Calculate the enthalpy of formation for calcium oxide using the information given above.   [3 marks]

b) The electron affinity of the O$^-$ ion is +790 kJ mol^{-1}. Explain why the electron affinity of O$^-$ is positive.   [2 marks]

Q2 Use the data below to calculate the lattice energy of magnesium chloride, MgCl$_2$.

Enthalpy of atomisation of magnesium = +148 kJ mol^{-1}	First ionisation energy of magnesium = +738 kJ mol^{-1}
Second ionisation energy of magnesium = +1451 kJ mol^{-1}	Enthalpy of atomisation of chlorine = +122 kJ mol^{-1}
Electron affinity of a chlorine atom = –349 kJ mol^{-1}	Enthalpy of formation of MgCl$_2$(s) = –641 kJ mol^{-1}

[4 marks]

I've always loved sheltering ships — people say I'm a Born-Haber...

There's a good reason why some compounds exist and not others, and it's all to do with $\Delta H_f^\ominus$. If that's a pretty meaningless squiggle as far as you're concerned, now's the time to make friends with it — and to understand all the other bits that make up a Born-Haber cycle. Oh, and don't forget to practise those nice calculations for lattice energy and whatnot.

Bond Enthalpies

If it weren't for copyright law, there'd be pictures of James Bond in his swimwear on this page.
These pages are for AQA (Unit 2), OCR A (Unit 2), OCR B (Unit 1) and Edexcel (Unit 1).

Reactions are all about **Breaking** and **Making** Bonds

When reactions happen, **reactant bonds** are **broken** and **product bonds** are **formed**.

1) You **need** energy to break bonds, so bond breaking is **endothermic** (ΔH is **positive**).
2) Energy is **released** when bonds are formed, so this is **exothermic** (ΔH is **negative**).
3) The **enthalpy change** for a reaction is the **overall effect** of these two changes. If you need **more** energy to **break** bonds than is released when bonds are made, ΔH is **positive**. If it's less, ΔH is negative.

You can only break bonds if you've got enough energy.

You need **Energy** to **Break** the **Attraction** between **Atoms** or **Ions**

1) In ionic bonding, **positive** and **negative ions** are attracted to each other. In covalent molecules, the **positive nuclei** are attracted to the **negative** charge of the shared electrons in a covalent bond.
2) You need energy to **break** this attraction — **stronger** bonds take more energy to break. The **amount of energy** you need **per mole** is called the **bond dissociation enthalpy**, or just **bond enthalpy**. (Of course it's got a fancy name — this is chemistry.)
3) Bond dissociation enthalpies always involve bond breaking in **gaseous compounds**. This makes comparisons fair.
4) Bond enthalpies influence **how quickly** a reaction will occur. In general, the **smaller** the **bond enthalpies** of the bonds that need to be broken, the **faster** a reaction will be. That's because **less energy** has to be taken in from the surroundings to break the reactant bonds.
5) You can use bond enthalpy values to make **predictions** about rate of reaction. For example, take this nucleophilic substitution reaction (see page 136) between a haloalkane and sodium hydroxide solution:

$$C_2H_5X + NaOH \rightarrow C_2H_5OH + NaX \quad \longleftarrow \quad \text{X is a halogen — e.g. Cl, Br, or I.}$$

- For this reaction to occur, the carbon–halogen bond (C–X) has to break. So the **weaker** the C–X bond (the **smaller** the bond enthalpy), the **faster** this reaction will be.
- Here are the bond enthalpies of some C–X bonds: C–Cl: 346 kJ mol^{-1}, C–Br: 292 kJ mol^{-1}, C–I: 228 kJ mol^{-1}
- From these C–X bond enthalpy values you can predict that **iodoethane** will react the **fastest** in aqueous alkali, while **chloroethane** will react the **slowest**.

Average Bond Enthalpies are **Not Exact**

1) There isn't just one bond enthalpy value between two particular atoms. For example, water (H_2O) has **two O–H bonds**. You'd think it'd take the same amount of energy to break them both... but it **doesn't** — because breaking the first bond changes the 'environment' of the remaining bond:

- Breaking the **first** bond, H–OH$_{(g)}$, takes **492 kJ mol^{-1}**. This is written **E(H–OH) = +492 kJ mol^{-1}**.
- Breaking the **second** bond, H–O$_{(g)}$, needs a bit less energy. E(H–O) = **+428 kJ mol^{-1}**. (OH$^-$ is easier to break apart than H_2O because there's extra electron repulsion.)

2) So what you can do is give the **mean** bond enthalpy — just take an average:

Using the data for water above, this would be $\dfrac{492+428}{2}$ = **+460 kJ mol^{-1}**.

3) The **data book** says the bond enthalpy for O–H is +463 kJ mol^{-1}. It's a bit different because it's the average for a **much bigger range** of molecules, not just water...

4) ... for example, the O–H bond in an **alcohol** molecule has carbon atoms and more hydrogen atoms nearby — its environment is different from that in a water molecule, so the bond's strength will be slightly different.

That's not quite what I meant by 'changing the environment'.

5) So when you look up an **average bond enthalpy**, what you get is:

the energy needed to break one mole of bonds in the gas phase, averaged over many different compounds

Breaking bonds is always an endothermic process, so average bond enthalpies are always **positive**.

Bond Enthalpies

Enthalpy Changes Can Be Calculated using Average Bond Enthalpies

Not Edexcel

1) In any chemical reaction there's a **rearrangement of atoms** — some existing bonds in the reactants are **broken** and new bonds are **formed** in the products.

2) Energy must be **absorbed** to break bonds but energy is **given out** during **bond formation**. The difference between the energy absorbed and released is the overall **enthalpy change of reaction**:

$$\begin{array}{ccc} \text{Enthalpy Change} & = & \text{Total Energy Absorbed} & - & \text{Total Energy Released} \\ \text{of Reaction} & & \text{to Break Bonds} & & \text{in Making Bonds} \end{array}$$

3) You might have to **calculate** an enthalpy change of reaction — it's fine, as long as you use the right numbers...

Example: Calculate the overall enthalpy change for this reaction:
$$N_2 + 3H_2 \rightarrow 2NH_3$$
Use the average bond enthalpy values in the table.

Bond	Average Bond Enthalpy
N≡N	945 kJ mol^{-1}
H–H	436 kJ mol^{-1}
N–H	391 kJ mol^{-1}

Bonds broken: 1 × N≡N bond broken = 1 × 945 = 945 kJ mol^{-1}
3 × H–H bonds broken = 3 × 436 = 1308 kJ mol^{-1}

Total Energy Absorbed = 945 + 1308 = **2253 kJ mol^{-1}**

Bonds formed: 6 × N–H bonds formed = 6 × 391 = 2346 kJ mol^{-1}

Total Energy Released = **2346 kJ mol^{-1}**

Now you just subtract 'total energy released' from 'total energy absorbed':
Enthalpy Change of Reaction = 2253 − 2346 = **−93 kJ mol^{-1}**

If you can't remember which value to subtract from which, just take the smaller number from the bigger one then add the sign at the end — positive if 'bonds broken' was the bigger number (endothermic), negative if 'bonds formed' was bigger (exothermic).

You Can Use Bond Enthalpies in Hess's Law Cycles

Not OCR A

There's not much you can't do with Hess's Law.* For example, here's how to calculate enthalpy changes using bond enthalpies:

Example: Calculate the enthalpy of formation of methane, $\Delta H_f^{\ominus}$ $CH_{4(g)}$, using the data below in a Hess's law energy cycle.

$\Delta H_{at}^{\ominus}$ $C_{\text{(graphite (s))}}$ = +715 kJ mol^{-1}, $\Delta H_{at}^{\ominus}$ $H_{(g)}$ = +218 kJ mol^{-1}, $E(C–H)$ = +412 kJ mol^{-1}

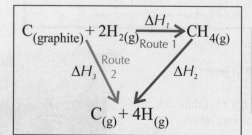

ΔH_1 = enthalpy of formation of methane (what you want to find)

ΔH_2 = 4 × $E(C–H)$ = 4 × +412 = +1648 kJ mol^{-1}

ΔH_3 = $\Delta H_{at}^{\ominus}$ $C_{(s)}$ + 4 × $\Delta H_{at}^{\ominus}$ $H_{(g)}$ = 715 + 4 × 218 = +1587 kJ mol^{-1}

Route 1 = Route 2
$\Delta H_1 + \Delta H_2 = \Delta H_3$
Enthalpy of formation of methane = ΔH_1 = $\Delta H_3 - \Delta H_2$ = 1587 − 1648 = **−61 kJ mol^{-1}**

For those few things, you need duct tape instead.

Bond Enthalpies

The **Length** of a Bond depends on its **Strength** | *OCR B and Edexcel only*

1) In covalent bonds, there isn't just an **attraction** between the nuclei and the shared electrons.
   The two **positively charged nuclei** also **repel** each other, as do the **electrons**.

2) The distance between the **two nuclei** is the distance where the **attractive**
   and **repulsive** forces balance each other. This distance is the **bond length**.

3) The **stronger** the attraction between the atoms, the higher the **bond dissociation enthalpy** and the **shorter**
   the bond length. It makes sense really. If there's more attraction, the nuclei will pull **closer** together.

> A C=C bond has a greater bond dissociation enthalpy and is shorter than a C–C bond.
> Four electrons are shared in C=C and only two in C–C, so the electron density between
> the two carbon atoms is greater. C≡C has an even higher bond dissociation enthalpy
> and is shorter than C=C — six electrons are shared here.

Bond	C–C	C=C	C≡C
Average Bond Dissociation Enthalpy (kJ mol^{-1})	+347	+612	+838
Bond length (nm)	0.154	0.134	0.120

Practice Questions

Q1 Is energy taken in or released when bonds are broken?

Q2 What state must compounds be in when bond dissociation enthalpies are measured?

Q3 Which is shorter — a single C–C bond or a double C=C bond?

Q4 Define average bond dissociation enthalpy.

Exam Questions

Q1

Bond	Compound	Bond length (nm)	Bond enthalpy (kJ mol^{-1})
C–O	alcohols	0.143	336
C=O	ketones	0.122	749

Explain why the bond energy of C=O in ketones is greater than the C–O bond energy in alcohols
and the bond length of C=O is less than that of C–O.   [6 marks]

Q2 a) Construct a Hess's law energy cycle to show the standard enthalpy change of formation
   of ammonia and the standard enthalpy changes of atomisation of its elements.   [4 marks]

   b) Use the cycle from part a) and the enthalpy changes given below to calculate the
      standard enthalpy change for the formation of ammonia.

   E(N–H) in ammonia $\Delta H^{\ominus}= +391$ kJ mol^{-1}

   $\frac{1}{2}N_{2(g)} \rightarrow N_{(g)}$ $\Delta H^{\ominus}= +473$ kJ mol^{-1}

   $\frac{1}{2}H_{2(g)} \rightarrow H_{(g)}$ $\Delta H^{\ominus}= +218$ kJ mol^{-1} [4 marks]

   c) The data book value for the average bond enthalpy of N–H is +388 kJ mol^{-1}.
      Why is there a discrepancy between this value and the value used above?   [1 mark]

I bonded with my friend. Now we're waiting to be surgically separated...

*Reactions are like pulling your Lego spaceship apart and building something new. Sometimes the bits get stuck together and
you need to use loads of energy to pull 'em apart. Okay, so energy's not really released when you stick them together, but
you can't have everything — and it wasn't that bad an analogy up till now. Ah, well... you'd best get on and learn this stuff.*

Reaction Rates

The rate of a reaction is just how quickly it happens. Lots of things can make it go faster or slower — like heating it up.
These pages are for AQA (Unit 2), OCR A (Unit 2), OCR B (Unit 2) and Edexcel (Unit 2).

Particles **Must Collide** to **React**

1) Particles in liquids and gases are **always moving** and **colliding** with **each other**.
   Most of the time they **don't** react though — they only react when the **conditions** are right.
   A reaction **won't** take place between two particles **unless** —

   > • They collide in the **right direction**. They need to be **facing** each other the right way.
   > • They collide with at least a certain **minimum** amount of kinetic (movement) **energy**.

   This stuff's called **Collision Theory**.

2) The **minimum amount of kinetic energy** particles need to react is called the **activation energy**.
   The particles need this much energy to **break the bonds** to start the reaction.

3) Reactions with **low activation energies** happen **pretty easily**. But reactions with **high activation energies** don't.
   You need to give the particles extra energy by **heating** them.

To make this a bit clearer, here's an **enthalpy profile diagram** (see page 88 for more on enthalpy profiles).

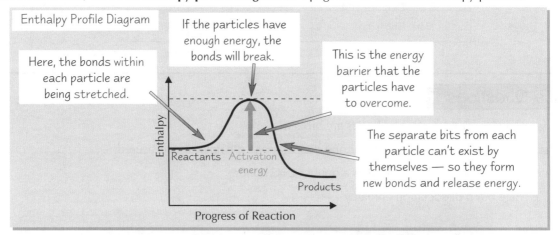

Enthalpy Profile Diagram

Here, the bonds within each particle are being stretched.

If the particles have enough energy, the bonds will break.

This is the energy barrier that the particles have to overcome.

The separate bits from each particle can't exist by themselves — so they form new bonds and release energy.

Reactants   Activation energy   Products

Enthalpy

Progress of Reaction

Molecules in a Gas **Don't** all have the **Same Amount of Energy**

Imagine looking down on **Oxford Street** when it's teeming with people. You'll see some people
ambling along **slowly**, some hurrying **quickly**, but most of them will be walking with a **moderate speed**.
It's the same with the **molecules** in a gas. Some **don't have much kinetic energy** and move **slowly**.
Others have **loads of kinetic energy** and **whizz** along. But most molecules are somewhere **in between**.

If you plot a **graph** of the **numbers of molecules** in a gas with different **kinetic energies** you get a
Maxwell-Boltzmann distribution. It looks like this:

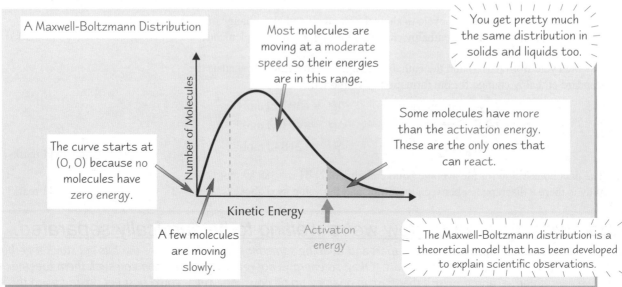

A Maxwell-Boltzmann Distribution

Most molecules are moving at a moderate speed so their energies are in this range.

You get pretty much the same distribution in solids and liquids too.

The curve starts at (0, 0) because no molecules have zero energy.

Some molecules have more than the activation energy. These are the only ones that can react.

Number of Molecules

Kinetic Energy

A few molecules are moving slowly.

Activation energy

The Maxwell-Boltzmann distribution is a theoretical model that has been developed to explain scientific observations.

Reaction Rates

Increasing the Temperature makes Reactions Faster

1) If you increase the **temperature**, the particles will on average have more **kinetic energy** and will move **faster**.

2) So, a **greater proportion** of molecules will have energies greater than the **activation energy** and be able to **react**. This changes the **shape** of the **Maxwell-Boltzmann distribution curve** — it pushes it over to the **right**.

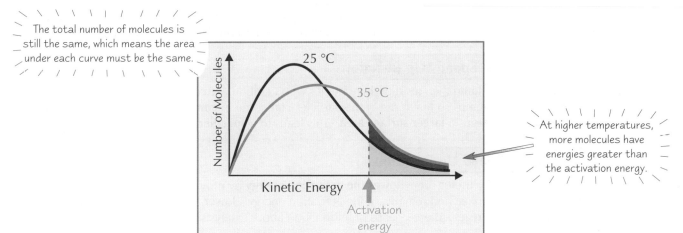

The total number of molecules is still the same, which means the area under each curve must be the same.

At higher temperatures, more molecules have energies greater than the activation energy.

3) And because the molecules are flying about **faster**, they'll **collide more often**. This is **another reason** why increasing the temperature makes a reaction faster.

> **Small temperature increases** can lead to **large increases in reaction rate**.

Practice Questions

Q1 Explain the term 'activation energy'.

Q2 Sketch an enthalpy profile diagram for a reaction.

Q3 What does a Maxwell-Boltzmann distribution show?

Q4 Sketch Maxwell-Boltzmann distributions for molecules at two different temperatures.

Exam Questions

Q1 Nitrogen monoxide (NO) and ozone (O_3) sometimes react to produce nitrogen dioxide (NO_2) and oxygen (O_2). A collision between the two molecules does not always lead to a reaction. Explain why. [2 marks]

Q2 Use collision theory to explain why the reaction between a solid and a liquid is generally faster than that between two solids. [2 marks]

Q3 On the right is a Maxwell-Boltzmann distribution curve for a sample of a substance at 25 °C.

a) Which of the curves X or Y shows the Maxwell-Boltzman distribution curve for the same sample at 15 °C ? [1 mark]

b) Explain how this curve shows that the reaction rate will be lower at 15 °C than at 25 °C. [2 marks]

Reaction Rates — cheaper than water rates

This page isn't too hard to learn — no equations, no formulas... what more could you ask for? The only tricky thing might be the Maxwell-Boltzmann thingymajiggle. Remember, particles don't react every time they collide — only if they have enough energy, and are at the correct angle. The more often they collide and the more energy they have, the faster the reaction is.

More on Reaction Rates

Carrots and sticks won't do a lot of good. But here's some more things that will.
These pages are for AQA (Unit 2), OCR A (Unit 2), OCR B (Unit 2) and Edexcel (Unit 2).

Concentration, Surface Area and Catalysts Affect the Reaction Rate Too

Increasing Concentration (Or Pressure) Speeds Up Reactions

Increasing the **concentration** of reactants in a **solution** (or the **pressure** of a **gas**) means the particles are **closer together** on average. If they're closer, they'll **collide more often**. More collisions mean **more chances** to react.

Increasing Surface Area Speeds Up Reactions

If one reactant is in a **big lump** then most of the particles won't collide with other reactants. You need to **crush** these lumps so that more of the particles can come in **contact** with the other **reactants**. A **smaller particle size** means a **larger surface area**. This leads to a **speedier** reaction.

Catalysts Can Speed Up Reactions

Catalysts are really useful. They **lower the activation energy** by providing a **different way** for the bonds to be broken and remade. If the activation energy's **lower**, more particles will have **enough energy** to react. There's heaps of information about catalysts on **pages 104-107**.

And Don't Forget About Temperature

Temperature is a biggie. I told you how it affects reaction rate on the last page, but it's so important that I'll tell you again. Increasing the temperature gives the particles **more energy**, so that they're **more likely to react** when they collide. And because they're moving faster, they collide more often too. It's win-win all the way.

You Can Measure the Volume of Gas Given Off to Investigate Reaction Rate

1) This involves using a **gas syringe** to collect the gas given off.
2) The **more** gas given off during a given **time interval**, the **faster** the reaction.
3) By taking regular readings of the amount of gas evolved, you can get data to plot a graph of **gas volume** against **time elapsed** (see example below).
   Watch out though — if too much gas is evolved too vigorously, you can easily blow the plunger out.
4) Like with most experiments, you should **repeat it** several times to check your results are **reliable**.
5) You can use this method to investigate the rate of any reaction in which one of the **products** is a **gas**.

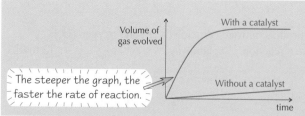

The steeper the graph, the faster the rate of reaction.

For example, this method is great for investigating the effect of the catalyst **manganese(IV) oxide** on the **decomposition of hydrogen peroxide**.

hydrogen peroxide → oxygen gas + water

Oxygen is produced **more quickly** when the catalyst is added.

...Or You Can Measure the Decrease in Mass

1) Another way to investigate the rate of a reaction that gives off a **gas** is to use a **mass balance**. As the gas is released, the mass of the reaction mixture **decreases** — you can follow this on the balance.
2) The quicker the reading on the balance **drops**, the faster the reaction.

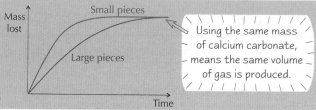

For example, you can use this method to investigate the effect of **surface area** on reaction rate. Add equal masses of **different sized pieces** of calcium carbonate to the same volume and concentration of acid.

Calcium carbonate reacts with acid to produce **carbon dioxide gas**. The flask gets lighter as the gas is lost.

Using the same mass of calcium carbonate, means the same volume of gas is produced.

More on Reaction Rates

You Can Time how Long a Precipitate Takes to Form

1) This can **only** be used when a product of the reaction is a **precipitate** which **clouds** the solution.
2) Observe a **mark** through the solution and measure how long it takes for it to **disappear**.
3) The **quicker** the mark disappears, the **quicker** the reaction.
4) This only works for reactions where the initial solution is **transparent**.
5) The result is very **subjective** — **different people** might not agree over the **exact** point when the mark 'disappears'.

> The reaction between **sodium thiosulfate solution and hydrochloric acid** makes a yellow **precipitate** of **sulfur**. So you can monitor the rate of this reaction using this method.
>
> For instance, you can investigate the effect of concentration by repeating the experiment using a **different concentration** of sodium thiosulfate solution each time. You need to keep everything else the same. You then **time** how long the mark takes to disappear each time.

> **Temperature** can also be investigated using this method. You warm the acid and sodium thiosulfate separately to a certain temperature, then mix them together. The **faster** the mark disappears, the **faster** the reaction.

Practice Questions

Q1 List the four factors that affect the rate of a reaction.

Q2 Why does decreasing the concentration decrease the rate of a reaction?

Q3 Which has the larger surface area: 1 gram of small crystals or 1 gram of large crystals of the same substance?

Q4 Describe an experiment to show how a catalyst can affect the rate of reaction.

Exam Questions

Q1 Explain how catalysts speed up chemical reactions. [2 marks]

Q2 Carbon dioxide gas is produced when hydrochloric acid reacts with calcium carbonate.
Curve A shows how the amount of carbon dioxide gas evolved increased over time.
The calcium carbonate is present in excess.

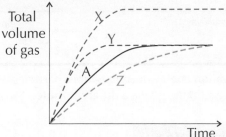

a) Which curve shows
   i) that the concentration of acid has been doubled but the volume of acid has been halved? [1 mark]
   ii) that the concentration of acid has been halved but the volume of acid has doubled? [1 mark]

b) Explain your choices for parts a)i) and a)ii). [3 marks]

My mate Dave stared at some juice for an hour — it said concentrate...

*Remember, increasing concentration and pressure do exactly the same thing. The only difference is you increase the concentration of a **solution** and the pressure of a **gas**. Don't get them muddled. Remember, the type of experiment you do to investigate the rate of a reaction depends on whether a gas or a precipitate is produced.*

Catalysts

Catalysts were tantalisingly mentioned a couple of pages ago — here's the full story...
These pages are for AQA (Unit 2), OCR A (Unit 2), OCR B (Units 1 and 2) and Edexcel (Unit 2).

Catalysts Increase the Rate of Reactions

You can use **catalysts** to make chemical reactions happen **faster**. Learn this definition:

> A **catalyst** increases the **rate** of a reaction by providing an **alternative reaction pathway** with a **lower activation energy**. The catalyst is **chemically unchanged** at the end of the reaction.

1) Catalysts are **great**. They **don't** get used up in reactions, so you only need a **tiny bit** of catalyst to catalyse a **huge** amount of stuff. They **do** take part in reactions, but they're **remade** at the end, so they're not used up.

2) Catalysts are **very fussy** about which reactions they catalyse. Many will **only** work on a single reaction.

> An example of a catalyst is **iron**. It's used in the **Haber process** to make ammonia.
> $$N_{2(g)} + 3H_{2(g)} \underset{}{\overset{Fe_{(s)}}{\rightleftharpoons}} 2NH_{3(g)}$$

3) **Enzymes** are **biological catalysts** — they're produced in living cells. Because of this, they work best close to room temperatures and pressures. They're also very fussy and only work on a **single reaction**. This is useful in industry for making specific products or for analysis in medicine. E.g. the enzyme glucose oxidase is used to find the glucose content of blood.

4) **Catalysis** is the process of changing the rate of a chemical reaction by using a catalyst.

Enthalpy Profiles and Boltzmann Distributions Show Why Catalysts Work

If you look at an **enthalpy profile** together with a **Maxwell-Boltzmann distribution** (see p100), you can see **why** catalysts work.

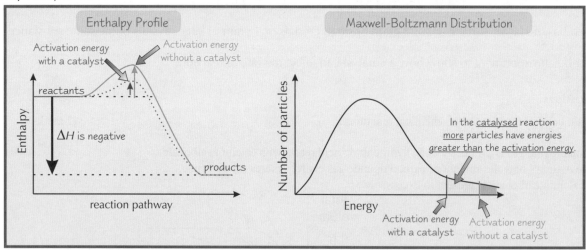

The catalyst **lowers the activation energy**, meaning **more particles** have **enough energy** to react when they collide. It does this by allowing the reaction to go **via a different route**. So, in a certain amount of time, **more particles react**.

Catalysts Can Be Poisoned

Catalysts can be **poisoned** so they don't work any more. For instance:

1) **Carbon monoxide**, CO, poisons the solid **iron catalyst** used in the **Haber process**.
2) **Lead** poisons **catalytic converters**, which are used to remove pollutants from car exhausts. This **was** a problem when lead was added to **all** petrol, but it's OK now there's **unleaded petrol**.

Heterogeneous catalysts (have a peep at **page 107**) often get poisoned because the **poison** clings to the catalyst's surface **more strongly** than the reactant does. So, the catalyst is **prevented** from getting involved in the reaction it's meant to be **speeding up**.

Catalysts

Catalysts — Good for Industry...

Loads of industries rely on **catalysts**. Catalysts can dramatically lower production costs, and help make better products. Here are a few examples:

Iron is used as a catalyst in **ammonia** production. If it wasn't for the catalyst, they'd have to raise the **temperature** loads to make the reaction happen **quickly enough**. Not only would this be bad for their fuel bills, it'd **reduce the amount of ammonia** produced.

	Made without a catalyst	Made with a catalyst (a Ziegler-Natta catalyst to be precise)
Using a catalyst can change the properties of a product to make it more useful, e.g. **poly(ethene)**.		
Properties of poly(ethene)	less dense, less rigid	more dense, more rigid, higher melting point

Catalysts are used **loads** in the **petroleum industry** too. They're used for **cracking**, **isomerisation**, and **reforming** alkanes.

...And for the Environment

1) Using catalysts means that lower temperatures and pressures can be used. So **energy is saved**, meaning **less CO_2** is released, and fossil fuel reserves are preserved. Catalysts can also **reduce waste** by allowing a different reaction with a better **atom economy** to be used. (*See page 34 for more on atom economy.*)

> For example, making the painkiller ibuprofen by the traditional method involves 6 steps and has an atom economy of 32%. Using catalysts it can be made in **3 steps** with an **atom economy of 77%**.

2) **Catalytic converters** on cars are made from **alloys of platinum, palladium and rhodium**. They reduce the pollution released into the atmosphere by speeding up this reaction **$2CO + 2NO \rightarrow 2CO_2 + N_2$**.

> **But catalysts don't last forever.** All catalysts eventually need to be disposed of. The trouble is, many contain nasty **toxic** compounds, which may leach into the soil if they're sent directly to **landfill**. So it's important to try to recycle them, or convert them to non-leaching forms.
>
> If a catalyst contains a **valuable metal**, such as platinum, it's worth recovering and recycling it — and there are special companies eager to do this for you. The decision whether to recycle the catalyst or to send it to landfill is made by balancing the **economic and environmental factors**.

Practice Questions

Q1 Draw an enthalpy profile diagram and a Maxwell-Boltzmann distribution diagram to show how a catalyst works.

Q2 Describe three important industrial processes that use a catalyst.

Q3 Describe two advantages of using catalysts in industrial processes.

Exam Questions

Q1 Sulfuric acid is manufactured by the Contact Process. In one of the stages, sulfur dioxide is converted into sulfur trioxide. A vanadium(V) oxide catalyst is used.

$$2SO_{2(g)} + O_{2(g)} \underset{V_2O_{5(s)}}{\rightleftharpoons} 2SO_{3(g)} \quad \Delta H = -197 \text{ kJ mol}^{-1}$$

a) Draw and label an enthalpy profile diagram for the catalysed reaction. Label the activation energy. [3 marks]

b) On your diagram from part a), draw a profile for the uncatalysed reaction. [1 mark]

c) Explain how catalysts work. [2 marks]

d) Although vanadium catalysts are less efficient than platinum, platinum is seldom used because it is susceptible to poisoning by arsenic. Explain how the poisoning happens. [2 marks]

Q2 The decomposition of hydrogen peroxide, H_2O_2, into water and oxygen is catalysed by manganese(IV) oxide, MnO_2.

a) Write an equation for the reaction. [2 marks]

b) Sketch a Maxwell-Boltzmann distribution for the molecules in hydrogen peroxide. Mark on the activation energy for the catalysed and uncatalysed processes. [3 marks]

c) Referring to your diagram from part b), explain how manganese(IV) oxide acts as a catalyst. [3 marks]

I'm a catalyst — I like to speed up arguments without getting too involved...

Whatever you do, do not confuse the Maxwell-Boltzmann diagram for catalysts with the one for a temperature change. Catalysts lower the activation energy without changing the shape of the curve. BUT, the shape of the curve does change with temperature. Get these mixed up and you'll be the laughing stock of the Examiners' tea room.

Homogeneous and Heterogeneous Catalysts

There are two types of catalyst — homogeneous and heterogeneous. Both types'll make reactions hurry up though.
These pages are for AQA (Unit 2), OCR A (Unit 2), OCR B (Units 1 and 2) and Edexcel (Unit 2).

Homogeneous Catalysts are in the Same State as the Reactants
OCR B (Unit 2) and Edexcel only

A **homogeneous catalyst** is in the **same state** as the **reactants**. So, if the reactants are **gases**, the catalyst must be a **gas** too. And if the reactants are **aqueous** (dissolved in water), the catalyst has to be **aqueous** too.

Enzymes are biological catalysts.

When **enzymes** catalyse reactions in your body **cells**, everything's **aqueous** — so it's **homogeneous catalysis**.

Homogeneous Catalysts Work by Forming Intermediates
OCR B (Unit 2) and Edexcel only

1) A homogeneous catalyst speeds up reactions by forming one or more **intermediate compounds** with the reactants. The products are then formed from the intermediate compounds.

2) The activation energy needed to form the **intermediates** (and to form the products from the intermediates) is **lower** than that needed to make the products directly from the reactants.

3) If a reaction is speeded up by a **homogeneous catalyst**, its enthalpy profile will have **two humps** in it.

The Enthalpy Profile of a Homogeneously Catalysed Reaction.
(What a hideous mouthful. But it had to be said.)

E' = the activation energy of the **first** step in the catalysed reaction.
E'' = the activation energy of the **second** step in the catalysed reaction.

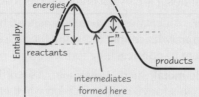

Mrs Watson tried everything to lower the camel's activation energy.

4) The catalyst is **reformed** again and carries on **catalysing** the reaction.

The Ozone Layer's being Destroyed by Homogeneous Catalysis
Not OCR B (Unit 1)

There's loads about the ozone layer on pages 144-145. Its destruction is a good example of homogeneous catalysis though, so this bit is here. The formula for ozone is O_3.

You've heard of how the **ozone layer's** being destroyed by **CFCs**, right. Well, here's what's happening.

1) **Chlorine free radicals**, $Cl\bullet$, are formed when **CFCs** (chlorofluorocarbons) are broken down by **ultraviolet radiation**. It's a carbon-chlorine bond that's broken.

Free radicals are formed when covalent bonds split in two — they've got an unpaired electron (shown by the dot), which makes them highly reactive.

E.g. $CCl_3F_{(g)} \rightarrow CCl_2F\bullet_{(g)} + Cl\bullet_{(g)}$

2) These free radicals are **catalysts**. They react with **ozone** to form an **intermediate** ($ClO\bullet$), and an oxygen molecule.

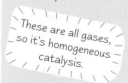
These are all gases, so it's homogeneous catalysis.

The chlorine free radical is regenerated. It goes straight on to attack another ozone molecule. It only takes one little chlorine free radical to destroy loads of ozone molecules.

$Cl\bullet_{(g)} + O_{3(g)} \rightarrow O_{2(g)} + ClO\bullet_{(g)}$
$ClO\bullet_{(g)} + O_{3(g)} \rightarrow 2O_{2(g)} + Cl\bullet_{(g)}$

3) So the **overall reaction** is...
$$2O_{3(g)} \rightarrow 3O_{2(g)}$$ ... and $Cl\bullet$ is the catalyst.

Homogeneous and Heterogeneous Catalysts

Heterogeneous Catalysts are in Different States from the Reactants

OCR A (Unit 2) and OCR B (Unit 1) only

Heterogeneous catalysts are in a **different physical state** from the reactants.
So, if the catalyst is **solid**, the reactants will have to be **gases** or **liquids**. Here are two examples:

> **Iron's** used as a **heterogeneous catalyst** in the **Haber process** to produce ammonia.
> Iron's a **solid** and the reactants are hydrogen **gas** and nitrogen **gas**.

Platinum is used as a **heterogeneous catalyst** in **catalytic converters**.
Catalytic converters sit quietly in a car **exhaust** and stop some **pollutants** from coming out.

Without catalytic converters, cars spew out **lots** of bad stuff, like **carbon monoxide** (which is poisonous), **oxides of nitrogen** and **unburnt hydrocarbons**. When the sun shines on nitrogen oxides and hydrocarbons, **low-level** (or ground level) **ozone** is produced. This **isn't** good ozone, like the stuff in the sky. This is **smog** — it makes you **cough** and **choke**, and generally doesn't do you much good.

Catalytic converters **get rid** of them by changing them to **harmless gases**, like **water vapour** and **nitrogen**, or to **less harmful** ones like **carbon dioxide**.

Reactions Happen On Heterogeneous Catalysts

OCR A (Unit 2) and OCR B (Unit 1) only

Solid heterogeneous catalysts can provide a **surface** for a reaction to take place on.

Here's how it works —

1) **Reactant molecules** arrive at the **surface** and **bond** with the solid catalyst. This is called **adsorption**.

2) The bonds between the **reactant's** atoms are **weakened** and **break up**. This forms **radicals**. These radicals then **get together** and make **new molecules**.

3) The new molecules are then detached from the catalyst. This is called **desorption**.

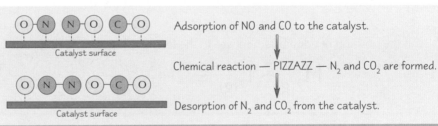

This example shows you how a catalytic converter changes the harmful gases **nitrogen monoxide, NO**, and **carbon monoxide, CO**, to **nitrogen** and **carbon dioxide**.

Adsorption of NO and CO to the catalyst.

Chemical reaction — PIZZAZZ — N_2 and CO_2 are formed.

Desorption of N_2 and CO_2 from the catalyst.

Remember — the adsorption **mustn't** be **too strong** or it won't **let go** of the atoms. **BUT** — it needs to be **strong enough** to **weaken** the bonds between the reactant molecules so that the new molecules can form.

Practice Questions

Q1 What is the difference between homogeneous catalysis and heterogeneous catalysis?

Q2 Give an example of a homogeneous catalyst and describe how it works.

Q3 What do 'adsorption' and 'desorption' mean in relation to heterogeneous catalysts?

Exam Questions

Q1 Enzymes are proteins that catalyse specific biological reactions.
Draw a fully labelled enthalpy profile for an enzyme-catalysed reaction and the uncatalysed reaction. [4 marks]

Q2 Heterogeneous catalysts are more common than homogeneous catalysts. In the manufacture of ammonia, finely divided iron is used as the catalyst. Explain why the iron is finely divided. [2 marks]

Don't get the hump now — you've gotta learn it...

CFCs used to be everywhere — in McDonald's cups, in deodorant and hairspray, and in fridges. When people realised the crazy amount of damage it was doing, they really cracked down on it. You need to practise writing out the ozone equations, and don't forget to dot your Cl's and O's. Oh, and wear sunscreen...or you'll be wrinkly before you know it.

Reversible Reactions

These pages are for AQA (Unit 2), OCR A (Unit 2), OCR B (Unit 2) and Edexcel (Unit 2).
There's a lot of to-ing and fro-ing on this page. Mind your head doesn't start spinning.

Reversible Reactions Can Reach Dynamic Equilibrium

1) Lots of chemical reactions are **reversible** — they go **both ways**. To show a reaction's reversible, you stick in a $\rightleftharpoons$.
   Here's an example:

> $$H_{2(g)} + I_{2(g)} \rightleftharpoons 2HI_{(g)}$$
> This reaction can go in **either direction** —
> forwards $H_{2(g)} + I_{2(g)} \rightarrow 2HI_{(g)}$ ....or backwards $2HI_{(g)} \rightarrow H_{2(g)} + I_{2(g)}$.

2) As the **reactants** get used up, the **forward** reaction **slows down** —
   and as more **product** is formed, the **reverse** reaction **speeds up**.

3) After a while, the forward reaction will be going at exactly the **same rate** as the backward reaction.
   The amounts of reactants and products **won't be changing** any more, so it'll seem like **nothing's happening**.
   It's a bit like you're **digging a hole**, while someone else is **filling it in** at exactly the **same speed**.
   This is called a **dynamic equilibrium**.

4) A **dynamic equilibrium** can only happen in a **closed system**. This just means nothing can get in or out.

Le Chatelier's Principle Predicts what will Happen if Conditions are Changed

If you **change** the **concentration**, **pressure** or **temperature** of a reversible reaction, you tend to **alter** the **position of equilibrium**. This just means you'll end up with **different amounts** of reactants and products at equilibrium.

> If the position of equilibrium moves to the **left**, you'll get more **reactants**.
>
> $$H_{2(g)} + I_{2(g)} \rightleftharpoons 2HI_{(g)}$$

> If the position of equilibrium moves to the **right**, you'll get more **products**.
>
> $$H_{2(g)} + I_{2(g)} \rightleftharpoons 2HI_{(g)}$$

Mr and Mrs Le Chatelier celebrate another successful year in the principle business

Le Chatelier's principle tells you how the **position of equilibrium** will change if a **condition changes**:

> If there's a change in **concentration, pressure** or **temperature**,
> the equilibrium will move to help **counteract** the change.

So, basically, if you **raise the temperature**, the position of equilibrium will shift to try to **cool things down**.
And, if you **raise the pressure or concentration**, the position of equilibrium will shift to try to **reduce it again**.

Catalysts Don't Affect The Position of Equilibrium

> **Catalysts** have **NO EFFECT** on the **position of equilibrium**.
> They **can't** increase **yield** — but they **do** mean equilibrium is reached **faster**.

Reversible Reactions

Here are Some **Handy Rules** for Using **Le Chatelier's Principle**

CONCENTRATION $2SO_{2(g)} + O_{2(g)} \rightleftharpoons 2SO_{3(g)}$

1) If you **increase** the **concentration** of a **reactant** (SO_2 or O_2), the equilibrium tries to **get rid** of the extra reactant. It does this by making **more product** (SO_3). So the equilibrium's shifted to the **right**.

2) If you **increase** the **concentration** of the **product** (SO_3), the equilibrium tries to remove the extra product. This makes the **reverse reaction** go faster. So the equilibrium shifts to the **left**.

3) **Decreasing** the concentrations has the **opposite effect**.

PRESSURE (changing this only affects **equilibria involving gases**)

1) **Increasing** the pressure shifts the equilibrium to the side with the **fewest** gas molecules. This **reduces** the pressure.

2) **Decreasing** the pressure shifts the equilibrium to the side with **most** gas molecules. This **raises** the pressure again.

There are 3 moles on the left, but only 2 on the right. So, an increase in pressure shifts the equilibrium to the right. $\longrightarrow$ $2SO_{2(g)} + O_{2(g)} \rightleftharpoons 2SO_{3(g)}$

TEMPERATURE

1) **Increasing** the temperature means **adding heat**. The equilibrium shifts in the **endothermic (positive ΔH) direction** to absorb this heat.

2) **Decreasing** the temperature **removes heat**. The equilibrium shifts in the **exothermic (negative ΔH) direction** to try to replace the heat.

3) If the forward reaction's **endothermic**, the reverse reaction will be **exothermic**, and vice versa.

This reaction's exothermic in the forwards direction. If you increase the temperature, the equilibrium shifts to the left to absorb the extra heat. Exothermic $\Longrightarrow$ $2SO_{2(g)} + O_{2(g)} \rightleftharpoons 2SO_{3(g)}$ $\Delta H = -197$ kJ mol^{-1} $\Longleftarrow$ Endothermic

Practice Questions

Q1 Using an example, explain the terms 'reversible reaction' and 'dynamic equilibrium'.

Q2 If the equilibrium moves to the right, do you get more products or reactants?

Q3 A reaction at equilibrium is endothermic in the forward direction. What happens to the position of equilibrium as the temperature is increased?

Exam Question

Q1 Nitrogen and oxygen gases were reacted together in a closed flask and allowed to reach equilibrium with the nitrogen monoxide formed. The forward reaction is endothermic.

$$N_{2(g)} + O_{2(g)} \rightleftharpoons 2NO_{(g)}$$

a) State Le Chatelier's principle. [1 mark]

b) Explain how the following changes would affect the position of equilibrium of the above reaction:
(i) Pressure is **increased**. [2 marks]
(ii) Temperature is **reduced**. [2 marks]
(iii) Nitrogen monoxide is removed. [1 mark]

c) What would be the effect of a catalyst on the composition of the equilibrium mixture? [1 mark]

Only going forward cos we can't find reverse...

Equilibria never do what you want them to do. They always **oppose** you. Be sure you know what happens to an equilibrium if you change the conditions. A word about pressure — if the equation has the same number of gas moles on each side, then you can raise the pressure as high as you like and it won't make a blind bit of difference to the position of equilibrium.

More About Equilibria

These pages are for AQA (Unit 2), OCR A (Unit 2), OCR B (Unit 2) and Edexcel (Unit 2).

Using Le Chatelier's principle you can shift the position of equilibrium to make more of a product.
This is really important in industry (as you'll see). But you can check it does actually work in the lab.

Simple Experiments can Show the Effect of Changes in Conditions

...And they don't even need much fancy equipment.

Changing the CONCENTRATION

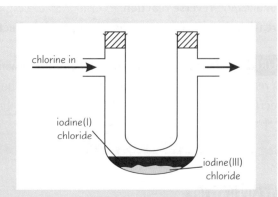

1) If you put **iodine(I) chloride** (a brown liquid) in the apparatus shown and pass **chlorine gas** over it, **iodine(III) chloride** (a yellow solid) forms.

   The reaction is:

   $$ICl_{(l)} + Cl_{2(g)} \rightleftharpoons ICl_{3(s)}$$

   brown liquid   yellow solid

2) If you pump more chlorine into the tube, you'll **increase** its **concentration**. The equilibrium moves to the **right** — so you get more of the yellow solid.

3) If you stop the supply of chlorine and let air in, the **concentration** of chlorine **decreases**. The equilibrium moves back to the **left**, so the **yellow solid** starts turning back into the **brown liquid**.

Changing the TEMPERATURE

1) The **colourless gas** dinitrogen tetroxide (N_2O_4) changes **reversibly** to **brown** nitrogen dioxide gas (NO_2). Here's the equation:

   $$N_2O_{4(g)} \rightleftharpoons 2NO_{2(g)} \qquad \Delta H = +58 \text{ kJ mol}^{-1}$$

   colourless gas   brown gas

   It's an endothermic reaction.

2) If you stick a **sealed syringe** full of this equilibrium mixture in a beaker of **hot water**, the gas gets **darker** because more brown NO_2 forms.

3) The extra heat sends the equilibrium in the **endothermic** direction.

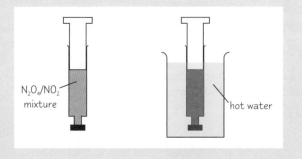

Changing the PRESSURE

1) This one also uses the syringe containing the N_2O_4 / NO_2 **mixture**.

2) If you compress the gas in the syringe, it gets **darker** at first — that's because the **concentration** has increased. But then the mixture gets **paler** as some NO_2 is converted into colourless N_2O_4.

3) The equilibrium has moved towards the side with **fewest moles** of gas to reduce the pressure again.

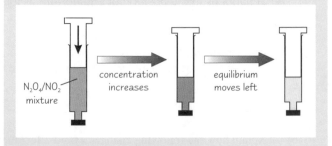

Businesses want to find the Best Conditions for their Processes

1) **Le Chatelier's principle** is also used in **industry** with chemical processes that involve **reversible reactions**.

2) The big bosses want to make bags of **money**. That means finding a way to make as much of the **useful products** as they can, as **cheaply** as possible.

3) So they need to pick the **best conditions** for their processes.

More About Equilibria

This page is for AQA and OCR A only.

Ethanol can be formed from Ethene and Steam

$$C_2H_{4(g)} + H_2O_{(g)} \rightleftharpoons C_2H_5OH_{(g)} \qquad \Delta H = -46 \text{ kJ mol}^{-1}$$

This reaction is reversible and exothermic.

Industrial Conditions

Pressure:	60-70 atmospheres
Temperature:	300 °C
Catalyst:	Phosphoric acid on silica

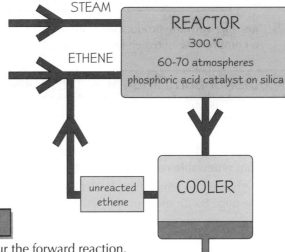

The Temperature Chosen is a Compromise

1) Because it's an **exothermic reaction**, **lower** temperatures favour the forward reaction. This means **more** ethene and steam is converted to ethanol — you get a better **yield**.

2) The trouble is, **lower temperatures** mean a **slower rate of reaction**.

3) You'd be **daft** to try to get a **really high yield** of ethanol if it's going to take you 10 years. So the 300 °C is a **compromise** between **maximum yield** and **a faster reaction**.

High Pressure would give a Big Yield — but it'd be Expensive

1) **Higher pressures** favour the **forward reaction**, so a pressure of **60-70 atmospheres** is used.

2) This is because **high pressure** moves the reaction to the side with **fewer molecules of gas**. There are **2 moles** of gas on the **reactant side** ($C_2H_{4(g)} + H_2O_{(g)}$) and only **1 mole** on the **product side** ($C_5H_5OH_{(g)}$).

3) **Increasing the pressure** also increases the **rate** of reaction.

4) Cranking up the pressure as high as you can sounds like a great idea so far. But **high pressures** are **expensive** to produce. You need **stronger pipes** and **containers** to withstand high pressure. In this process, increasing the pressure can also cause **side reactions** to occur.

5) So the **60-70 atmospheres** is a **compromise** between **maximum yield** and **expense**. In the end, it all comes down to **minimising costs**.

A Catalyst Doesn't Affect the Equilibrium Position but will Increase the Rate

Without a **catalyst** the **reaction** is **slow**. The phosphoric acid **catalyst** makes the **reaction** reach equilibrium more quickly.

Recycling Unreacted Ethene Also Saves Money

1) Only a **small proportion** of the ethene reacts each time the gases pass through the catalyst.

2) To save money, the **unreacted ethene** is separated from the liquid ethanol and **recycled** back into the reactor.

3) Thanks to this around **95%** of the ethene is eventually converted to ethanol.

More About Equilibria

Methanol can be Produced from Hydrogen and Carbon Monoxide — AQA only

1) **Methanol** is also made industrially in a **reversible reaction**. It's made from **hydrogen** and **carbon monoxide**:

$$2H_{2(g)} + CO_{(g)} \rightleftharpoons CH_3OH_{(g)} \qquad \Delta H = -90 \text{ kJ mol}^{-1}$$

Industrial conditions — **pressure:** 50-100 atmospheres, **temperature:** 250 °C, **catalyst:** mixture of copper, zinc oxide and aluminium oxide

2) Just like with the production of **ethanol**, the conditions used are a **compromise** between keeping **costs** low and **yield** high.

Methanol and Ethanol are Important Liquid Fuels — AQA only

1) Methanol is mainly used to make other chemicals, but both **methanol** and **ethanol** can also be used as **fuels for cars** — either on their own, or added to petrol.

2) Ethanol and methanol are thought of as **greener** than petrol — they can be made from **renewable resources** and they produce **fewer pollutants** (like NO_x and CO).

3) Methanol and ethanol can both be **carbon neutral fuels** (pretty much). See page 85 for more on why ethanol is thought of as carbon neutral.

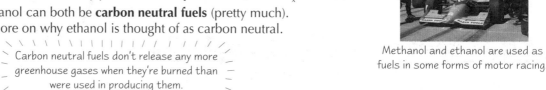

Carbon neutral fuels don't release any more greenhouse gases when they're burned than were used in producing them.

Methanol and ethanol are used as fuels in some forms of motor racing.

Practice Questions

Q1 How could you show using a simple experiment that changing temperature can change the position of equilibrium?

Q2 State the advantages and disadvantages of using high pressure in the production of ethanol from ethene and steam.

Q3 What effect does a catalyst have on an equilibrium reaction?

Q4 State an advantage of adding ethanol to petrol.

Q5 Explain what a 'carbon neutral fuel' is.

Exam Question

Q1 The manufacture of ethanol can be represented by the reaction

$$C_2H_{4(g)} + H_2O_{(g)} \rightleftharpoons C_2H_5OH_{(g)} \qquad \Delta H = -46 \text{ kJ mol}^{-1}$$

Typical conditions are 300 °C and 60-70 atmospheres.

a) Explain, in molecular terms, why a temperature lower than the one quoted is not used. [3 marks]

b) Explain why a pressure higher than the one quoted is not often used. [2 marks]

c) The gases are passed through a conversion chamber containing a catalyst of phosphoric acid, adsorbed onto the surface of silica. Describe and explain the effect of the catalyst on:
   (i) the rate of production of ethanol, [3 marks]
   (ii) the amount of ethanol in the equilibrium mixture. [2 marks]

d) Under the conditions given above only about 5% of the ethene is converted to ethanol when it passes through the catalyst. Without changing the conditions, explain how the overall yield is improved. [1 mark]

It's all about money — it's what makes the world go around...

Lots of lovely stuff here folks. It just goes to show you Le Chatelier's principle isn't just something they make you learn to fill up the AS Chemistry syllabus. It has uses in real life. Everyone in the manufacturing business wants to make as much stuff as they can, as quickly as they can and as cheaply as they can. It's just a fact of life.

Extracting Metals From Their Ores

These pages are for AQA (Unit 2) only.
Metals are handy for making metal things. Sadly, you don't tend to find big lumps of pure metal lying about, ready to use...

Sulfide Ores are Usually Converted to Oxides First

1) An **ore** is a natural substance that a metal can be **economically extracted** from. In other words, a rock that you can get **enough metal** out of to more than cover the cost of extracting it.

2) Metals are often found in ores as **sulfides** (such as lead sulfide and zinc sulfide), or **oxides** (like titanium dioxide and iron(III) oxide). Getting the metal out of these compounds is where the chemistry comes in.

3) The first step to extract a metal from a **sulfide ore** is to turn it into an **oxide**. You simply **roast** the sulfide in air.

When extracting metals, Jimmy liked to use his ores and cart.

E.g.

| zinc sulfide | + | oxygen | $\rightarrow$ | zinc oxide | + | sulfur dioxide |
| $ZnS_{(s)}$ | + | $3O_{2(g)}$ | $\rightarrow$ | $2ZnO_{(s)}$ | + | $2SO_{2(g)}$ |

Acid rain harms plants and aquatic life. It damages limestone buildings too.

Sounds simple — but the bad news is **sulfur dioxide** gas causes **acid rain**.

4) But there's a silver lining to the cloud — you can convert the sulfur dioxide to **sulfuric acid**. Not only does this avoid a pollutant, but you make a **valuable product** — sulfuric acid's in demand because it's used in many chemical and manufacturing processes.

Oxides are Reduced to the Metal

1) The method for **reducing** the oxide depends on the metal you're trying to extract.

2) **Carbon** (as coke) and **carbon monoxide** are used as **reducing agents** for quite a few metals — usually the ones that are **less reactive** than carbon.

Coke is a solid fuel made from coal.

You need to know these **three examples** of metal extraction with carbon and carbon monoxide:

REDUCTION OF IRON(III) OXIDE

Iron(III) oxide is reduced by **carbon** or **carbon monoxide** to iron and carbon dioxide.

$$2Fe_2O_3 + 3C \rightarrow 4Fe + 3CO_2$$
$$Fe_2O_3 + 3CO \rightarrow 2Fe + 3CO_2$$

This happens in a blast furnace at temperatures greater than 700 °C.

REDUCTION OF MANGANESE(IV) OXIDE (MANGANESE DIOXIDE)

Manganese(IV) oxide is reduced with **carbon** or **carbon monoxide** in a blast furnace.

$$MnO_2 + C \rightarrow Mn + CO_2$$
$$MnO_2 + 2CO \rightarrow Mn + 2CO_2$$

This needs higher temperatures than iron(III) oxide — about 1200 °C.

REDUCTION OF COPPER CARBONATE

Copper can be extracted using **carbon**.

One ore of copper is **malachite**, containing $CuCO_3$. This can be heated directly with carbon.

$$2CuCO_3 + C \rightarrow 2Cu + 3CO_2$$

Another method involves heating the carbonate until it decomposes, then reducing the oxide with carbon.

$$CuCO_3 \rightarrow CuO + CO_2$$
$$2CuO + C \rightarrow 2Cu + CO_2$$

Carbon and **carbon monoxide** are the first choices for extracting metals because they're **cheap**.
But they're not always suitable — some metals have to be extracted by other methods.
You'll see three examples on the next page...

Extracting Metals From Their Ores

These pages are for AQA (Unit 2) only.

Tungsten *is Extracted Using* Hydrogen

1) **Tungsten** can be extracted from its oxide with carbon, but that can leave **impurities** which make the metal **brittle**. If pure tungsten is needed, the ore is reduced using **hydrogen** instead.

$$WO_{3(s)} + 3H_{2(g)} \rightarrow W_{(s)} + 3H_2O_{(g)}$$

This happens in a furnace at temperatures above 700 °C.

2) Tungsten is the **only metal** reduced on a large scale using **hydrogen**. Hydrogen is more **expensive** but it's worth the extra cost to get pure tungsten, which is much easier to work with.

3) Hydrogen is **highly explosive** when mixed with air though, which is a bit of a hazard.

Aluminium *is Extracted by* Electrolysis

1) **Aluminium** is **too reactive** to extract by reduction by carbon — a very **high temperature** would be needed and it's **too expensive** to be worthwhile. Electrolysis is used instead.

2) Aluminium's ore is called **bauxite** and it's mainly aluminium oxide, Al_2O_3, with various impurities. First of all, these impurities are removed. Next, it's dissolved in **molten cryolite** (sodium aluminium fluoride, Na_3AlF_6), which lowers its **melting point** from a scorching 2050 °C, to a cool **970 °C**. This reduces the operating costs.

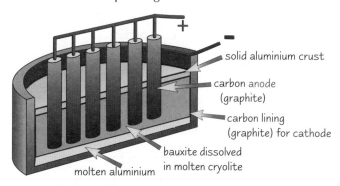

solid aluminium crust

carbon anode (graphite)

carbon lining (graphite) for cathode

bauxite dissolved in molten cryolite

molten aluminium

ELECTROLYSIS OF ALUMINIUM

1) Aluminium is produced at the **cathode** and collects as the molten liquid at the bottom of the cell.

$$Al^{3+} + 3e^- \rightarrow Al$$

2) Oxygen is produced at the **anode**.

$$2O^{2-} \rightarrow O_2 + 4e^-$$

The current used in electrolysis is high (200 000 A), so the process is carried out where cheap electricity is available, often near hydroelectric power stations.

Titanium is used in the bodies of modern planes.

Titanium *is* Great *but a bit too* Expensive

1) Titanium is a pretty **abundant** metal in the Earth's crust. In its pure form, titanium is a **strong**, **light** metal that is highly resistant to **corrosion**. Pretty much perfect really, so how come it's not used more... Well basically, it's just a bit too **difficult** and **expensive** to produce.

2) The main ore is **rutile** (titanium(IV) oxide, TiO_2). You can't extract titanium from it by carbon reduction because you get titanium carbide which ruins it... $TiO_{2\ (s)} + 3C_{(s)} \rightarrow TiC_{(s)} + 2CO_{(g)}$

THE EXTRACTION OF TITANIUM

...is a **batch** process with several stages.

1) The ore is converted to **titanium(IV) chloride** by heating it to about 900 °C with carbon in a stream of chlorine gas.

$$TiO_{2\ (s)} + 2Cl_{2\ (g)} + 2C_{(s)} \rightarrow TiCl_{4\ (g)} + 2CO_{(g)}$$

2) The titanium chloride is purified by **fractional distillation** under an inert atmosphere of argon or nitrogen.

3) Then the chloride gets reduced in a **furnace** at almost 1000 °C. It's heated with a **more reactive** metal such as sodium or magnesium. An inert atmosphere is used to prevent side reactions.

$$TiCl_{4\ (g)} + 4Na_{(l)} \rightarrow Ti_{(s)} + 4NaCl_{(l)}$$
$$TiCl_{4\ (g)} + 2Mg_{(l)} \rightarrow Ti_{(s)} + 2MgCl_{2\ (l)}$$

Na and Mg are reducing agents.

Extracting Metals From Their Ores

Recycling can be Good for the Environment and Save Money

Once you've got the metal out of the ore, you can keep **recycling** it again and again.
As usual, there are pros and cons:

Advantages of recycling metals:
- Saves raw materials — ores are a finite resource.
- Saves energy — recycling metals takes less energy than extracting metal. This saves money too.
- Reduces waste sent to landfill.
- Mining damages the landscape and spoil heaps are ugly. Recycling metals reduces this.

Disadvantages of recycling metals:
- Collecting and sorting metals from other waste can be difficult and expensive.
- The purity of recycled metal varies — there's usually other metals and other impurities mixed in.
- Recycling metals may not produce a consistent supply to meet demand.

Scrap Iron can be used in Copper Extraction

1) Some scrap metal can be put to other uses. For example, **scrap iron** can be used to extract **copper** from solution. This method is mainly used with **low grade** ore — ore that only contains a **small percentage** of copper.

2) Acidified water **dissolves** the copper compounds in the ore.
The solution is collected and **scrap iron** is then added. The iron dissolves and **reduces** the copper(II) ions.
The copper precipitates out of the solution. $Cu^{2+}_{(aq)} + Fe_{(s)} \rightarrow Cu_{(s)} + Fe^{2+}_{(aq)}$

3) This process produces copper **more slowly** than carbon reduction and has a **lower yield**, which is why it's not used with ores that have a high copper content. It's **cheaper** than carbon reduction though, because you don't need **high temperatures**, and better for the environment because there's no **CO_2** produced.

Practice Questions

Q1 What is used to reduce manganese(IV) oxide to manganese?
Q2 Write an equation for the conversion of zinc sulfide ore to zinc oxide.
Q3 Write the equation for the displacement of titanium from titanium chloride using sodium.
Q4 Why is sodium (or magnesium) chosen to reduce titanium chloride?
Q5 Give one environmental and one economic reason for recycling metals.

Exam Questions

Q1 The iron ore in a blast furnace contains a mixture of oxides, one of which is Fe_3O_4.
When Fe_3O_4 is reduced, both carbon and carbon monoxide act as reducing agents.
Write equations to show
a) how carbon monoxide reduces Fe_3O_4.   [1 mark]
b) how carbon reduces Fe_3O_4.   [1 mark]

Q2 Hydrogen is used to extract tungsten from its ore.
Give an advantage and a disadvantage of using hydrogen in place of carbon.   [2 marks]

Q3 Aluminium is extracted from its purified ore by electrolysis.
a) What important step is taken to reduce the cost of extracting aluminium?   [2 marks]
b) Write equations for the reactions occurring at each electrode.   [2 marks]
c) Explain why aluminium is more expensive to extract than iron.   [1 mark]

Extraction can be heavy going — in fact, it's like pulling teeth...

It might look like there are loads of equations to learn here — in fact, come to think of it, there are quite a few. But at least most of those oxide reduction ones are pretty similar, e.g. oxide + carbon monoxide → metal + carbon dioxide. There's actually <u>nothing too hard</u> on these pages at all. But there is <u>plenty</u> to get stuck into with your revision shovel.

Dissolving and Entropy

There are two types of solvent — polar and non-polar. Some things dissolve better in polar solvents, while other things dissolve better in non-polar solvents. And guess what — you need to know why.
This page is for Edexcel (Unit 2) only.

Solubility is Affected by Bonding

1) When a substance dissolves, bonds in the **substance** have to **break**, bonds in the **solvent** have to **break**, and bonds **between** the **substance** and the **solvent** have to **form**.

2) Usually a substance will only dissolve if the strength of the new bonds **formed** is about **the same as**, or **greater than**, the strength of the bonds that are **broken**.

3) There are two main **types of solvent**.
   • **Polar solvents** such as water. Water molecules bond to each other with **hydrogen bonds**.
   • **Non-polar solvents** such as hexane. Hexane molecules bond to each other by **van der Waals forces**.

Ionic Substances Dissolve in Polar Solvents such as Water

1) The ions are attracted to the **oppositely charged ends** of the water molecules.

2) The ions are pulled away from the ionic lattice by the water molecules, which surround the ions. This process is called **hydration**.

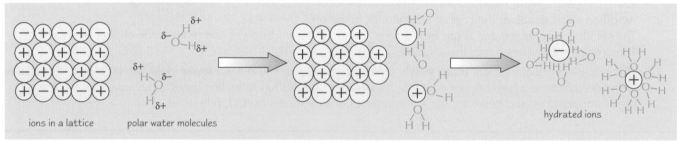

ions in a lattice   polar water molecules   hydrated ions

3) Some ionic substances **don't dissolve** because the bonding between their ions is **too strong**. E.g. Aluminium oxide (Al_2O_3) is insoluble in water because the bonds between the ions are stronger than the bonds they'd form with the water molecules. (Al^{3+} has a high charge density, so it's highly polarising — see p49.)

Alcohols also Dissolve in Polar Solvents such as Water

1) Alcohols are **covalent** but they dissolve in water because the polar O-H bond in an alcohol is attracted to the polar O-H bonds in water. **Hydrogen bonds** form between the lone pairs on the oxygen atoms and the δ+ hydrogen atoms.

2) The **carbon chain** part of the alcohol isn't attracted to water, so the more carbon atoms there are, the **less soluble** the alcohol will be.

Not All Molecules with Polar Bonds Dissolve in Water

1) **Haloalkanes** contain **polar bonds** but their dipoles aren't strong enough to form **hydrogen bonds** with water. (See p51 for what's needed to form hydrogen bonds.)

2) The hydrogen bonding **between** water molecules is **stronger** than the bonds that would be formed with haloalkanes, so haloalkanes don't dissolve.

E.g. the haloalkane chlorobutane doesn't mix with water. The substances instead separate into two layers.

chlorobutane layer
water layer

Non-polar Substances Dissolve Best in Non-polar Solvents

1) Non-polar substances such as **iodine**, or **alkanes** have **van der Waals forces** between their molecules. They form **similar bonds** with **non-polar solvents** such as hexane — so they tend to dissolve in them.

2) Molecules of **polar solvents** such as water are attracted to **each other** more strongly than they are to **non-polar molecules** such as iodine or alkanes — so non-polar substances don't tend to dissolve easily in polar solvents.

Like dissolves like (usually) — substances usually dissolve best in solvents that have **similar bonds**.

Dissolving and Entropy

OK, so entropy's not got a lot to do with dissolving. But when you dissolve one thing in another, the entropy increases.

Entropy Tells you How Much Disorder there is   OCR B (Unit 1) only

To explain **entropy** we need to go back to the good old **solid-liquid-gas** particle explanation thingies...

1) So... in **solids**, everything's nice and orderly. The particles don't move about freely — they just wobble about a fixed point. This means it's pretty easy to **predict** where a particle's going to be.

2) In **liquids**, the particles are still close together, but they can move about freely. So it's not quite so orderly and it's harder to **predict** the position of a particle.

3) In **gases**, the particles are very far apart, whizzing around wherever they like. There's **no order** — in fact, it's absolutely **random**. The position of a particle is totally **unpredictable**.

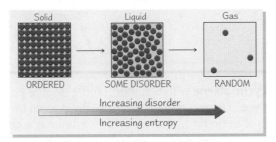

Looks like someone else has been reading the dissolving and entropy stuff again...

Entropy is a measure of the **number of ways** the particles can be **arranged** — but it's basically just a measure of disorder. Now get this: substances **like** disorder. Particles will naturally move to give a substance the **maximum possible entropy**...

– Gases diffuse to fill all the available space because there are more ways of arranging particles in a bigger space.
– When something dissolves, the **solute** particles spread out in the **solvent**, and entropy increases.

Increasing the **number of particles** increases the entropy — a greater number of particles can be **arranged in more ways**.

Also, a **mixture** of two different types of particle has more entropy than the same number of one type of particle.

LESS ENTROPY

MORE ENTROPY

Practice Questions

Q1 Which type of solvent would you choose to dissolve: a) sodium chloride?   b) iodine?

Q2 What type of bonding occurs between an alcohol and water?

Q3 Explain why steam has a greater entropy than ice.

Q4 In terms of entropy, why do gases diffuse to fill all the available space?

Exam Questions

Q1 a) What type of bonding is present between molecules of water?   [1 mark]

   b) Explain why alcohols often dissolve in water while haloalkanes do not.   [4 marks]

Q2 a) Describe how you could determine that an unknown substance, X, was likely to be a non-polar covalent compound by testing with two different solvents. Name the solvents chosen and give the expected results.   [4 marks]

   b) Explain these results in terms of the bonding within X and the solvents.   [3 marks]

Q3 State and explain how you would expect entropy to change in the following reaction
$$2Na_{(s)} + 2H_2O_{(l)} \rightarrow 2NaOH_{(aq)} + H_{2(g)}$$ [3 marks]

My bedroom has the maximum possible entropy...

Entropy's another one of those science words that scare everybody away because it sounds like something complicated. But it's actually not too bad once you get your head round it, honest. As for solutions, it's not enough just to remember that 'like dissolves like' — though that's a useful thing to know — make sure you also learn <u>why</u> that's usually the case.

Alkenes

I'll warn you now — some of this stuff gets a bit heavy — but stick with it, as it's pretty important.
These pages are for AQA (Units 1 and 2), OCR A (Unit 2), OCR B (Unit 2) and Edexcel (Unit 1).

Alkenes are **Unsaturated Hydrocarbons**

1) Alkenes have the **general formula** C_nH_{2n}. They're just made of carbon and hydrogen atoms, so they're **hydrocarbons**.

2) Alkene molecules **all** have at least one **C=C double covalent bond**. Molecules with C=C double bonds are **unsaturated** because they can make more bonds with extra atoms in **addition** reactions.

   Here are a few pretty diagrams of **alkenes**:

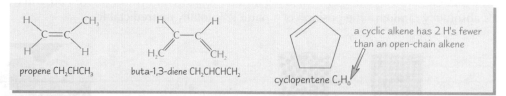

propene CH$_2$CHCH$_3$ buta-1,3-diene CH$_2$CHCHCH$_2$

a cyclic alkene has 2 H's fewer than an open-chain alkene

cyclopentene C$_5$H$_8$

benzene

Benzene (C_6H_6) is like a **cyclic alkene** with 6 carbons and 3 double bonds. It's more **stable** (less reactive) than you'd expect though, because the double bond electrons are **delocalised** around the carbon ring. That's why its symbol has a **circle** in it.

3) Compounds with **benzene ring structures** are called **arenes**, or **aromatic compounds**. All other organic compounds (e.g. alkanes and alkenes) are called **aliphatic compounds**.

Alkene Names *Follow the* **Same Pattern** *as* **Alkane Names**

To name an alkene molecule, just follow the steps that you saw on page 79. Here's a reminder:

1) Find the longest carbon chain in the molecule. Count the carbon atoms in it — this gives you the **stem** of the name.

2) The **suffix** for an alkene molecule is always '**ene**'.

3) If the double bond can go in more than one place, you need to include a **number** to show where it is. Number the carbons so that the first carbon in the double bond has the **lowest** possible number.

Example — CH$_3$CH$_2$CHCHCH$_3$

1) The longest chain is **5** carbons, so the stem of the name is **pent-**.

2) The functional group is **C=C**, so it's **pentene**.

3) Number the carbons from right to left (so the double bond starts on the lowest possible number). The first carbon in the double bond is **carbon 2**. So this is **pent-2-ene**.

H–C₅H₂–C₄H₂–C₃H=C₂H–C₁H₃–H

If the alkene has two double bonds the suffix becomes diene — like buta-1,3-diene above.

The stem of the name usually gets an extra 'a' (e.g. but<u>a</u>-, pent<u>a</u>- not but-, pent-) when there's more than one double bond. And you might see the numbers written first, e.g. 1,3-butadiene.

Alkenes are **Much More Reactive** than Alkanes

AQA (Unit 2), OCR A and Edexcel

1) Each **double bond** in an alkene is made up of a σ **bond and a** π **bond**. It's a bit like a hot dog. The π **bond** is the bun and the σ **bond** is sandwiched in the middle like the sausage.

2) Because there are two pairs of electrons in the bond, the C=C double bond has a really **high electron density**. This makes alkenes pretty reactive.

3) Another reason for the high reactivity is that the π **bond** sticks out above and below the rest of the molecule. So, the π **bond** is likely to be attacked by **electrophiles** (see the next page).

4) As the double bond's so **reactive**, alkenes are handy **starting points** for making other organic compounds and for making **petrochemicals**.

5) The two pairs of electrons in the double bond and the electron pairs in the two C–H single bonds repel each other **equally**. This give the molecule its **trigonal planar** shape — see page 122 for more about this.

See page 40 for more about σ and π bonds.

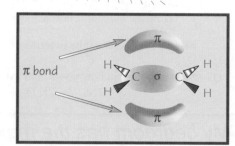

Alkenes

Adding **Hydrogen** to C=C Bonds Produces **Alkanes**   *Not AQA*

1) Ethene will react with **hydrogen** gas to produce ethane. It needs a **nickel catalyst** and a temperature of **150 °C** though.

$$H_2C=CH_2 + H_2 \xrightarrow[150\,°C]{Ni} CH_3CH_3$$

2) Other **alkenes** will react with **hydrogen** in a **similar way**. Here's the equation for the hydrogenation of **propene**:

$$CH_3CH=CH_2 + H_2 \xrightarrow[150\,°C]{Ni} CH_3CH_2CH_3$$

3) **Margarine** is made by '**hydrogenating**' **unsaturated vegetable oils**. By removing some **double bonds**, you raise the **melting point** of the oil so that it becomes **solid** at room temperature.

Electrophilic Addition Reactions Happen to Alkenes   *Not AQA (Unit 1)*

Electrophilic addition reactions of alkenes aren't too complicated.

1) The **double bond** opens up, and another atom is **added** to each of its carbons.

2) Addition reactions happen because the double bond has got plenty of electrons and is easily attacked by an **electrophile**.

3) The double bond is also **nucleophilic** — it's attracted to places that don't have enough **electrons**.

> **Electrophiles** are **electron-pair acceptors** — they're usually a bit short of electrons, so they're **attracted** to areas where there's lots of them about. Here are a couple of examples of electrophiles:
> - **Positively charged ions**, like H^+, NO_2^+.
> - **Polar molecules** — the $\delta+$ atom is attracted to places with lots of electrons

There's loads about electrophilic addition reactions on the next page — this bit was just to get you all excited.

See page 48 for a reminder about polar molecules.

Practice Questions

Q1 What's the general formula for an alkene?

Q2 What is an electrophile?

Q3 Why do alkenes react with electrophiles?

Q4 Write an equation for the hydrogenation of ethene.

Exam Questions

Q1 Ethene has the molecular formula C_2H_4. Explain why it is described as being unsaturated. [2 marks]

Q2 The alkene myrcene can be isolated from bay leaves.
The structural formula of myrcene is $(CH_3)_2CCHCH_2CH_2C(CH_2)CHCH_2$.
a) What is its molecular formula? [1 mark]
b) How many double bonds does myrcene contain, assuming there are no cyclic groups in its structure? [1 mark]
c) Draw the displayed formula of myrcene. [2 marks]

Q3 a) There are two straight-chain alkenes with the molecular formula C_4H_8.
Give the structural formulae and the names of both isomers. [2 marks]
b) Write an equation for the reaction of one of these alkenes with hydrogen. [1 mark]
c) Will the product of this reaction be more reactive or less reactive than the alkene from which it was formed? Explain your answer. [2 marks]

Double bond hot dog — Brosnan's the bun, Dalton's the dog...

What ON EARTH are you talking about, man? Search me — I'm just here to tell you about Organic Chemistry. Alkenes are really important. Make sure you understand why they're so much more reactive than alkanes. It's all to do with the double bond. So get that Double Bond Hot Dog thingy learned. And remember — Connery's the ketchup, Moore's the mustard...

Reactions of Alkenes

Alkenes do loads of weird and wacky stuff — and I've squished plenty of it on this double-page spread.
These pages are for AQA (Unit 2), OCR A (Unit 2), OCR B (Unit 2) and Edexcel (Unit 1).

Bromine *Reacts With* Alkenes *by* Electrophilic Addition

On the last page I mentioned **electrophilic addition reactions**, and why they happen to alkenes.
Well, here's one — if you mix an alkene and bromine, the bromine adds across the double
bond to form a **dibromoalkane**. Here's the mechanism...

Other halogens, like chlorine and iodine, do this with alkenes too.

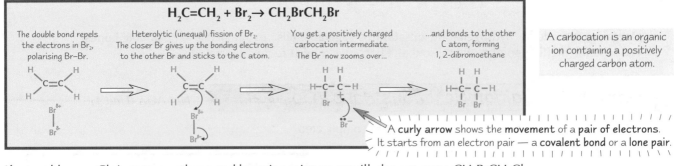

$$H_2C=CH_2 + Br_2 \rightarrow CH_2BrCH_2Br$$

The double bond repels the electrons in Br_2, polarising Br–Br.

Heterolytic (unequal) fission of Br_2. The closer Br gives up the bonding electrons to the other Br and sticks to the C atom.

You get a positively charged carbocation intermediate. The Br^- now zooms over...

...and bonds to the other C atom, forming 1, 2-dibromoethane

A carbocation is an organic ion containing a positively charged carbon atom.

A **curly arrow** shows the **movement** of a **pair of electrons**. It starts from an electron pair — a **covalent bond** or a **lone pair**.

If you add some Cl^- ions to an ethene and bromine mixture, you'll also get some CH_2BrCH_2Cl.
This is evidence for the suggested mechanism — once the the ethene has reacted with bromine to form the **carbocation**
(**positively** charged), it can react with **either** another **bromide ion or** a **chloride ion** (**negatively** charged).

Use Bromine Water *to Test for* C=C *Double Bonds*

1) When you shake an alkene with **orange bromine water**, the solution **decolourises**.
   This happens because the bromine molecules add across the double bonds
   to make colourless dibromoalkanes.

2) You can use this reaction as a **test** for **C=C double bonds**.

bromine water + alkene

SHAKE

solution goes colourless

Edexcel only — actually that isn't quite the whole story...

Bromine water is a **dilute solution** — it contains more **water molecules** than bromine atoms. The **carbocation** is
more likely to react with H_2O than Br^- — so an **OH** group will add to the second carbon rather than another Br atom.
This means that the product of the reaction between an alkene and bromine water is mostly **bromoalcohol**.
The result of the test doesn't change — the bromine water is still decolourised if there are C=C bonds present.

bromoethanol

Adding Hydrogen Halides *to* Unsymmetrical Alkenes *Forms* Two Products

1) Alkenes also undergo **electrophilic addition** reactions with HBr, to form **bromoalkanes**.

2) If the HBr adds to an **unsymmetrical** alkene, like propene, there are two possible products. The amount
   of each product formed depends on how **stable** the **carbocation** formed in the middle of the reaction is.

3) Carbocations with more **alkyl groups** are more stable, because the alkyl groups feed **electrons** towards the
   positive charge. The **more stable carbocation**
   is much more likely to form.

Alkyl groups are alkanes with a hydrogen removed, e.g. methyl, CH_3.

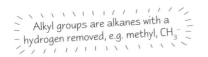

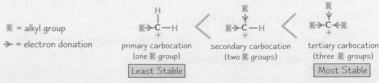

R = alkyl group
→ = electron donation

primary carbocation (one R group)
Least Stable

secondary carbocation (two R groups)

tertiary carbocation (three R groups)
Most Stable

Here's how hydrogen bromide reacts with propene:

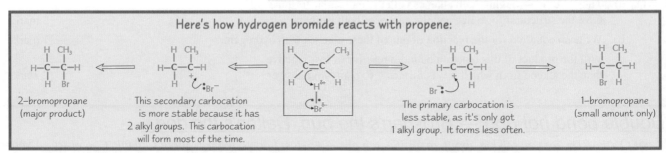

2-bromopropane (major product)

This secondary carbocation is more stable because it has 2 alkyl groups. This carbocation will form most of the time.

The primary carbocation is less stable, as it's only got 1 alkyl group. It forms less often.

1-bromopropane (small amount only)

4) If you do this reaction in the lab, you do get **mostly** 2-bromopropane, and just **a little** 1-bromopropane.

Reactions of Alkenes

Reacting Alkenes with *Water* and an H_2SO_4 Catalyst Makes *Alcohols*   *AQA and OCR B*

1) Cold concentrated **sulfuric acid** reacts with an alkene in an **electrophilic addition** reaction.

$$H_2C=CH_2 \ + \ H_2SO_4 \longrightarrow CH_3CH_2OSO_2OH$$
ethene   sulfuric acid   ethyl hydrogen sulfate

> Hydrolysis is the breaking of covalent bonds by reaction with water.

2) If you then add cold **water** and warm the product, it's **hydrolysed** to form an alcohol.

$$CH_3CH_2OSO_2OH \ + \ H_2O \longrightarrow CH_3CH_2OH \ + \ H_2SO_4$$
ethyl hydrogen sulfate   ethanol

3) The **sulfuric acid** isn't used up — it acts as a **catalyst**.

Ethanol is Manufactured by *Steam Hydration*   *Not Edexcel*

1) Ethene can be **hydrated** by **steam** at 300 °C and a pressure of 60 atm. It needs a solid **phosphoric(V) acid catalyst**.

2) The reaction's **reversible** and the reaction yield is low — only about 5%. This sounds rubbish, but you can **recycle** the unreacted ethene gas, making the overall yield a much more profitable **95%**.

$$H_2C=CH_{2(g)} + H_2O_{(g)} \underset{\substack{300\ °C \\ 60\ atm}}{\overset{H_3PO_4}{\rightleftharpoons}} CH_3CH_2OH_{(g)}$$

Alkenes are *Oxidised* by *Acidified Potassium Manganate(VII)*   *Edexcel only*

If you shake an alkene with **acidified potassium manganate(VII)**, the purple solution is decolourised. You've **oxidised** the alkene and made a diol (an alcohol with two -OH groups).

This is another useful **test** for a double C=C bond.

Here's how **ethene** reacts with acidified potassium manganate(VII) ⟶

[O] is often used to show an oxidising agent in an organic equation.

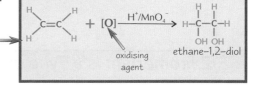
ethane-1,2-diol
oxidising agent

Practice Questions

Q1 In a mechanism diagram, what does a curly arrow show?

Q2 Which is the most stable kind of carbocation?

Q3 What colour change do you see when you shake acidified potassium manganate(VII) solution with an alkene?

Q4 Name the catalyst used in the reaction between ethene and steam to produce ethanol.

Exam Question

Q1 But-1-ene is an alkene. Alkenes contain at least one C=C double bond.

    a) Describe how bromine water can be used to test for C=C double bonds.   [2 marks]

    b) Name the reaction mechanism involved in the above test.   [2 marks]

    c) Hydrogen bromide will react with but-1-ene by this mechanism, producing two isomeric products.

      (i) Write a mechanism for the reaction of HBr with $CH_2=CHCH_2CH_3$, showing the formation of the major product only. Name the product.   [3 marks]

      (ii) Explain why it is the major product for this reaction.   [2 marks]

This section is free from all GM ingredients...

Wow... these pages really are jam-packed. There's not one, not two, but three mechanisms to learn. And learn them you must. Get the book shut and scribble them out. Make sure you know the tests for double bonds too. They mightn't be as handy in real life as, say, a tin opener, but you won't need a tin opener in the exam. Unless your exam paper comes in a tin.

E/Z Isomerism

The chemistry on these pages isn't so bad. And don't be too worried when I tell you that a good working knowledge of both German and Latin would be useful. It's not absolutely essential... and you'll be fine without.
These pages are for AQA (Unit 2), OCR A (Unit 2), OCR B (Unit 2) and Edexcel (Unit 1).

Double Bonds Can't Rotate

1) Carbon atoms in a C=C double bond and the atoms bonded to these carbons all lie in the **same plane** (they're **planar**).
Because of the way they're arranged, they're actually said to be **trigonal planar** — the atoms attached to each double-bond carbon are at the corners of an imaginary equilateral triangle.

The bond angles in the planar unit are all 120°.

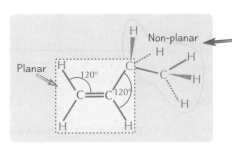

2) Ethene, **C₂H₄** (like in the diagram above) is completely planar, but in larger alkenes, only the >C=C< unit is planar.

3) Another important thing about C=C double bonds is that atoms **can't rotate** around around them like they can around single bonds (because of the way the p orbitals **overlap** to form a π **bond** — see p40).
In fact, double bonds are fairly **rigid** — they don't bend much either.

4) Even though atoms can't rotate about the **double bond**, things can still still rotate about any **single bonds** in the molecule — like in this molecule of pent-2-ene.

5) The **restricted rotation** around the C=C double bond is what causes **E/Z isomerism**.

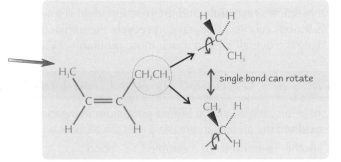

single bond can rotate

E/Z isomerism is a Type of Stereoisomerism

1) **Stereoisomers** have the same structural formula but a **different arrangement** in space.
(Just bear with me for a moment... that will become clearer, I promise.)

2) Because of the **lack of rotation** around the double bond, some **alkenes** can have stereoisomers.

3) Stereoisomers happen when the two double-bonded carbon atoms each have **different atoms** or **groups** attached to them. Then you get an '**E-isomer**' and a '**Z-isomer**'.

For example, the double-bonded carbon atoms in but-2-ene each have an **H** and a **CH₃** group attached.

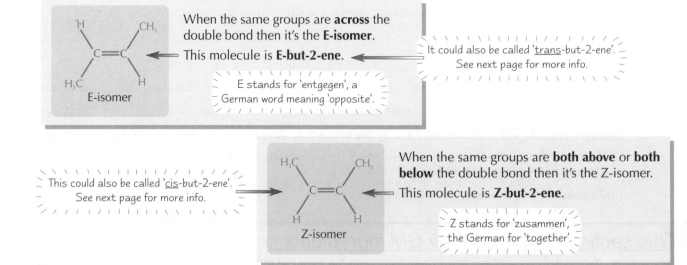

When the same groups are **across** the double bond then it's the **E-isomer**.
This molecule is **E-but-2-ene**.

It could also be called 'trans-but-2-ene'. See next page for more info.

E stands for 'entgegen', a German word meaning 'opposite'.

This could also be called 'cis-but-2-ene'. See next page for more info.

When the same groups are **both above** or **both below** the double bond then it's the Z-isomer.
This molecule is **Z-but-2-ene**.

Z stands for 'zusammen', the German for 'together'.

E/Z Isomerism

E/Z Isomers Can Sometimes Be Called Cis-Trans Isomers

1) E/Z isomerism is sometimes called **cis-trans isomerism**, where...
   (i) 'cis' means the **Z-isomer**, and
   (ii) 'trans' means the **E-isomer**.

   So E-but-2-ene can be called trans-but-2-ene, and Z-but-2-ene can be called cis-but-2-ene.

   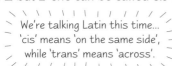
   We're talking Latin this time...
   'cis' means 'on the same side',
   while 'trans' means 'across'.

   Here's another example:
   The **Br** atom and the **CH₃** group are on **opposite** sides of the double bond, so this is **trans-1-bromopropene**.
   No problems there.

   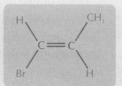

2) But if the carbon atoms each have totally **different** groups attached to them, the cis-trans naming system can't cope.

   Oh dear. This could be **trans-1-bromo-1-fluoropropene**, because the **Br** and **CH₃** are on **opposite** sides, or it could be **cis-1-bromo-1-fluoropropene**, because the **F** and **CH₃** are on the same side...

   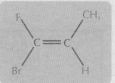

3) The E/Z system keeps on working though. This is because each of the groups linked to the double-bonded carbons is given a **priority**.

   If the two carbon atoms have their 'higher priority group' on **opposite** sides, then it's an **E isomer**.
   If the two carbon atoms have their 'higher priority group' on the **same** side, then it's a **Z isomer**.

   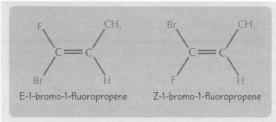
   E-1-bromo-1-fluoropropene   Z-1-bromo-1-fluoropropene

4) In the E/Z system, Br has a **higher priority** than F, so the names depend on where the Br atom is in relation to the CH₃ group.

   You don't need to know the rules for deciding the order of these priorities.

Practice Questions

Q1 Which of the following is the Z-isomer of but-2-ene?

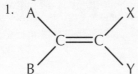

Q2 Define the term 'stereoisomers'.

Q3 Which corresponds to the 'cis-isomer,' the E-isomer or Z-isomer?

Exam Questions

Q1 a) Draw and name the E/Z isomers of pent-2-ene. [4 marks]
   b) Explain why alkenes can have E/Z isomers but alkanes cannot. [2 marks]

Q2 An alkene has 4 different groups attached: A, B, X and Y.
   Which of the following is the E-isomer if A and X have priority?

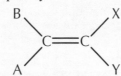

[1 mark]

And there you have it, folks — two E/Z pages in an AS Chemistry book...

Cis and trans are fairly easy to remember... 'cis' — think of sisters standing next to each other, while 'trans' means 'across' in things like transmit, transfer, and the Trans-Siberian Railway. And for E/Z isomers, remember that Z-isomers are the ones with the groups on 'ze zame zide'. Or if you prefer, you could learn to speak German...

Polymers

Polymers are long stringy molecules made by joining lots of little molecules together.
These pages are for AQA (Unit 2), OCR A (Unit 2), OCR B (Unit 2) and Edexcel (Unit 1).

Alkenes *Join Up* to form *Addition Polymers*

1) The **double bonds** in alkenes can open up and join together to make long chains called **polymers**.
   It's kind of like they're holding hands in a big line. The individual, small alkenes are called **monomers**.

2) This is called **addition polymerisation**.
   For example, **poly(ethene)** is made by
   the **addition polymerisation** of **ethene**.

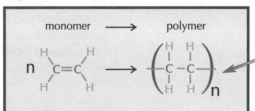

The bit in brackets is the 'repeat unit' (or 'repeating unit'). n represents the number of repeat units.

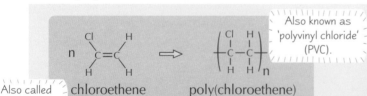

polymer
(polypropene)   repeat unit   monomer
                                        (propene)

3) To find the **monomer** used to form an
   addition polymer, take the **repeat unit**
   and add a **double bond**.

4) Because of the loss of the double bond, poly(alkenes), like alkanes, are **unreactive**.

5) **Copolymers** are made from more than one type of
   monomer — they join together in a **random** order.

   $nA + mB \longrightarrow -A-A-B-B-B-A-B-A-A-B-A-A-B-A-A-B-B-$

   For example, ethene can be combined with propene to produce a polymer
   with different properties from either poly(ethene) or poly(propene).

Different Alkenes give Polymers with Different Properties   *Not Edexcel*

1) Different polymer **structures** have different **properties**,
   which means they're suited to different **uses**.

   Some typical uses of **poly(ethene)** and **poly(propene)**
   are shown in the table.

	Properties	Uses
Low density poly(ethene)	Soft Flexible	Plastic bags Squeezy bottles
Poly(propene)	Tough Strong	Bottle crates Rope

2) You can polymerise molecules other than basic alkenes:

   Also known as 'polyvinyl chloride' (PVC).

   Also called 'vinyl chloride'.

   chloroethene   poly(chloroethene)   tetrafluoroethene   poly(tetrafluoroethene)
                                                                          (PTFE)

   Also known as Teflon®

   Poly(chloroethene) is **durable** and **flexible**.
   It has a wide range of uses — for example,
   it's used to make water pipes, for insulation
   on electric wires and as a building material.

   Poly(tetrafluoroethene) is chemically **inert** and
   has **non-stick** properties.
   This makes it ideal as a coating for frying pans.

3) Other examples of useful polymers are:

   Poly(phenylethene) — also known as **polystyrene**.
   It's cheap, and can be made into **expanded polystyrene**, which is light and a good **insulator**.
   This means it's good for making things like disposable cups.

   Poly(methyl-2-methylpropenoate) — also known as **Perspex®**.
   This is transparent and pretty strong, so it can be used in place of glass for certain applications.

Polymers

Hydrogen Bonding *Means Some Polymers* Dissolve in Water
OCR B only

1) A substance will **dissolve** in water if the molecules of the substance are able to form **bonds** with the water molecules instead of with each other (see p116).

2) Polymers that have -OH groups can form **hydrogen bonds** (p51) with water molecules. But the polymer molecules also bond to **each other** by hydrogen bonds.

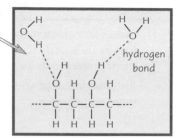

   • If the polymer has **loads** of -OH groups, the hydrogen bonding between its molecules will be very **strong** — meaning too much energy is needed to break it down. The polymer will be **insoluble**.

   • If the polymer has **very few** -OH groups, then there won't be many hydrogen bonds formed with water molecules — and the polymer will also be **insoluble**.

   • For a polymer to be **soluble**, you need something in between — not too many hydrogen bonds, and not too few.

Cross-Linking *Affects how Polymers Behave when they're* Heated
OCR B only

Thermoplastic polymers, like poly(ethene), don't have cross-linking between chains. It's only **weak intermolecular forces** that hold the chains together. These forces are really easy to overcome, so it's dead easy to **melt** the plastic. When it **cools**, the thermoplastic hardens into a new shape. You can melt these plastics and **remould** them as many times as you like.

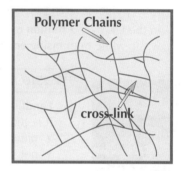

Thermosetting polymers, like bakelite, have **covalent cross-links**. These hold the chains together in a **3D giant covalent structure**. The polymer doesn't soften when it's heated — but too much heat makes it **burn**. Thermosetting polymers are the **tough guys** of the plastic world. They're **strong**, **hard**, **rigid** and **insoluble**.

Practice Questions

Q1 Explain what is meant by the term 'copolymer'.

Q2 Give a typical use for poly(ethene) and for poly(propene).

Q3 Why can thermoplastic polymers be melted easily but thermosetting polymers can't?

Exam Questions

Q1 Part of the structure of a polymer is shown on the right.
   a) Draw the repeating unit of the polymer. [1 mark]
   b) Draw the monomer from which the polymer was formed. [1 mark]

Q2 Poly(ethanol) has the repeating unit shown on the right.
   a) Draw part of the polymer consisting of three of the repeating units. [1 mark]
   b) Poly(ethanol) is water soluble.
      Describe, in terms of intermolecular forces, what happens when it dissolves in water. [2 marks]
   c) Explain why a polymer with many more -OH groups than poly(ethanol) would not dissolve in water. [2 marks]

Q3 The chains of polymer A form covalent cross-links with each other.
   The chains of polymer B do not form cross-links, and are held together by van der Waals forces.
   Predict TWO differences in the physical properties of polymers A and B that may result from this. [2 marks]

Barbie plastic surgery — gas mark 4, 20 minutes...

You can have hours of fun melting stuff — chocolate, cheese, CDs, candles, crayons, laundry baskets... you're only limited by your imagination. The potential for setting stuff on fire is a bit of a problem though, and some things'll give off nasty fumes. So maybe you'd better find yourself a different pastime instead. Like learning AS Chemistry. That'll keep you busy.

More About Polymers

Polymers are amazingly useful. But they have one big drawback...
These pages are for AQA (Unit 2), OCR A (Unit 2) and Edexcel (Unit 1).

Polymers — *Useful* but Difficult to *Get Rid Of*

1) Synthetic polymers have loads of **advantages**, so they're incredibly widespread these days — we take them pretty much for granted.

   Just imagine what you'd have to live without if there were no polymers...

   (Okay... I could live without the polystyrene head, but the rest of this stuff is pretty useful.)

2) One of the really useful things about many everyday polymers is that they're very **unreactive**. This means food doesn't react with the PTFE coating on pans, plastic windows don't rot, plastic crates can be left out in the rain and they'll be okay, and so on.

3) But this **lack** of reactivity also leads to a **problem**. Most polymers aren't **biodegradable**, and so they're really difficult to **dispose of**.

4) In the UK over **2 million** tonnes of plastic waste are produced each year. It's important to find ways to get rid of this waste while minimising **environmental damage**. There are various possible approaches...

Waste Plastics can be *Buried*

1) **Landfill** is one option for dealing with waste plastics. It is generally used when the plastic is:
   - difficult to separate from other waste,
   - not in sufficient quantities to make separation financially worthwhile,
   - too difficult technically to recycle.

   Landfill means taking waste to a landfill site, compacting it, and then covering it with soil.

2) But because the **amount of waste** we generate is becoming more and more of a problem, there's a need to **reduce** landfill as much as possible.

Waste Plastics can be *Recycled*

Because many plastics are made from non-renewable **oil-fractions**, it makes sense to recycle plastics as much as possible.

There's more than one way to recycle plastics. After **sorting** into different types:

- some plastics (poly(propene), for example) can be **melted** and **remoulded**,
- some plastics can be **cracked** into **monomers**, and these can be use to make more plastics or other chemicals.

Plastic products are usually marked to make sorting easier. The different numbers show different polymers e.g.

$\triangle_3 \triangle$ = PVC,   and $\triangle_5 \triangle$ = poly(propene)

Flowchart:
Waste plastics → burying in landfill
Waste plastics → burning as fuel (see below)
Waste plastics → sorting → cracking → processing → other chemicals / new plastics
sorting → remoulding → new objects

Waste Plastics can be *Burned*

Rex and Dirk enjoy some waist plastic.

1) If recycling isn't possible for whatever reason, waste plastics can be burned — and the heat can be used to generate **electricity**.

2) This process needs to be carefully **controlled** to reduce **toxic** gases. For example, polymers that contain **chlorine** (such as **PVC**) produce **HCl** when they're burned — this has to be removed.

3) Waste gases from the combustion are passed through **scrubbers** which can **neutralise** gases such as HCl by allowing them to react with a **base**.

More About Polymers

Biodegradable Polymers Decompose in the Right Conditions   Not AQA

Scientists can now make **biodegradable** polymers — ones that naturally **decompose**.

1) **Biodegradable polymers** decompose pretty quickly in certain conditions — because organisms can digest them.
   (You might get asked about 'compostable' polymers as well as 'biodegradable' ones. These two terms mean more or less the same thing — 'compostable' just means it has to decay fairly quickly, "at the speed of compost".)

2) Biodegradable polymers can be made from materials such as **starch** (from maize and other plants) and from the hydrocarbon **isoprene** (2-methyl-1,3-butadiene). So, biodegradable polymers can be produced from **renewable** raw materials or from **oil fractions**:

   > Using **renewable** raw material has several **advantages**.
   >
   > (i) Raw materials aren't going to **run out** like oil will.
   >
   > (ii) When polymers biodegrade, **carbon dioxide** (a greenhouse gas — see p146) is produced. If your polymer is **plant-based**, then the CO_2 released as it decomposes is the same CO_2 absorbed by the plant when it grew. But with an **oil-based** biodegradable polymer, you're effectively transferring carbon from the oil to the atmosphere.
   >
   > (iii) Over their 'lifetime' some plant-based polymers **save energy** compared to oil-based plastics.

   But whatever raw material you use, at the moment the energy for making polymers usually comes from fossil fuels.

3) Even though they're biodegradable, these polymers still need the right conditions before they'll decompose. You **couldn't** necessarily just put them in a landfill and expect them to perish away — because there's a lack of moisture and oxygen under all that compressed soil. You need to chuck them on a big compost heap. This means that you still need to **collect** and **separate** the biodegradable polymers from non-biodegradable plastics. At the moment, they're also **more expensive** than oil-based equivalents.

4) There are various potential uses — e.g. plastic sheeting used to protect plants from the frost can be made from poly(ethene) with **starch grains** embedded in it. In time the starch is broken down by **microorganisms** and the remaining poly(ethene) crumbles into dust. There's no need to collect and dispose of the old sheeting.

Practice Questions

Q1 Many plastics are unreactive. Describe one benefit and one disadvantage of this.

Q2 Which harmful gas is produced during the combustion of PVC?

Q3 Describe three ways in which waste polymers such as poly(propene) can be dealt with.

Q4 Give two potential benefits of starch-based polymers over oil-based equivalents.

Exam Questions

Q1 Waste plastics can be disposed of by burning.
   a) Describe one advantage of disposing of waste plastics by burning. [1 mark]
   b) Describe a disadvantage of burning waste plastic that contains chlorine, and explain how the impact of this disadvantage could be reduced. [2 marks]

Q2 Describe one way in which waste poly(propene) could be recycled into new plastic objects. [2 marks]

Q3 Apart from being biodegradable, describe TWO benefits of using starch- or maize-based polymers instead of oil-based polymers. [2 marks]

Phil's my recycled plastic plane — but I don't know where to land Phil...

You might have noticed that all this recycling business is a hot topic these days. And not just in the usual places, such as Chemistry books. No, no, no... recycling even makes it regularly onto the news as well. This suits examiners just fine — they like you to know how useful and important chemistry is. So learn this stuff, pass your exam, and do some recycling.

Alcohols

Alcohol — evil stuff, it is. I could start preaching, but I won't, because this page is enough to put you off alcohol for life...
These pages are for AQA (Unit 2), OCR A (Unit 2), OCR B (Unit 2) and Edexcel (Unit 2).

Alcohols can be Primary, Secondary or Tertiary

1) The alcohol homologous series has the **general formula** $C_nH_{2n+1}OH$.

2) An alcohol is **primary**, **secondary** or **tertiary**, depending on which carbon atom the hydroxyl group **–OH** is bonded to...

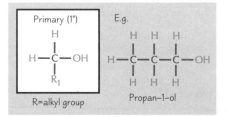

R=alkyl group Propan–1–ol

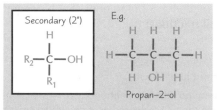

Propan–2–ol

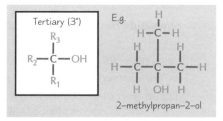

2–methylpropan–2–ol

The Hydroxyl Group –OH can form Hydrogen Bonds   *Not AQA*

The **polar –OH** group on alcohols helps them to form **hydrogen bonds** (see p51), which gives them certain properties...

1) Hydrogen bonding is the **strongest** kind of intermolecular force, so it gives alcohols **high boiling points** compared to non-polar compounds, e.g. alkanes of similar sizes.

You might also hear it said that alcohols have relatively low volatility. Volatility is the tendency of something to evaporate into a gas.

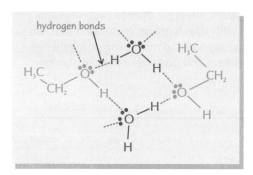

hydrogen bonds

2) When you mix an alcohol with water, hydrogen bonds can also form between the **–OH** and **H_2O**.

3) If it's a **small** alcohol (e.g. methanol, ethanol or propan-1-ol), hydrogen bonding lets it mix freely with water — it's **miscible** with water.

4) In **larger alcohols**, most of the molecule is a non-polar carbon chain, so there's less attraction for the polar H_2O molecules. This means that as alcohols **increase in size**, their miscibility in water **decreases.**

5) Small alcohols are also miscible in some **non-polar solvents** like cyclohexane.

Ethanol can be Produced Industrially by Fermentation   *Not OCR B or Edexcel*

At the moment most industrial ethanol is produced by **steam hydration of ethene** with a **phosphoric acid catalyst** (see page 111). The ethene comes from cracking heavy fractions of crude oil. But in the future, when crude oil supplies start **running out**, petrochemicals like ethene will be expensive — so producing ethanol by **fermentation** will become much more important...

Industrial Production of Ethanol by Fermentation

1) Fermentation is an **exothermic** process, carried out by **yeast** in **anaerobic conditions** (without oxygen).

2) Yeast produces an **enzyme** which converts sugars, such as glucose, into **ethanol** and **carbon dioxide**.

3) The enzyme works at an **optimum** (ideal) temperature of **30-40 °C**. If it's too cold, the reaction is **slow** — if it's too hot, the enzyme is **denatured** (damaged).

4) When the solution reaches about **15% ethanol**, the yeast dies. **Fractional distillation** is used to increase the concentration of ethanol.

5) Fermentation is **low-tech** — it uses cheap equipment and **renewable resources**. The ethanol produced by this method has to be **purified** though.

$$C_6H_{12}O_{6\,(aq)} \xrightarrow[\text{yeast}]{30\text{-}40\,°C} 2C_2H_5OH_{(aq)} + 2CO_{2\,(g)}$$

glucose

Rate of reaction

0   Optimum temperature   50   Temperature °C

Alcohols

Ethanol can also be Produced Industrially by **Hydration of Ethene**

Not OCR B or Edexcel

1) Ethene reacts with **steam** at **high temperature** (300 °C) and **high pressure**, in the presence of a **phosphoric acid catalyst**, to form ethanol (see p121).

$$CH_2=CH_2 + H_2O \rightleftharpoons C_2H_5OH$$

See p152 for more about batch and continuous processes.

2) Both methods for making ethanol have their **pros** and **cons**.

Method	Rate of reaction	Quality of product	Raw material	Process/Costs
Hydration of ethene	Very fast	Pure	Ethene from oil — a finite resource	Continuous process, so expensive equipment needed, but low labour costs.
Fermentation	Very slow	Very impure — needs further processing	Sugars — a renewable resource	Batch process, so cheap equipment needed, but high labour costs.

Alcohols Have a **Wide Variety** of Uses

1) **Ethanol** is the alcohol found in **alcoholic drinks**.

2) **Methylated spirits** is an important **solvent**. It's basically ethanol, with some toxic methanol and purple dye added to make it **undrinkable** and tax-exempt (sneaky). Ethanol will dissolve **polar**, **non-polar** and some **ionic compounds**.

3) Methanol is important as a **feedstock** (starting point) for manufacturing organic chemicals, e.g. plastics and dyes.

4) **Unleaded petrol** contains 5% methanol and 15% MTBE (an ether made using methanol) to improve combustion.

5) Ethanol is also being used increasingly as a **fuel**, particularly in countries with few oil reserves. E.g. in Brazil, **sugars** from sugar cane are **fermented** to produce alcohol, which is a **biofuel** added to petrol. (See p85 for an explanation of why bioethanol is regarded as a carbon neutral biofuel.)

Practice Questions

Q1 What is the general formula for an alcohol?

Q2 How do the boiling points of alcohols compare with the boiling points of similarly-sized alkanes?

Q3 Explain why $C_6H_{13}OH$ is less soluble in water than ethanol, C_2H_5OH.

Q4 Give two examples of how alcohol is used as fuel.

Exam Questions

Q1 Butanol C_4H_9OH has four chain and positional isomers. Name each isomer and class it as primary, secondary or tertiary. [8 marks]

Q2 Ethanol is a useful alcohol.
   a) State whether ethanol is a primary, secondary or tertiary alcohol, and explain why. [2 marks]
   b) Industrially, ethanol can be produced by fermentation of glucose, $C_6H_{12}O_6$.
      (i) Write a balanced equation for this reaction. [1 mark]
      (ii) State the optimum conditions for fermentation. [3 marks]
   c) At present most ethanol is produced by the acid-catalysed hydration of ethene. Why is this? Why might this change in the future? [3 marks]
   d) Ethanol is an important solvent. Explain why this is, with reference to the structure and intermolecular forces in ethanol. [4 marks]
   e) Describe the advantages of producing ethanol by fermentation instead of by hydration of ethene. [2 marks]

Euuurghh, what a page... I think I need a drink...

Not much to learn here — a few basic definitions, some fiddly explanations of properties in terms of bonding, an industrial process, the advantages and disadvantages of it compared to another industrial process, 4 or 5 uses... Like I said, not much here at all. Think I'm going to faint. [THWACK]

Reactions of Alcohols

Another page about alcohols — jam-packed tighter than 25 elephants in a tube of Smarties.
These pages are for AQA (Unit 2), OCR A (Unit 2), OCR B (Unit 2) and Edexcel (Unit 2).

–OH can be Swapped for a Halogen to make a Haloalkane   *OCR B and Edexcel only*

1) **Alcohols** are a good starting point for making haloalkanes. You need to replace the alcohol's **-OH** group with a **halogen**.

2) **Tertiary** alcohols are more **reactive** than either primary or secondary alcohols, so it's easiest to start with one of these.

3) To make a **chloroalkane** you can just shake a tertiary alcohol with hydrochloric acid. This gives you an impure chloroalkane, which you can purify using the method shown on p140.

4) **Primary** and **secondary** alcohols react **too slowly** to be made this way. You need to use the phosphorus(III) halide method below.

Haloalkanes are just alkanes that have halogens in place of one or more of their hydrogens (see p134).

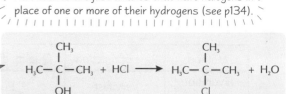

$$H_3C-\underset{\underset{OH}{|}}{\overset{\overset{CH_3}{|}}{C}}-CH_3 + HCl \longrightarrow H_3C-\underset{\underset{Cl}{|}}{\overset{\overset{CH_3}{|}}{C}}-CH_3 + H_2O$$

tertiary alcohol
(2-methylpropan-2-ol)

haloalkane
(2-chloro-2-methylpropane)

Edexcel only:

Bromoalkanes and **iodoalkanes** are a bit trickier to make than chloroalkanes — HBr and HI aren't always available 'off the shelf'. Some books suggest using concentrated H_2SO_4 and a **metal halide** (e.g. KBr or KI) to produce HBr or HI 'in situ' (i.e. during the reaction process itself).

The drawback is that HBr and HI are both oxidised by the H_2SO_4, so you end up with by-products (Br_2 and I_2) and a reduced yield of haloalkane. You get so little iodoalkane that it's better to use **phosphoric(V) acid** instead of sulfuric.

You Can Make Haloalkanes Using Phosphorus(III) Halides Too   *Edexcel only*

1) This is the general equation: $3ROH + PX_3 \rightarrow 3RX + H_3PO_3$ X represents Cl, Br or I.

2) It's straightforward to make a **chloroalkane** by reacting an alcohol with PCl_3. But, PBr_3 and PI_3 are usually made **in situ** by refluxing the alcohol with 'red phosphorus' and either bromine or iodine.

Chloroalkanes can Also be Made Using Phosphorus(V) Chloride

Here's the equation: $ROH_{(l)} + PCl_{5(l)} \rightarrow RCl_{(l)} + HCl_{(g)} + POCl_{3(l)}$

This reaction's used to **test** for alcohols...

Test for the Hydroxyl Group (–OH)
Add **phosphorus(V) chloride** to the unknown liquid.
If -OH is present, you'll get **steamy fumes** of HCl gas, which turn moist **blue litmus red** (because HCl dissolves to form a strong acid).

Here are a Few More Alcohol Reactions to Learn

Sodium Reacts with Alcohols to Produce Alkoxides   *Edexcel only*

$$2CH_3CH_2OH + 2Na \rightarrow 2CH_3CH_2O^-Na^+ + H_2$$

1) **Sodium metal** reacts gently with **ethanol**, breaking the **O–H** bonds to produce ionic sodium ethoxide and hydrogen.

2) The longer the **hydrocarbon chain** of the alcohol gets, the **less** reactive it is with sodium.

Reacting a Carboxylic Acid with Ethanol Produces an Ester   *OCR A only*

This stuff smells of pear drops — aliphatic esters generally smell fruity.

1) If you warm **ethanol** with a **carboxylic acid** (like ethanoic acid) and a **strong acid catalyst** (concentrated sulfuric acid will do), it forms an ester (**ethyl ethanoate** in this case).

2) The **O–H** bond in ethanol is broken in the **esterification** reaction.

$$C_2H_5OH + CH_3COOH \rightleftharpoons CH_3C\overset{\displaystyle O}{\underset{\displaystyle O-CH_2CH_3}{\big<}} + H_2O$$

Reactions of Alcohols

Alcohols can be **Dehydrated** to Form **Alkenes**   *Not Edexcel*

1) You can make ethene by **eliminating** water from **ethanol** in a **dehydration reaction** (i.e. elimination of **water**).

$$C_2H_5OH \longrightarrow CH_2=CH_2 + H_2O$$

In an elimination reaction, a small group of atoms breaks away from a larger molecule. It's not replaced by anything else.

There are two ways to go about it:

Dehydrating Alcohols to form Alkenes

Method 1: **Reflux** (see p140) ethanol with **concentrated sulfuric acid**.

The reaction occurs in two stages:

This is the reverse of the hydrolysis reaction on p121.

$$C_2H_5OH + H_2SO_4 \longrightarrow C_2H_5OSO_2OH + H_2O$$
$$C_2H_5OSO_2OH \longrightarrow CH_2=CH_2 + H_2SO_4$$

The H_2SO_4 is unchanged at the end of the reaction, so it's acted as a catalyst. Phosphoric acid (H_3PO_4) can also be used as a catalyst for this reaction.

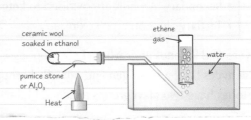

Reflux Apparatus — water out, water in, Ethanol and concentrated H_2SO_4, heat

Method 2:
(OCR B only) Ethanol vapour is passed over a hot catalyst of pumice stone or aluminium oxide, Al_2O_3 — the catalyst provides a large surface area for the reaction.

ceramic wool soaked in ethanol, pumice stone or Al_2O_3, Heat, ethene gas, water

2) These methods allows you to produce alkenes from **renewable** resources.

Remember... you can produce ethanol by fermentation of glucose, which you can get from plants (see p128-129).

3) This is important, because it means that you can produce **polymers** (poly(ethene), for example) **without** needing **oil**.

Practice Questions

Q1 Describe two reactions that can be used to produce a chloroalkane.

Q2 What do you get if you react an alcohol with a carboxylic acid?

Q3 What is the purpose of the H_2SO_4 in the elimination reaction that forms ethene from ethanol?

Q4 Describe how poly(ethene) can be obtained without having to use oil fractions.

Exam Questions

Q1 Ethanol undergoes various chemical reactions.
Fill in the missing products in the diagram below:

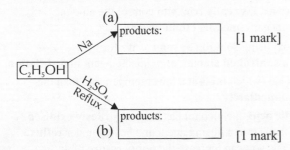

(a) products: [ ] [1 mark]

C_2H_5OH — Na, H_2SO_4 Reflux

(b) products: [ ] [1 mark]

Q2 Chloroalkanes can be made by reacting ethanol with phosphorus(V) chloride.

a) Write a balanced equation for this reaction. [2 marks]

b) Phosphorus(V) chloride is used to test for the presence of hydroxyl groups.
What would you observe happening if hydroxyl groups were present? [2 marks]

Carboxylic acid + ethanol produces Ester — well, that's life...

Oh, my goodness me... these alcohol reaction blighters are a bit of a pain, aren't they... but don't get stressed about them. Just read them really carefully, and do your best to get them in your head. Then, shut the book and try and scribble them out from memory. Then check you've got them right. It's the only way to really lock them in your brain...

Oxidation of Alcohols

Another page of alcohol reactions. Probably not what you wanted but at least it's the last one.
And you're getting closer to the end of the book... and your wits, probably.
These pages are for AQA (Unit 2), OCR A (Unit 2), OCR B (Units 1 and 2) and Edexcel (Unit 2).

The Simple way to Oxidise Alcohols is to **Burn Them** | *OCR B (Unit 1), OCR A and Edexcel*

It doesn't take much to set ethanol alight and it burns with a **pale blue flame**. The C–C and C–H bonds are broken as the ethanol is **completely oxidised** to make carbon dioxide and water. This is a **combustion** reaction.

$$C_2H_5OH_{(l)} + 3O_{2(g)} \rightarrow 2CO_{2(g)} + 3H_2O_{(g)}$$

But you don't get the most exciting products by doing this. If you want to end up with something more interesting at the end, you need a more sophisticated way of oxidising...

How Much an Alcohol can be **Oxidised** Depends on its **Structure** | *Not OCR B (Unit 1)*

You can use the **oxidising agent acidified potassium dichromate(VI)** to **mildly** oxidise alcohols.

- **Primary** alcohols are oxidised to **aldehydes** and then to **carboxylic acids**.
- **Secondary** alcohols are oxidised to **ketones** only.
- **Tertiary** alcohols aren't oxidised.

The orange dichromate(VI) ion is reduced to the green chromium(III) ion, Cr^{3+}.

Aldehydes and **ketones** are **carbonyl** compounds — they have the functional group C=O. Their general formula is $C_nH_{2n}O$.

1) **Aldehydes** have a **hydrogen** and **one alkyl group** attached to the carbonyl carbon atom. E.g.
2) **Ketones** have **two alkyl groups** attached to the carbonyl carbon atom.

propanone
CH_3COCH_3

propanal
CH_3CH_2CHO

Primary Alcohols will Oxidise to **Aldehydes** and **Carboxylic Acids** | *Not OCR B (Unit 1)*

[O] = oxidising agent

$R-CH_2-OH + [O] \longrightarrow R-C\overset{O}{\underset{H}{\big\langle}} + [O] \xrightarrow{reflux} R-C\overset{O}{\underset{OH}{\big\langle}}$
$+ H_2O$

primary alcohol   aldehyde   carboxylic acid

You can control how **far** the alcohol is oxidised by controlling the **reaction conditions**:

Oxidising Primary Alcohols

1) Gently heating ethanol with potassium dichromate(VI) solution and sulfuric acid in a test tube should produce "apple" smelling **ethanal** (an aldehyde). However, it's **really tricky** to control the amount of heat and the aldehyde is usually oxidised to form "vinegar" smelling **ethanoic acid**.

2) To get just the **aldehyde**, you need to get it out of the oxidising solution **as soon** as it's formed. You can do this by gently heating excess alcohol with a **controlled** amount of oxidising agent in **distillation apparatus**, so the aldehyde (which boils at a lower temperature than the alcohol) is distilled off **immediately**.

Reflux Apparatus
water out
Liebig condenser
water in
round bottomed flask
anti-bumping granules (added to make boiling smoother)
heat

3) To produce the **carboxylic acid**, the alcohol has to be **vigorously oxidised**. The alcohol is mixed with excess oxidising agent and heated under **reflux**. Heating under reflux means you can increase the **temperature** of an organic reaction to boiling without losing **volatile** solvents, reactants or products. Any vaporised compounds are cooled, condense and drip back into the reaction mixture. Handy, hey.

See page 140 for more on distillation and reflux.

Oxidation of Alcohols

Secondary Alcohols will Oxidise to **Ketones** — *Not OCR B (Unit 1)*

$$R_1 - \underset{\underset{R_2}{|}}{\overset{\overset{H}{|}}{C}} - OH + [O] \xrightarrow{\text{reflux}} \overset{R_1}{\underset{R_2}{>}}C=O + H_2O$$

1) Refluxing a secondary alcohol, e.g. propan-2-ol, with acidified dichromate(VI) will produce a **ketone**.
2) Ketones can't be oxidised easily, so even prolonged refluxing won't produce anything more.

Tertiary Alcohols **Can't** be Oxidised Easily

Tertiary alcohols don't react with potassium dichromate(VI) at all — the solution stays orange. The only way to oxidise tertiary alcohols is by **burning** them.

Use **Oxidising Agents** to Distinguish Between **Aldehydes** and **Ketones** — *AQA only*

Aldehydes and ketones can be distinguished using **oxidising agents** — aldehydes are easily oxidised but ketones aren't.

1) **Fehling's solution** and **Benedict's solution** are both deep blue Cu^{2+} complexes, which reduce to brick-red Cu_2O when warmed with an aldehyde, but stay blue with a ketone.
2) **Tollen's reagent** is $[Ag(NH_3)_2]^+$ — it's reduced to **silver** when warmed with an aldehyde, but not with a ketone. The silver will coat the inside of the apparatus to form a **silver mirror**.

Practice Questions

Q1 Write the equation for the combustion of ethanol in air.

Q2 Describe the difference between the structures of an aldehyde and a ketone.

Q3 What will acidified potassium dichromate(VI) oxidise secondary alcohols to?

Q4 What is the colour change when potassium dichromate(VI) is reduced?

Exam Question

Q1 A student wanted to produce propanal from propanol.
He set up reflux apparatus using acidified potassium dichromate(VI) as the oxidising agent.

a) Draw a labelled diagram of a reflux apparatus. Explain the purpose of the reflux apparatus. [3 marks]

b) The student tested his product and found that he had not produced propanal.
(i) Describe a test for an aldehyde. [2 marks]
(ii) What is the student's product? [1 mark]
(iii) Write equations to show the two-stage reaction. Use [O] to represent the oxidising agent. [2 marks]
(iv) What technique should the student have used and why? [2 marks]

c) The student also tried to oxidise 2-methylpropan-2-ol, unsuccessfully.
(i) Draw the full structural formula for 2-methylpropan-2-ol. [1 mark]
(ii) Why is it not possible to oxidise 2-methylpropan-2-ol with an oxidising agent? [1 mark]

I.... I .... just can't do it, R2...

Don't give up now. Only as a fully-trained Chemistry Jedi, with the force as your ally, can you take on the Examiner.
If you quit now, if you choose the easy path as Wader did, all the marks you've fought for will be lost. Be strong.
Don't give in to hate — that leads to the dark side... (Just haloalkanes to go now on the organic reactions front...)

Haloalkanes

Don't worry if you see haloalkanes called halogenoalkanes. It's a government conspiracy to confuse you.
These pages are for AQA (Unit 2), OCR A (Unit 2), OCR B (Unit 2) and Edexcel (Unit 2).

Haloalkanes are Alkanes with Halogen Atoms

A **haloalkane** is an alkane with at least one **halogen atom** in place of a hydrogen atom.

E.g.

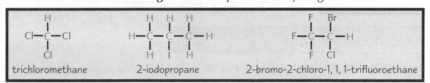

trichloromethane   2-iodopropane   2-bromo-2-chloro-1,1,1-trifluoroethane

Haloalkanes are special amongst alkanes...

Haloalkanes can be Primary, Secondary or Tertiary   *Edexcel only*

Haloalkanes with just **one halogen atom** can be **primary**, **secondary** or **tertiary** haloalkanes.

On the **carbon** with the **halogen** attached:

1) A **primary** haloalkane has **two hydrogen atoms** and just **one alkyl group**.
2) A **secondary** haloalkane has **just one hydrogen atom** and **two alkyl groups**.
3) A **tertiary** haloalkane has **no hydrogen atoms** and **three alkyl groups**.

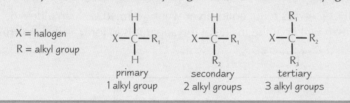

X = halogen
R = alkyl group

primary — 1 alkyl group   secondary — 2 alkyl groups   tertiary — 3 alkyl groups

This is just the same as for alcohols.

Primary, Secondary and Tertiary Haloalkanes Have Different Reactivities   *Edexcel only*

You can **compare the reactivity** of primary, secondary and tertiary haloalkanes by doing an experiment.

1) When you mix a **haloalkane** with water, it reacts to form an **alcohol**.
$$R–X + 2H_2O \rightarrow R–OH + H_3O^+ + X^-$$

2) If you put **silver nitrate solution** in the mixture too, the silver ions react with the **halide ions** as soon as they form, giving a **silver halide precipitate** (see page 73).
$$Ag^+_{(aq)} + X^-_{(aq)} \rightarrow AgX_{(s)}$$

3) To compare the reactivities, set up three test tubes each containing a different haloalkane, ethanol (as a solvent) and dilute silver nitrate solution:

The haloalkanes should all be isomers to make it a fair test.

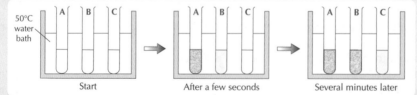

Start   After a few seconds   Several minutes later

A = 2-bromo-2-methylpropane (**tertiary**)
B = 2-bromobutane (**secondary**)
C = 1-bromobutane (**primary**)

4) In the tube with the **tertiary** haloalkane, a precipitate of silver bromide forms **immediately**.
In the tube with the **secondary** haloalkane, the silver bromide precipitate takes **several seconds** to form.
In the tube with the **primary** haloalkane, the silver bromide precipitate takes **several minutes to** form.

From the results of this experiment you can tell that the **tertiary haloalkane** is the most reactive, since it reacted **fastest** with the water, and the primary haloalkane is the least reactive.

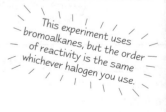

This experiment uses bromoalkanes, but the order of reactivity is the same whichever halogen you use.

The reasons for this difference in reactivity are quite complicated. Primary and tertiary haloalkanes each react with water via a different mechanism, and the secondary haloalkane reacts via both. You don't need to worry about the details of these mechanisms though. All you need to know is the reactivity order — tertiary > secondary > primary.

Haloalkanes

The **Boiling Points** of the **Haloalkanes Increase Down** the Group   *OCR B only*

1) The boiling points of the haloalkanes depend on the **strength** of their **intermolecular forces** – the stronger the forces between the molecules, the higher the boiling point.

2) As you go **down** Group 7 from fluorine to iodine, the **atomic radius** of the halogen atoms, and the **number of electron shells** that they have, **increases**.

3) This leads to stronger **Van der Waals forces** (see page 50) between molecules — you have to put in **more energy** to overcome them.

4) So the boiling point of the haloalkanes **increases** down the group.

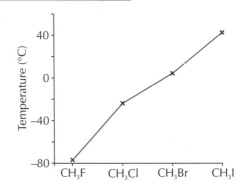

Chlorofluorocarbons (CFCs) are Haloalkanes

1) **Chlorofluorocarbons** (**CFCs**) are haloalkane molecules where all of the hydrogen atoms have been replaced by **chlorine** and **fluorine** atoms.

$$Cl-\underset{\underset{F}{|}}{\overset{\overset{Cl}{|}}{C}}-Cl$$
trichlorofluoromethane

$$F-\underset{\underset{Cl}{|}}{\overset{\overset{F}{|}}{C}}-F$$
chlorotrifluoromethane

2) CFCs used to be used for lots of things, because they're pretty **unreactive**. There's loads more about this on page 145.

3) Both **CFCs** and **chloroalkanes** were used as **solvents** in dry cleaning and degreasing.

4) In the 1970s scientists discovered that CFCs were causing **damage** to the **ozone layer** (see page 144). The **advantages** of CFCs couldn't outweigh the **environmental problems** they were causing, so they were **banned**.

Practice Questions

Q1 What is a haloalkane?

Q2 What is a tertiary haloalkane?

Q3 What factor causes the boiling point of the haloalkanes to increase as you go down the group?

Q4 Describe the structure of a CFC.

Exam Questions

Q1 (a) A haloalkane has the molecular formula C_4H_9I.
       Draw and label a possible primary, secondary and tertiary isomer of the haloalkane.   [3 marks]

  (b) Samples of your three isomers are mixed with water and silver nitrate solution.
       Which isomer will form a precipitate first?   [1 mark]

  (c) Write an equation for the reaction of the primary isomer with water.   [2 marks]

Q2 A chemist has samples of three haloalkanes in tubes labelled A, B and C.

   The boiling points of the three haloalkanes are: Tube A = 71 °C, Tube B = 46 °C, Tube C = 102 °C.

   The haloalkanes in the three tubes are 1-chloropropane, 1-bromopropane and 1-iodopropane.
   Which haloalkane is in which tube? Explain your answer.   [4 marks]

Chlorofluorocarbon — a word invented by scrabble playing scientists...

I don't reckon there's anything too complicated here. Just learn the facts and you'll be fine. **Learn the difference between a primary, a secondary and a tertiary haloalkane.** *And make sure that you can remember what a CFC is — because with my amazing powers I foretell that you'll see more about them later in the book. And meet a tall dark stranger. Maybe.*

More About Haloalkanes

*If you haven't had enough of haloalkanes yet, there's more. If you **have** had enough — there's still more.*
These pages are for AQA (Unit 2), OCR A (Unit 2), OCR B (Unit 2) and Edexcel (Unit 2).

The Carbon–Halogen Bond in Haloalkanes is Polar

1) Halogens are much more **electronegative** than carbon. So, the carbon–halogen bond is **polar**.
2) The **δ+ carbon** doesn't have enough electrons. This means it can be attacked by a **nucleophile**.
   A nucleophile's an **electron-pair donor**. It donates an electron pair to somewhere without enough electrons.
3) **OH^-, CN^-, NH_3 and H_2O** are all **nucleophiles** that can react with haloalkanes.

Haloalkanes can Undergo Nucleophilic Substitution

Haloalkanes react with **hydroxide ions** by **nucleophilic substitution**.
You have to use **warm aqueous sodium hydroxide** or it won't work.

Here's how the reaction happens:

Heterolytic fission is when both the electrons are taken by one of the atoms — in this case, the Br.

The OH⁻ ion acts as a nucleophile, attacking the positive carbon atom.

The C–Br bond is polar. The $C^{δ+}$ attracts a lone pair of electrons from the OH⁻ ion.

The C–Br bond breaks heterolytically, and a new bond forms between the C and the OH⁻ ion

Here's the general equation for this reaction: **R–X + NaOH → ROH + NaX**

R represents an alkyl group. X stands for one of the halogens (F, Cl, Br or I).

Water Can Act as a Nucleophile Too   *Not AQA*

Warming a **haloalkane** with **water** also results in a **nucleophilic substitution** reaction:

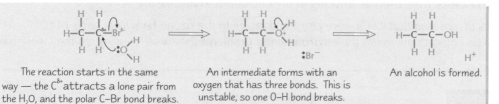

The reaction starts in the same way — the $C^{δ+}$ attracts a lone pair from the H_2O, and the polar C–Br bond breaks.

An intermediate forms with an oxygen that has three bonds. This is unstable, so one O–H bond breaks.

An alcohol is formed.

*This is a **hydrolysis** reaction.*

Haloalkanes React with Ammonia to Form Amines   *Not OCR A*

If you **warm** a haloalkane with excess **ethanolic** ammonia, the **ammonia** swaps places with the **halogen** — yes, it's another one of those **nucleophilic substitution reactions**.

Ethanolic ammonia is just ammonia dissolved in ethanol.

The first step is the same as in the mechanisms above, except this time the nucleophile is NH_3.

In the second step, an ammonia molecule removes a hydrogen from the NH_3 group to form an ammonium ion (NH_4^+).

The ammonium ion can react with the bromine ion to form ammonium bromide. So the overall reaction is this:

$$CH_3{-}\overset{\overset{\displaystyle H}{|}}{\underset{\underset{\displaystyle H}{|}}{C}}{-}Br + 2NH_3 \xrightarrow[\text{ethanol}]{\text{reflux}} CH_3{-}\overset{\overset{\displaystyle H}{|}}{\underset{\underset{\displaystyle H}{|}}{C}}{-}NH_2 + NH_4Br$$

You can use Haloalkanes to Form Nitriles   *AQA only*

If you **warm** a haloalkane with **ethanolic potassium cyanide**, you get a **nitrile**.

Nitriles have $-C{\equiv}N$ groups.

It's yet another **nucleophilic substitution reaction** — the **cyanide ion**, CN^-, is the **nucleophile**.

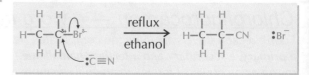

More About Haloalkanes

Iodoalkanes are the **Most Reactive** *Haloalkanes*

Bonds between carbon atoms and halogen atoms are polarised, with **C–F** the **most polar** and **C–I** the **least**.
You might expect that the more polar the bond is, the more likely it is to break, but this turns out **not** to be the case.

Experimental evidence shows that **iodoalkanes** are the **most reactive** — so reactivity can't be due to bond polarisation.
Here are two experiments you can use to show this reactivity series:

React the Haloalkanes with Water: *This is pretty much the same as the experiment on page 134.*

1) In each of three test tubes, you mix a **haloalkane, silver nitrate** solution, and some
ethanol (as a solvent), just like on p134. You need to use a chloroalkane, a bromoalkane, *To make it a fair*
and an iodoalkane this time though so you can compare their **reactivities**. *test, the haloalkanes*
must be identical in
2) A precipitate forms fastest with the **iodoalkane** — so that must be the **most reactive**. *all other ways.*
Bromoalkanes react slower than iodoalkanes, and **chloroalkanes** the slowest of the three.

or: React the Haloalkanes with NaOH:

1) Warm **aqueous NaOH** with the **haloalkanes**. The **OH⁻ ion** acts as the nucleophile (as on the previous page).

2) Add dilute **nitric acid** to **neutralise** any spare OH⁻ ions **before** adding the **silver nitrate** solution (or else the
silver nitrate will react with the OH⁻ ions to form a silver oxide precipitate, which messes up your results).

It's actually the carbon-halogen bond strength that decides reactivity:

Despite being the most polar, the **C-F bond** is the **strongest**
— it has the highest **bond enthalpy**. For any reaction
to occur the carbon-halogen bond needs to **break**.
The **stronger** that bond is, the **slower** the reaction will be.

bond	bond enthalpy kJ mol⁻¹
C–F	467
C–Cl	346
C–Br	290
C–I	228

Faster hydrolysis as bond enthalpy decreases (the bonds are getting weaker).

The **Carbon-Iodine** Bond is Easiest to Split with **UV** Too *OCR B only*

The haloalkanes all react similarly when they absorb UV — the carbon-halogen bond splits **homolytically** to create two
free radicals (see p86). The ease with which this happens is also related to the enthalpy of the carbon-halogen bond.
So it's easiest to split the C-I bond, and hardest to split the C-F bond.

Practice Questions

Q1 What is a nucleophile?

Q2 Why is the carbon-halogen bond polar?

Q3 Why does iodoethane react faster than chloro- or bromoethane with warm, aqueous sodium hydroxide?

Q4 Give two examples of nucleophiles that can react with haloalkanes.

Exam Question

Q1 The equation for the reaction between water and 2-bromopropane is shown below.

$CH_3CHBrCH_3 + H_2O \rightarrow CH_3CH(OH)CH_3 + HBr$

a) (i) What is the name of this type of reaction? [1 mark]

(ii) Name the organic product formed. [2 marks]

b) Under the same conditions, 2-iodopropane was used in place of 2-bromopropane in the reaction above.
What difference would you expect in the rate of the reaction? Explain your answer. [2 marks]

c) Draw the mechanism for the reaction between 2-bromopropane and aqueous potassium hydroxide. [3 marks]

I get irritable when it rains — it's a precipitation reaction...

*Polar bonds get in just about every area of Chemistry. If you still think they're something to do with either bears or mints, flick
back to Section 3 and have a good read of pages 48 and 49. And make sure you can draw out all the reaction mechanisms,
and explain the reactivity series. This stuff's always coming up in exams. Ruin the examiner's day and get them right.*

Haloalkanes and Reaction Types

Breathe a huge sigh of relief — it's the last page about haloalkane reactions.

These pages are for AQA (Unit 2), OCR A (Unit 2), OCR B (Unit 2) and Edexcel (Unit 2).

Haloalkanes also Undergo Elimination Reactions
This bit's just for AQA and Edexcel

You saw on p136 that if you react a haloalkane with a warm **aqueous solution** of hydroxide ions, a nucleophilic substitution reaction happens, and you end up with an alcohol. **BUT** — if you warm a haloalkane with hydroxide ions dissolved in **ethanol** instead, an **elimination reaction** happens, and you end up with an **alkene**. This is how you do it:

1) Heat the mixture **under reflux** or you'll lose volatile stuff.

$$CH_3CHBrCH_3 + KOH \xrightarrow[\text{reflux}]{\text{ethanol}} CH_2=CH_2CH_3 + H_2O + KBr$$

These conditions are anhydrous (there's no water).

2) Here's how the reaction works:

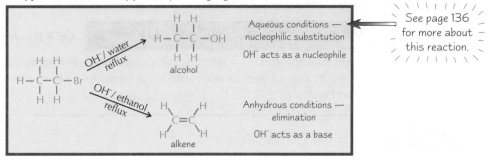

OH⁻ acts as a base and takes a proton, H⁺, from the carbon on the left. This makes water. The left carbon now has a spare electron, so it forms a double bond with the other carbon. To form the double bond, the right carbon has to let go of the Br, which drops off as a Br⁻ ion.

3) This is an example of an **elimination reaction**. In an elimination **reaction**, a **small group** of atoms breaks away from a larger molecule. This **small group** is **not replaced** by anything else (whereas it would be in a substitution reaction). In the reaction above, H and Br have been eliminated from CH_3CH_2Br to leave $CH_2=CH_2$

The Type of Reaction That Happens Depends on the Conditions
AQA and Edexcel only

You can control what **type of reaction** happens by **changing the conditions**.

See page 136 for more about this reaction.

Both of these reactions have their uses...

1) The **elimination** reaction is a **good way** of getting a **double bond** into a molecule. Loads of other organic synthesis reactions use **alkenes**, so the elimination reaction is a good starting point for making lots of different organic chemicals.

2) The **substitution** reaction allows you to produce any **alcohol** molecule that you need. And alcohols can be the starting point for synthesis reactions that produce **aldehydes**, **ketones**, **esters**, and **carboxylic acids**.

So haloalkanes are very useful as a **starting material** for making other organic compounds.

You Can Classify Reactions by Reaction Type

Here's a quick reminder of all the reaction types that you've come across in this section:

Polymerisation – joining together lots of simple molecules to **form a giant molecule**.

Elimination – when a **small group of** atoms **breaks away** from a larger molecule.

Substitution – when **one species is replaced by another**.

Hydrolysis – splitting a molecule into two new molecules by **adding H⁺ and OH⁻** derived from **water**.

Oxidation – any reaction in which an atom **loses electrons**.

Reduction – any reaction in which an atom **gains electrons**.

Redox – any reaction where **electrons are transferred** between two species.

A species is an atom, an ion, or a molecule.

Haloalkanes and Reaction Types

Classifying Reagents *Helps to Predict What Reactions Will Happen*

Knowing the **type of reagent** that you have helps you **predict** which chemicals will react together and what products you're likely to end up with.

1) **Nucleophiles** are **electron pair donors**. Because they're **electron rich**, they're **attracted** to places that are electron poor. So they like to react with **positive** atoms and ions. Molecules with **polar bonds** are often attacked by nucleophiles too, as they have $\delta+$ areas.

> Nucleophiles are attracted to the $C^{\delta+}$ atom in a **polar carbon-halogen bond**. The carbon-halogen bond breaks and the nucleophile takes the halogen's place — and that's **nucleophilic substitution** (see page 136).

Frank put safety first when he tested his nuclear file...

2) **Electrophiles** are **electron pair acceptors**. Because they're **electron poor**, they're **attracted** to places that are electron rich. This means that they like to react with **negative** atoms and ions — and the **electron-rich** area around a **C=C bond**.

> **Alkene** molecules undergo electrophilic addition. In a molecule with a polar bond, like HBr, the $H^{\delta+}$ acts as an **electrophile** and is strongly attracted to the C=C double bond, (which **polarises** the H–Br bond even more, until it finally breaks). There's more about this reaction on page 120.

electron rich area

$$\begin{array}{c} H \\ C=C \\ H \quad\quad H \end{array}$$

$H^{\delta+}$
$Br^{\delta-}$ electrophile

3) **Free radicals** have an **unpaired electron**, e.g. the chlorine atoms produced when UV light splits a Cl_2 molecule. Because they have unpaired electrons, they're very, very **reactive**. Unlike electrophiles and nucleophiles, they'll react with anything, positive, negative or neutral.

$$UV$$
$$Cl{-}Cl \rightarrow 2Cl\cdot$$

Because a free radical will react with anything in sight, you'll probably end up with a mixture of products. So free radical reactions aren't much use if you're after a pure product.

> **Free radicals** will even attack stable non-polar bonds, like C–C and C–H (so they're one of the few things that will react with alkanes). There's loads about the reactions of free radicals with alkanes on page 86.

Practice Questions

Q1 Explain what an elimination reaction is.

Q2 Give an example of an elimination reaction.

Q3 What is an electrophile?

Exam Questions

Q1 Two reactions of 2-bromopropane, $CH_3CHBrCH_3$, are shown on the right.

For each reaction, name the reagent and solvent used. [4 marks]

$$CH_3CHBrCH_3 \xrightarrow{reaction\ 1} CH_3CH(OH)CH_3$$
$$\xrightarrow{reaction\ 2} CH_3CH(NH_2)CH_3$$

Q2 Propene can be produced from 2-bromopropane.

a) Give the reagents and conditions needed for this reaction. [3 marks]

b) What type of reaction is it? [1 mark]

c) Write a balanced equation for the reaction that occurs. [3 marks]

Oxidising agent SALE NOW ON — everything's reduced...

Scientists do love to classify everything, and have it neatly in order. I knew one who liked to alphabetise his socks. But that's a whole other issue. Just learn the different products you end up with if you change the haloalkane reaction conditions, and the definitions for types of reactions and reagents and you'll have this page sorted. Without having to alphabetise anything.

Doing Organic Chemistry

I'm sure learning all this organic chemistry has got you itching to get into the lab and do some experiments.
Well, hold your horses and read these pages before you go throwing chemicals around willy-nilly...
This page is for OCR B (Unit 2) and Edexcel (Unit 2).

Organic Chemistry Uses some Specific Techniques

There are some **practical techniques** that get used a lot in organic chemistry. The products from organic reactions are often **impure** — so you've got to know how to get rid of the unwanted by-products or leftover reactants. The method for turning an **alcohol** into a **chloroalkane** is a really useful example because it involves quite a few of those techniques.

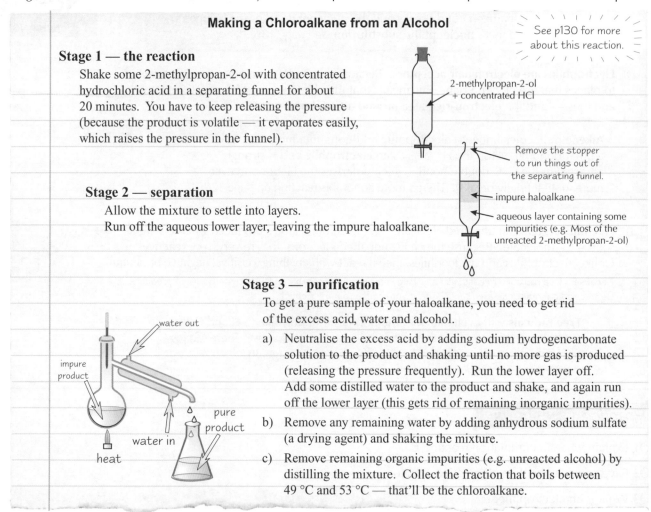

Making a Chloroalkane from an Alcohol

See p130 for more about this reaction.

Stage 1 — the reaction

Shake some 2-methylpropan-2-ol with concentrated hydrochloric acid in a separating funnel for about 20 minutes. You have to keep releasing the pressure (because the product is volatile — it evaporates easily, which raises the pressure in the funnel).

2-methylpropan-2-ol + concentrated HCl

Remove the stopper to run things out of the separating funnel.

Stage 2 — separation

Allow the mixture to settle into layers.
Run off the aqueous lower layer, leaving the impure haloalkane.

impure haloalkane

aqueous layer containing some impurities (e.g. Most of the unreacted 2-methylpropan-2-ol)

Stage 3 — purification

To get a pure sample of your haloalkane, you need to get rid of the excess acid, water and alcohol.

water out

impure product

water in

heat

pure product

a) Neutralise the excess acid by adding sodium hydrogencarbonate solution to the product and shaking until no more gas is produced (releasing the pressure frequently). Run the lower layer off. Add some distilled water to the product and shake, and again run off the lower layer (this gets rid of remaining inorganic impurities).

b) Remove any remaining water by adding anhydrous sodium sulfate (a drying agent) and shaking the mixture.

c) Remove remaining organic impurities (e.g. unreacted alcohol) by distilling the mixture. Collect the fraction that boils between 49 °C and 53 °C — that'll be the chloroalkane.

Volatile Liquids Need to be Heated under Reflux

1) **Volatile liquids** (ones with a low boiling point) can be tricky to work with. If you need to heat a volatile liquid for a reaction, you can end up with most of the liquid **evaporating** before it's had chance to react.

2) You can get around this by fitting a **reflux condenser** — that's just a condenser fitted vertically to the reaction flask.

3) The volatile liquid evaporates, but then condenses and drips back into the flask where it has another chance to react.

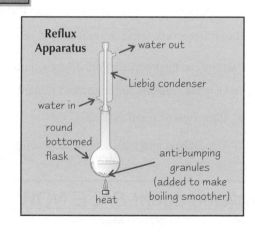

Reflux Apparatus

water out

Liebig condenser

water in

round bottomed flask

anti-bumping granules (added to make boiling smoother)

heat

Frankie says 'reflux'

Doing Organic Chemistry

This page is for Edexcel (Unit 1)(except for the questions — some of them are for OCR B (Unit 2) and Edexcel (Unit 2).)

Hazards and Risks Aren't the Same

You need to know the difference between **hazard** and **risk**:

> A **hazard** is anything that can cause **harm**.
> **Risk** is the **chance** that what you're doing will cause harm.

Using Organic Chemicals can be Hazardous

You should already know the chemical **hazard symbols**. The ones below are common hazards of **organic chemicals**.

 Most organic chemicals are flammable. Some (like ethanol and methane) are **highly flammable**.

 You won't see the '**explosive**' symbol in the lab much, but highly flammable gases can cause explosions if they're released in the air.

 Irritant: e.g. propan-1-ol, pentane. These chemicals can irritate or blister your skin, but won't cause permanent damage.

 Harmful: e.g. butan-1-ol, 1-chloropropane. Pretty nasty stuff — harmful chemicals can damage your health, but aren't as dangerous as toxic ones.

 Toxic: e.g. methanol, chloroethene. Really nasty stuff — these chemicals can kill you if you swallow or inhale them, or sometimes even if you get them on your skin.

 This symbol means **dangerous for the environment**. You'll find it on chemicals that can cause very serious environmental damage (e.g. hexane).

A Risk Assessment can Help to Make Lab Work Safer

1) Most laboratory chemicals can cause harm if you aren't careful with them. Before you do **anything** with chemicals in a lab, you should do a **risk assessment**.

2) A risk assessment looks at the **hazards** of all the **reactants**, **products** and **procedures** involved in an experiment and considers how to make the risks from them as **small as possible**.

3) You can **reduce risks** by:
   - working on a smaller scale
   - taking appropriate precautions — like eye protection, plastic gloves and fume cupboards
   - using different, safer chemicals or lower concentrations if possible

4) It's impossible to **completely** get rid of all risk. But the point of doing a risk assessment is to systematically think about ways to **minimise the risks**. Despite all the hazardous chemicals, science labs are actually pretty safe. If you follow all the lab safety rules, you're less likely to get injured in a chemistry lesson than you are travelling in a car or playing sport.

Practice Questions

Q1 What is meant by the term risk? What is meant by the term hazard?

Q2 Name a suitable drying agent to use in the purification of an organic liquid.

Exam Questions

Q1 What is meant by reflux and why is the technique sometimes used in organic chemistry? [2 marks]

Q2 Explain how distillation can help to purify a liquid product. [2 marks]

Q3 The preparation of an organic compound involves chemicals with the hazard signs shown on the right. Suggest two sensible ways to reduce the risks involved, other than wearing protective clothing such as goggles, laboratory overalls and plastic gloves.   [2 marks]

If you're going to bake a cake, don't forget to do a whisk assessment...

Risk assessments might be a bit dull if you just want to get on with an experiment, but it's a good idea to make sure you're not going to blow your head off before you start. The hazards and risks stuff applies to all chemistry, not just the organic. In fact, it could be useful in life in general — I know a few people who could do with 'irritant' or 'toxic' labels...

The Atmosphere

The atmosphere wasn't always like it is today. A few billion years ago it was full of carbon dioxide, with just a teeny-weeny bit of oxygen. Luckily, it evolved so we could breathe and stuff. We're starting to mess it up again with pollutants though.

These pages are for OCR B (Unit 2) and Edexcel (Units 1 and 2).

Most of the **Atmosphere** is **Nitrogen** and **Oxygen**   *OCR B only*

Here's what the atmosphere's made of. The percentages are by **volume** of dry air (in the lower atmosphere).

Nitrogen	**78%**
Oxygen	**21%**
Argon	**1%**
Carbon dioxide	**0.035%**

Also:
1) Varying amounts of **water vapour**.
2) **Other gases** in tiny amounts.

It comes to over 100% because the percentages are rounded off slightly.

So every **100 cm³** of air contains about **78 cm³** of nitrogen, **21 cm³** of oxygen and **1 cm³** of argon. And **tiny bits** of other stuff too.

We're also putting **pollutants** like **methane**, **sulfur dioxide**, **oxides of nitrogen** and **CFCs** into the atmosphere. These are bad — they add to the **greenhouse effect** (p146-148), **acid rain**, **smog** (p84) and the destruction of the **ozone layer** (page 144-145).

Parts Per Million is used for **Really Small Quantities**   *Not Edexcel (Unit 2)*

1) The **major gases** in the atmosphere are normally given as **percentages** of the **total volume**. But some gases are present in such **tiny amounts** that it's **not very convenient** to write their quantities like this. For instance, **xenon** makes up only **0.000 009%** of the atmosphere. Numbers this small are a pain to work with.

2) So to get round this problem, another type of measurement is used. It is called **parts per million** or **ppm**.

3) So if there's **0.000 009 parts** of xenon in every **one hundred parts of air**, you can multiply both quantities by **10 000** to make the quantity **large enough** to work with, like this:

$$0.000\,009\% = \begin{array}{c} 0.000\,009 \\ \text{parts per 100} \\ \text{parts of air} \end{array} \longrightarrow \begin{array}{c} 0.000\,009 \times 10\,000 = 0.09 \\ 100 \times 10\,000 = 1\,000\,000 \end{array} \longrightarrow 0.09 \text{ parts per million}$$

4) So there's 0.09 ppm xenon. The atmosphere also contains **0.1 ppm** carbon monoxide and **0.3 ppm** nitrous oxide.

The **Earth's Atmosphere** Absorbs **Radiation**   *OCR B only*

1) The Sun gives out **electromagnetic radiation** because of the nuclear processes going on in its core. Electromagnetic radiation is energy that's transmitted as waves, with a **spectrum** of different frequencies.

2) The Sun mainly gives out **visible** radiation (light) and **infrared** radiation (heat), along with a smaller amount of **ultraviolet** radiation.

The Sun's main radiations

| RADIO WAVES | MICRO- WAVES | INFRA- RED | VISIBLE LIGHT | ULTRA- VIOLET | X-RAYS | GAMMA RAYS |

INCREASING FREQUENCY AND ENERGY →

3) The **Earth's atmosphere** absorbs some of the Sun's infrared radiation and most of the ultraviolet radiation — more on this on the next page.

4) The **Earth's surface** also absorbs radiation from the Sun and is warmed. It then re-emits **radiation**, mostly as **infrared**. The Earth emits much **lower frequency** radiation than the Sun (because it's much cooler).

The Atmosphere

Infrared Radiation Makes Some Bonds Vibrate More   *Not Edexcel (Unit 1)*

1) Some molecules absorb energy from **infrared radiation**.
   The extra energy makes their covalent bonds **vibrate** more.

2) Only molecules made of **different atoms** can absorb infrared radiation.
   This is because the **polarities** of their bonds change as they vibrate.

3) So, oxygen (O_2) and nitrogen (N_2) don't absorb infrared radiation,
   but **carbon dioxide, water, nitric oxide (NO)** and **methane** do.
   Gases that **do** absorb infrared radiation are called **greenhouse gases** because they stop
   some of the radiation emitted by the Earth from escaping into space (see page 146).

4) Gas molecules' bonds have **certain fixed energy levels**. These are called **quantised** levels.
   So a bond's energy can only **jump** from one level to another — like moving up a **staircase** in steps.

5) This means that only frequencies of radiation corresponding to particular amounts of energy are absorbed.
   Different molecules absorb **different frequencies** of radiation.

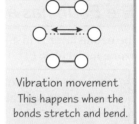

Vibration movement
This happens when the
bonds stretch and bend.

UV and Visible Light Radiation Give Electrons More Energy   *OCR B only*

1) The **electrons** in molecules also have **fixed energy levels** that they can **jump between**.

2) When **ultraviolet radiation** or **visible light** hit a molecule of **gas** the **electrons** can **absorb** the energy and **jump up**
   to their **next energy level**. Because the energy needed for these changes is **quantised** too, **only specific frequencies**
   are absorbed.

3) If enough energy is absorbed bonds
   break, forming **free radicals**.

UV radiation O_2

If O_2 molecules absorb the right amount of UV energy they
split into oxygen atoms or free radicals — this is the first
step in the formation of ozone, O_3 (see page 144).

The Energy from Radiation can be Calculated   *OCR B only*

You saw this equation
on page 11.

The **energy** depends on the **frequency** of the radiation. I reckon we're about due for an **equation**:

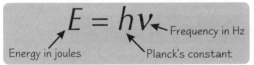

$$E = h\nu$$

Energy in joules — Planck's constant — Frequency in Hz

Planck's constant
= 6.63×10^{-34} Js

So, if you know **Planck's constant** and the
frequency of the radiation, you can calculate
how much energy the molecule absorbed.

Example: What is the energy supplied to a molecule by infrared radiation of frequency 0.5×10^{14} Hz?

$$E = h\nu = (6.63 \times 10^{-34}) \times (0.5 \times 10^{14}) = \mathbf{3.315 \times 10^{-20} \ J}$$

Practice Questions

Q1 What is the difference between 'per cent' and 'parts per million'?

Q2 What does the word 'quantised' mean?

Q3 How can you tell if a gas will be a greenhouse gas? Name two greenhouse gases and two non-greenhouse gases.

Q4 What happens when molecules absorb UV radiation?

Exam Questions

Q1 The Earth absorbs radiation from the Sun. It also emits radiation.
   a) What are the main types of radiation emitted by the Sun and by the Earth?   [2 marks]
   b) Describe what happens within a molecule when it absorbs infrared radiation.   [1 mark]

Q2 Calculate the energy absorbed when one molecule of HCl changes from its ground vibrational level
   to the next level, given that the frequency of radiation absorbed is 8.19×10^{13} Hz.   [2 marks]

The atmosphere — it ain't made of custard...

*If there were no atmospheric gases, bad sunburn would be the least of our worries. There'd be no oxygen, so we
wouldn't be able to breathe. But at least there'd be no AS Chemistry either. I don't think this has been too bad a page
— I hope you weren't too bored by the stuff on Planck's constant. Cor blimey, if ever there was a lame joke, that was it.*

The Ozone Layer

The ozone layer seems to have been forgotten about lately, with all the worries about climate change. It's still there though.
This page is for AQA (Unit 2), OCR A (Unit 2), OCR B (Unit 2) and Edexcel (Unit 2).

The Earth has a Layer of **Ozone** at the Edge of the **Stratosphere**   *Not AQA*

The **ozone layer** is in a layer of the atmosphere called the **stratosphere**. It contains most of the atmosphere's **ozone molecules**, O_3. Ozone is formed when **UV radiation** from the Sun hits oxygen molecules.

> If the right amount of **UV radiation** is absorbed by an oxygen molecule, the oxygen molecule splits into separate atoms or **free radicals**. The free radicals then **combine** with other oxygen molecules to form **ozone molecules**, O_3.
>
> $$O_2 + h\nu \rightarrow O\bullet + O\bullet \longrightarrow O_2 + O\bullet \rightarrow O_3$$
>
> a quantum of UV radiation

The Ozone Layer is Constantly Being **Replaced**   *Not AQA*

1) UV radiation can also **reverse** the formation of ozone.

$$O_3 + h\nu \rightarrow O_2 + O\bullet$$

The radical produced then forms more ozone with an O_2 molecule, as shown above.

2) So, the ozone layer is continuously being **destroyed** and **replaced** as UV radiation hits the molecules. An **equilibrium** is set up, so the concentrations stay fairly constant:

$$O_2 + O\bullet \rightleftharpoons O_3$$

The Ozone Layer **Protects** the Earth   *Not Edexcel*

UVA   UVB   UVC

INCREASING FREQUENCY AND ENERGY

1) The **UV radiation** from the Sun is made up of **different frequencies**. These are grouped into **three bands**:

2) The ozone layer removes all the high energy **UVC radiation** and about 90% of the **UVB**. These types of UV radiation are harmful to humans and most other life on Earth.

3) **UVB** can damage the DNA in cells and cause **skin cancer**. It's the main cause of **sunburn** too. **UVA** can also lead to **skin cancer**. Both types of UV break down collagen fibres in the skin causing it to **age faster**.

4) When the skin's exposed to UV, it **tans**. This helps protect **deeper tissues** from the effects of the radiation.

5) **BUT...** UV radiation isn't all bad — in fact it's **essential** for us humans. We need it to produce **vitamin D**.

Scientists Discovered that the **Ozone Layer** Was a **Bit Thin** in Places

1) In the 1970s, a team from the **British Antarctic Survey** found that the concentration of ozone over Antarctica was very low compared to previous measurements. In 1985 they measured it again and they found that it was **even lower**.

2) The decrease was so **dramatic** that they thought their measuring instruments were faulty. They got some **new instruments**, but these gave the same results. Eeeek.

3) As all good scientists do, they **published** their results so that others could check them out.

4) A **satellite** had mapped the ozone levels at about the same time. But it was programmed to treat measurements below a certain value as **errors** and to ignore them — so this evidence for the thinning of the ozone layer was **overlooked**. When the British Antarctic Survey published their findings the satellite data was re-examined and found to show the 'hole' too.

5) The ozone layer over the **Arctic** has been found to be thinning too. These 'holes' in the ozone layer are bad because they allow more harmful **UVB radiation** to reach the Earth.

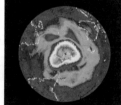

LABORATORY FOR ATMOSPHERES, NASA GODDARD/SPACE FLIGHT CENTER/SCIENCE PHOTO LIBRARY

Here's a satellite map showing the 'hole' in the ozone layer over Antarctica. The 'hole' is shown by the white and pink area.

CFCs and **Nitrogen Oxides** Were Breaking the Ozone Down   *Not OCR B*

1) **CFCs** (see the next page) absorb UV radiation and split to form **chlorine free radicals**. These free radicals **destroy ozone molecules** and are then **regenerated** to destroy more ozone. One chlorine atom can destroy 10 000 ozone molecules before it forms a stable compound. There's more detail on this on page 106.

2) **NO•** free radicals from **nitrogen oxides** destroy ozone too. Nitrogen oxides are produced by **car and aircraft engines** and **thunderstorms**. NO• free radicals affect ozone in the **same way** as chlorine radicals.

3) The overall reactions can be represented by these equations, where **R** represents either Cl• or NO•.

$$R + O_3 \rightarrow RO + O_2$$
$$RO + O\bullet \rightarrow R + O_2$$

NO• and Cl• aren't the only culprits — free radicals are produced from other haloalkanes too.

The free radicals acts as **catalysts** for the destruction of the ozone — see page 106.   Formed when UV breaks down O_2.   The harmful radical is regenerated.

The Ozone Layer

CFCs Have Great Properties — But Alternatives Had to be Found

1) **CFCs (chlorofluorocarbons)** are a group of compounds made by replacing all of the hydrogen atoms in alkanes with chlorine and fluorine. They're **haloalkanes** — see page 134.

2) They're **unreactive**, **non-flammable** and **non-toxic**. They were used in fire extinguishers, as propellants in aerosols, as the coolant gas in fridges and to foam plastics to make insulation and packaging materials.

3) The **Montreal Protocol** of 1989 was an **international treaty** to phase out the use of CFCs and other ozone-destroying haloalkanes by the year 2000. There were a few **permitted uses** such as in medical inhalers and in fire extinguishers used in submarines.

4) Scientists supported the treaty, and worked on finding **alternatives** to CFCs.

   - **HCFCs (hydrochlorofluorocarbons)** and **HFCs (hydrofluorocarbons)** are being used as temporary alternatives to CFCs until safer products are developed. **Hydrocarbons** are also used.
   - **HCFCs** are broken down in the atmosphere in 10-20 years. They still damage the ozone layer, but their effect is much smaller than CFCs.
   - **HFCs** are broken down in the atmosphere too **and** they don't contain chlorine, so don't affect the ozone layer.
   - Unfortunately, **HFCs and HCFCs are greenhouse gases** — they're 1000 times worse than carbon dioxide.
   - Some **hydrocarbons** are being used in fridges but these are greenhouse gases too.
   - Nowadays, most aerosols have been replaced by **pump spray systems** or use **nitrogen** as the propellant. **Ammonia** is used as a coolant in industrial refrigerators, and CO_2 is used to make foamed polymers.

   These substances do have **drawbacks**, but they're currently the **least environmentally damaging** of all the alternatives.

5) The ozone holes **still** form in the spring but the **rate of decrease** of ozone is **slowing** — so things are looking up.

Ozone Occurs at Ground Level Too — OCR A and OCR B only

1) Ozone occurs in the **troposphere** (the lowest part of the atmosphere) due to the effect of **sunlight** on mixtures of **nitrogen dioxide and hydrocarbons**. Nitrogen dioxide and hydrocarbons occur **naturally** from a variety of sources but **vehicle engines** and **power stations** contribute large amounts too.

2) In heavily industrialised areas and cities with lots of cars, the ozone mixes with **solid particles** of carbon and many other substances — the effect is called **photochemical smog**. Mexico City is particularly badly affected.

3) Ozone is **toxic** to humans. At the levels often found in cities it can affect the **lungs** and trigger **asthma attacks**.

Practice Questions

Q1 What is ozone, and where is the ozone layer?

Q2 Which has higher energy — UVA, UVB, or UVC?

Q3 Write equations to show how ozone is destroyed, using R to represent the radical.

Q4 Where's photochemical smog found and what's it made of? Why is it bad?

Exam Questions

Q1 The 'ozone layer' lies mostly between 15 and 30 km above the Earth's surface.
   a) Explain how ozone forms in this part of the atmosphere. [3 marks]
   b) What are the benefits to humans of the ozone layer? [2 marks]
   c) How does the ozone layer absorb harmful radiation without being permanently destroyed? [2 marks]

Q2 CFCs were invented in 1928. They were widely used in the 20th century.
   a) Give three important uses of CFCs. [3 marks]
   b) What useful properties do CFCs have? [3 marks]
   c) Why was the use of CFCs banned by the Montreal Protocol? [1 mark]
   d) What alternatives to CFCs have been used and what are their drawbacks? [6 marks]

A scarecrow won a Nobel Prize — He was outstanding in his field...
I know it's completely irrelevant, but I like it.

How scientists found the hole in the ozone layer, repeated their experiments, then published their results is a super example of How Science Works. What's more, the evidence was used to instigate an international treaty — it's a beauty of an example of how science informs decision-making. And remember — think about any anomalous results before chucking them away.

The Greenhouse Effect

Now I'm sure you know this already but it's good to be sure — the greenhouse effect, global warming and climate change are all different things. They're linked (and you need to know how) — but they are not the same. Ahem.
This page is for AQA (Units 1 and 2), OCR A (Unit 2), OCR B (Unit 2) and Edexcel (Unit 2).

The Greenhouse Effect Keeps Us Alive

1) The Sun emits **electromagnetic radiation**, mostly as visible light, UV radiation and infrared radiation.

2) When radiation from the Sun reaches **Earth's atmosphere**, most of the UV and infrared is **absorbed by atmospheric gases** (see pages 142-144), and some radiation is **reflected back into space** from **clouds**.

3) The energy that reaches the **Earth's surface** is mainly **visible light**, with some UV and a little infrared. Some of this radiation is reflected into space by light-coloured, shiny surfaces like ice and snow. The rest is **absorbed** by the Earth, which causes it to heat up.

4) The Earth then **radiates energy** back towards space as **infrared radiation** (heat).

5) Some of this infrared (IR) radiation **escapes** (through the so-called 'IR window' — the range of IR frequencies that are not absorbed by atmospheric gases). But various gases in the troposphere (the lowest layer of the atmosphere) **absorb** other infrared radiation... and **re-emit** it in **all directions** — including back towards Earth, keeping us warm.

6) This is called the **'greenhouse effect'** (even though a real greenhouse doesn't actually work like this, annoyingly).
Without this absorption and re-emission of heat by 'greenhouse gases', the average surface temperature on Earth would be about 30 °C cooler than it is — and we wouldn't be here.

Visible and UV radiation from the Sun

Some infrared radiation emitted by the Earth is absorbed by greenhouse gases

Some infrared radiation emitted by the Earth escapes through the 'IR window'

A bit more on greenhouse gases

1) The main greenhouse gases are **water vapour, carbon dioxide** and **methane**. They're greenhouse gases because their molecules **absorb IR radiation** to make the bonds in the molecule **vibrate more** (see page 143).

2) This extra vibrational energy is passed on to other molecules in the air through **collisions**, giving the other molecules more kinetic energy and so raising the overall temperature.

3) The greenhouse gas you hear about all the time is **carbon dioxide**, but actually water vapour makes a far greater contribution to the effect. The contribution of any particular gas depends on:
   • how much radiation one molecule of the gas absorbs
   • how much of that gas there is in the atmosphere (concentration in ppm, say)

   For example, one methane molecule traps far more heat than one carbon dioxide molecule, but there's much **less methane** in the atmosphere, so its overall contribution to the greenhouse effect is smaller.

An Enhanced Greenhouse Effect Causes Global Warming... *OCR A and OCR B only*

1) You don't see newspaper headlines about H_2O emissions — even though water vapour's responsible for a large portion of the greenhouse effect — but we're constantly being encouraged to reduce our **CO_2 emissions**.

2) That's because the concentration of water vapour in the atmosphere has stayed pretty constant for many years, whereas the concentration of carbon dioxide (and methane) has **increased** and **is still increasing**.

3) Over the last 150 years or so, the world's **human population** has shot up and we've become more **industrialised**. To supply our energy needs, we've been **burning fossil fuels** at an ever-increasing rate, releasing **tons and tons** of CO_2 into the atmosphere. We've also been **chopping down forests** which used to absorb CO_2 by photosynthesis.

4) And it's not just carbon dioxide. **Methane** levels have also risen as we've had to grow more food for our rising population. **Cows** are responsible for large amounts of methane. From both ends. (There are, it turns out, quite simple ways to reduce the problem by altering their diet.)

Vegetarians can't feel entirely smug though. Paddy fields, in which rice is grown, kick out a fair amount of methane too.

5) These **human activities** have caused a rise in greenhouse gas concentrations, which **enhances** the greenhouse effect. So now **too much heat** is being trapped and the Earth is **getting warmer** — this is **global warming**.

The Greenhouse Effect

This page is for OCR A (Unit 2), OCR B (Unit 2) and Edexcel (Unit 2).

...which will Lead to **Sea Level Rise** and **Climate Change**   *OCR A only*

Global warming won't just make everywhere a bit warmer and affect the skiing:

1) The warmer oceans will expand and massive ice-sheets in the polar regions will melt, causing **sea levels** to rise and leading to more flooding. This is a particular worry for some Pacific islands and countries like Bangladesh and Holland, which are mostly very low-lying.

2) The **climate** in any region of the world depends on a **really complicated** system of ocean currents, winds, etc., and it's all driven by heat energy (it starts off with the tropics getting more heat from the Sun than higher latitudes do).

3) Global warming means there's **more heat energy** in the system. This could lead to **stormier**, less predictable weather. But it could also upset the whole climate system we're used to...

4) It's thought that melting ice and other changes will cause big changes in major ocean currents — and this would affect various regions of the world differently:

> In some places there could be much less rainfall, with droughts and crop failures causing famines and forcing entire populations to become refugees. The effect of this mass migration on other countries would be huge. In other regions, increased rainfall and flooding would bring diseases like cholera. Wildlife would also be affected — from photogenic polar bears becoming homeless to less appealing mosquitoes moving into Northern Europe.

Climate Change **Isn't New**...   *Edexcel only*

Climate change has happened quite **naturally** throughout the Earth's history, on various different timescales:

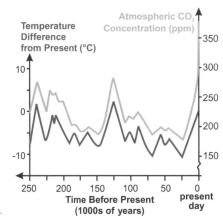

1) For example, regular changes in the Earth's orbit around the Sun are linked to **ice age** cycles — long cold periods (ice ages) with warmer periods (**interglacials**) in between. (We're in an interglacial period now).

2) Various changes in the **Sun's** activity (e.g. **sunspot** cycles every 11 years) also cause warming or cooling.

3) Not all natural changes are caused by regular cycles. For example, huge **volcanic eruptions** or **meteor impacts** have thrown vast amounts of smoke or dust into the air and caused significant global cooling.

... But **Anthropogenic Change Is**

A lot of scientific evidence shows that global warming **is** taking place now, more quickly than in the past.

1) For example, scientists regularly sample the air in unpolluted places (like remote islands). Both average temperatures and carbon dioxide levels are going up (they both change over the seasons, of course, so it's the yearly averages that count).

2) Monitoring of **sea water** shows that the oceans have become **more acidic** as more carbon dioxide dissolves in the water (because it forms carbonic acid, H_2CO_3). So we know that the chemistry of the oceans is changing.

3) Scientists have used **mass spectrometry** to analyse the composition of **air** trapped inside the ice in polar regions, to see how the atmosphere has changed in the past (when older, deeper ice formed), and compare that with changes in recent years.

4) Putting all the evidence together, it seems to show that the Earth's average temperature has increased **dramatically** in the last 50 years, and that carbon dioxide levels have increased at the same time.

5) The **correlation** between CO_2 and temperature is pretty clear, but there's been debate about whether rising carbon dioxide levels have **caused** the recent temperature rise. Just showing a correlation doesn't prove that one thing causes another — there has to be a plausible mechanism for how one change causes the other (in this case, the explanation is the enhanced greenhouse effect).

6) There is a consensus amongst climate scientists that the link **is** causal, and that recent warming is **anthropogenic** — **human activities** are to blame.

The Greenhouse Effect

This page is for OCR A (Unit 2) and OCR B (Unit 2).

Scientists are **Monitoring Global Warming**... *OCR A only*

1) Scientific evidence gathered by the Intergovernmental Panel on Climate Change (IPCC) persuaded most of the world's governments that global warming is happening. There's now global agreement that climate change could be very damaging for millions of people, the environment and economies, and that we should try to limit it.

2) In 1997 the **Kyoto protocol** was signed — industrialised countries (including the UK) promised to reduce their greenhouse gas emissions to agreed levels. Many chemists are now involved in **monitoring** greenhouse gas emissions to see if countries will meet the targets (it looks like many won't).

3) Chemists also continue to monitor the environment to see how it's changing now. The data they collect and analyse is used in **climate models** (a big load of equations run on a computer to simulate how the climate system works).

4) Climate scientists use these models to predict future changes. It's a big job — when new factors affecting the climate are discovered by other scientists, the modellers have to 'tweak' their models to take this into account.

HANK MORGAN / SCIENCE PHOTO LIBRARY

...and **Investigating** Ways to **Limit It**

Scientists are investigating various ways to help **reduce** carbon dioxide emissions. These include:

1) **Carbon capture and storage** (CCS). This means removing waste CO_2 from, say, power stations, and either
   - injecting it as a **liquid** into the **deep ocean**, or
   - storing it deep **underground** — one possibility is to use old oil- or gas-fields under the seabed, or
   - reacting it with metal oxides to form stable, easily stored **carbonate minerals**, e.g. calcium carbonate.

2) Developing alternative fuels. See page 85 for more on this.

3) Trying to **increase photosynthesis** to soak up more CO_2 — one idea is to increase the growth of **phytoplankton** (teeny green plants in the ocean) by 'seeding' the oceans with iron, an essential nutrient for the plankton.

Practice Questions

Q1 What type of electromagnetic radiation does the Earth emit?

Q2 What's the difference between the greenhouse effect and global warming?

Q3 Give three problems that climate change may cause.

Q4 Give two natural causes of climate change.

Exam Questions

Q1 a) Name the three main greenhouse gases. [3 marks]

b) Explain how greenhouse gases keep the temperature in the lower layer of the Earth's atmosphere higher than it would otherwise be. [3 marks]

c) What factors affect the contribution a gas makes to the greenhouse effect? [2 marks]

Q2 The concentration of carbon dioxide in the Earth's atmosphere has increased over the last 50 years.

a) Give two reasons for this increase. [2 marks]

b) Describe one piece of scientific evidence for the increase. [2 marks]

c) Describe two methods that chemists are developing as a way of reducing carbon dioxide emissions. [2 marks]

Global Warming probably just isn't funny...

You may be sick of global warming, because it's all over the news these days. Well, tough — just think of all those poor, seasick chemists hauling bucketfuls of water out of the ocean and sticking litmus paper in to test its acidity (that's not <u>actually</u> what they do, clearly, but there is a lot of careful measuring involved to monitor what's changing and how).

Green Chemistry

'Green' things are big news these days — they're everywhere. So it'll be no surprise to find them in AS Chemistry too.
The next three pages are for OCR A (Unit 2) and Edexcel (Unit 2).

Chemical Industries Could Be More Sustainable

1) Doing something **sustainably** means you do it **without stuffing things up** for future generations.
   So sustainable chemistry (or 'green chemistry') means **not using up** all the Earth's **resources**,
   and not putting loads of **damaging** chemicals into the environment.

2) Many of the chemical processes used in industry at the moment **aren't** very sustainable. Take the **plastics** industry,
   for example — the raw materials used often come from non-renewable **crude oil**, and the products themselves are
   usually **non-biodegradable** or **hard to recycle** when we're finished with them. (See pages 126-127 for more details.)

3) But there are things chemists can do to try and improve things. For example, they can...

1) Use Renewable Raw Materials

Loads of chemicals are traditionally made from **non-renewable** raw materials (e.g. crude oil fractions, or metal ores).
But chemists can often develop **alternative compounds** (or **alternative ways** to make existing ones) involving
renewable raw materials — e.g. some plastics are now made from **plant products** rather than oil fractions (p127).

2) Use Renewable Energy Sources, or just Use Less Energy

1) Many chemical processes use a lot of **energy**. At the moment, most of that energy
   comes from **fossil fuels**, which will soon run out. But there are potential **alternatives**...
   - **Plant-based fuels** can be used (e.g. bioethanol — see page 85 for more information).
   - **Solar power** — there are two ways to produce electricity from
     sunlight, and they're both developing rapidly at the moment.

     There are plenty of other renewable energy technologies too — geothermal, wind, wave...

     i) **photovoltaic cells** — solar panels like the ones on calculators
        (only much more efficient).
     ii) **'solar furnace'** power stations — large mirrors focus the Sun's rays onto a boiler full of water,
         heating it up and turning it into steam, which powers turbines to generate electricity.

2) Energy **efficiency** can be improved too. One technique used in the pharmaceutical industry is to use
   microwave radiation to heat the reacting mixture **directly**. (Conventional heating systems heat the
   reaction vessel, which then 'passes on' the heat to the reaction mixture — a less efficient system.)

3) Ensure All the Chemicals Involved are as Non-Toxic as Possible

1) Many common chemicals are **harmful** — either to **humans**, other **living things**, the **environment**, or all three.
   Where possible, it's generally a good thing to use a **safer** alternative. For example...
   - **Lead** (which can have some pretty unpleasant effects on your health) used to be used in paint, petrol and in
     solder for electrical components. But this meant lead got into the air from flaking paint, vehicle exhausts,
     and so on. Alternatives are now available — lead-free pigments are used in paints, unleaded petrol is
     standard now, and soldering is usually done with a mixture of tin, copper and silver.
   - Some **foams** used in fire extinguishers are very good at putting out fires, but leave hazardous products behind,
     including some that deplete the ozone layer. Again, alternatives are now available (see page 145).
   - **Dry cleaners** used to use a solvent based on chlorinated **hydrocarbons**, but these are known to be **carcinogenic**
     (i.e. they cause cancer). Safer alternatives are now available (liquid 'supercritical' carbon dioxide, as you asked).

2) Sometimes **redesigning** a **process** means you can do without unsafe chemicals completely — e.g. instead of
   using harmful organic solvents, some reactions can be carried out with one of the **reactants** acting as a solvent.

4) Make Sure that Products and Waste are Biodegradable or Recyclable

1) Chemists can also try to create **recyclable** products — a good way to conserve supplies
   of raw materials.

2) The amount of **waste** produced should also be kept to a **minimum**, and where possible it
   should be **recyclable** or **biodegradable** (see p127).

3) **Laws** can be used to encourage change. For example, when you buy a new TV, the shop now
   has to agree to recycle your old TV set, with the TV manufacturers paying some of the cost.
   This creates an incentive to design products that are easier and cheaper to recycle.

Plastics are
hard to recycle.
Dogs too.

Green Chemistry

Catalysts and High Atom Economy are Important | *Edexcel only*

1) For efficiency reasons, it's good if chemical reactions have a high **atom economy** (see pages 34-35) — this **reduces waste**, and makes the best use of **resources**.

2) Scientists can also improve the **efficiency** of a process by developing new **catalysts**.
   - A new catalyst may **speed up** an **unusably slow** (but otherwise very efficient) reaction to the point where it **can** be used.
   - A new catalyst might mean you can use a **lower** (and so more energy efficient) **temperature and pressure**, but still get your products reasonably **quickly**.

3) For example, the industrial production of **ethanoic acid** (CH₃COOH) has become much more efficient over the years...

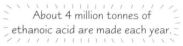
About 4 million tonnes of ethanoic acid are made each year.

① Ethanoic acid was first made on an **industrial scale** by the oxidation of butane or naphtha (crude oil fractions). The reaction needed conditions of 150-200 °C, 40-50 atm pressure and a **cobalt catalyst**.

The **atom economy** of this reaction was **low** (only about 35%) because lots of other products were made too, including methanoic acid, propanone and propanoic acid. (Most of these 'side-products' are actually useful, but separating everything took lots of energy.)

② In 1963 the chemical company BASF developed a process using methanol and carbon monoxide:

$$CH_3OH + CO \rightarrow CH_3COOH$$

The **atom economy** of this reaction is **100%** — all the reactant molecules end up as product. So it was a much more efficient use of resources than the previous method.

But it needed a higher temperature and a much higher pressure — about 300 °C and 700 atm. Using these conditions and a **cobalt iodide catalyst** gave a yield of about 90%.

See page 29 for info about percentage yields.

③
1) By 1970 a different company, Monsanto, had developed a **rhodium iodide** catalyst to use with the same reaction. With this new catalyst, **less extreme conditions** were needed — 150-200 °C and 30-60 atm. These conditions meant an improved yield of about 98%.

2) The 'Monsanto process' has been the main method used to produce ethanoic acid ever since.

3) At the moment, the **methanol** that's needed is derived from crude oil. However, it could be obtained from **biomass**, including household waste — this would make the process even more sustainable.

4) Recently BP Chemicals have developed the 'Cativa™ process'. It's based on the same reaction but uses different conditions and an **iridium iodide** catalyst. This process produces **fewer by-products** than the Monsanto Process, and makes **more efficient use** of resources.

Greener Chemistry Can Have Unexpected Consequences | *OCR A only*

1) Pretty much everyone agrees that making the chemical industry more sustainable is a good thing. But sometimes making things 'greener' can cause unwanted **knock-on effects**. Take biofuels, for example...

2) Growing grain crops for biodiesel (or sugar cane for ethanol) means that **less land** is available for growing **food**. So food gets **more expensive**. The effects of this will probably be worst for the **urban poor** — people living in towns and cities who already struggle to afford food (and can't grow their own).

3) Another worry is that large companies will buy up the **most fertile** land for biofuel production, forcing small farmers onto less fertile land where crop yields are poor.

4) There are other problems too — the land to grow biofuels often comes from clearing **forests**. And removing loads of trees means less CO₂ is absorbed in photosynthesis, and so more remains in the atmosphere — the very problem that the use of biofuels is supposed to be tackling...

5) And that's not all — destroying existing, varied habitats and replacing them all with vast swathes of the same crop will **reduce biodiversity** and could cause **soil degradation** (loss of nutrients, etc.).

Green Chemistry

International Cooperation *Is Needed to* Reduce Pollution OCR A *only*

1) Pollution doesn't stop at national borders — **rivers** flow from one country to the next, and the **atmosphere** and **oceans** are constantly moving and mixing. This means that eventually **everyone** suffers from **everyone else's** dirty ways.

2) **International cooperation** is important — there are already concerns about countries buying products made using **polluting technologies** from **abroad**, so that they can claim not to be producing the pollution themselves.

3) Various **international treaties** have been agreed. But usually, not all countries sign up because they're worried it will be bad for their **economy** (make things more expensive, cause job losses, and so on).

4) The **Montreal Protocol on Substances that Deplete the Ozone Layer** is probably the most successful 'green chemistry' global treaty to date — virtually everyone's signed up. Countries who signed up to this '**Montreal Protocol**' agreed to phase out production of substances that damaged the ozone layer (see p144-145).

5) Similarly, most countries have signed the **Stockholm Treaty** on persistent organic pollutants (POPs). POPs are organic chemicals (e.g. some pesticides and fungicides) that **accumulate** in the fatty tissues of living organisms. They're passed up the food chain and are **toxic** to humans and other animals.

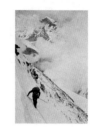

6) In 1992, the United Nations held a big conference about the environment and development (the '**Earth Summit**') in Rio de Janeiro. Governments agreed to a set of **27 principles** about sustainable development — the 'Rio Declaration'.

These principles were all very sensible (e.g. don't cause environmental harm, develop in a sustainable way, and so on) but they **aren't legally binding** — so **no punishment** can be dished out when countries don't keep to the principles.

The summit of the Earth... much harder to get to than the Earth Summit in Rio had been.

You <u>don't</u> need to memorise <u>every detail</u> about the examples on these last two pages, but you should understand the <u>basic principles</u> behind them.

Practice Questions

Q1 List four ways in which the chemical industry can be made more sustainable.

Q2 Explain why plants are a sustainable resource.

Q3 Why is a high atom economy desirable in chemical reactions?

Q4 Why are international treaties important in controlling pollution?

Exam Questions

Q1 In Brazil, ethanol is produced by fermenting sugar cane.
This ethanol is then used as fuel.

a) Explain the advantages of using ethanol made from sugar cane as a fuel, instead of petrol. [2 marks]

b) Suggest why not all countries produce ethanol for use as a fuel in this way. [1 mark]

c) Describe two possible negative effects of growing sugar cane to make ethanol. [2 marks]

Q2 Much research is currently done on new catalysts.

a) Explain why catalysts are important in making chemical processes 'greener'. [2 marks]

b) The discovery of a new catalyst has made it possible to make ethanoic acid very efficiently by reacting methanol with carbon monoxide:

$$CH_3OH + CO \rightarrow CH_3COOH$$

Describe one way in which this process could be considered 'green'. [2 marks]

Like the contents of my fridge, Chemistry's going greener by the day...

It's important stuff, all this. It'll be important for your exam, obviously, but it's my bet that you'll come across this stuff long after you've taken your exam as well, which makes it doubly useful. On a different note... isn't it weird how you can sign up for an AS level in Chemistry, and only then be told that you'll be studying international politics too...

The Chemical Industry

These pages are for OCR B (Unit 2) only.

I'm sure that with all your chemistry knowledge, you're thinking of starting up a chemical business.
But there are a few things you'll need to bear in mind before you do...

Production Processes are either **Batch** or **Continuous**

This bit is relatively straightforward. You can either make your product **continuously**, or in **batches**...

	Continuous	Batch
What is it?	Reactants continually enter the vessel, and products continually leave — the reaction doesn't need to be stopped.	Reactants enter the vessel and react. The product is removed, the vessel is cleaned and then used again.
Advantages	Lower labour costs as the process can be easily automated. Can make large quantities of product non-stop. Less variation in quality.	Small quantities can be made. The reaction vessel can be used to make other products. Cheaper to build.
Disadvantages	More expensive to build. More expensive to run unless the plant runs at full capacity.	More labour intensive as emptying and cleaning needed. Contamination can occur if cleaning is not thorough.
Examples	Making industrial ethanol (see p121). Haber process for making ammonia. Contact process for making sulfuric acid. Blast furnace.	Dye manufacture. Aspirin and paracetamol manufacture. Steel making. Production of ethanol by fermentation (p128).

It's Important to Choose a **Suitable Site**

This is where things get more complicated. You probably **won't** find a place that's absolutely **perfect** to build your plant. You'll probably need to find the best **compromise** to satisfy **competing demands**.

1) Ideally, you'd like your chemical plant to be near a source of **raw materials**, since they can be expensive to **transport** — especially if they're hazardous, bulky, or you just need lots of them. So it might make sense to build your plant near a **source** of your raw materials, or near a **port** you can ship them to.

2) But ideally, you'd also like to put your plant near your **customers** — to save on **delivery costs**. (If a product's going to be used by another plant to make other chemicals, it's usually a good idea to site the plants close together.)

3) Chemical processes often use large amounts of **water** for cooling. So you might want access to a **river** or the **sea**.

4) And if your process needs loads of **energy** (as in, say, the production of aluminium), you need to think about that too. (Aluminium ore is shipped long distances to get it to cheap sources of power, e.g. near a hydroelectric power station.)

5) You'll also need to think about your **workforce**. Are people with the necessary **skills** available **nearby**? If not, will people be willing to **relocate**?

6) It's pretty unlikely you'll be able to find a spot that satisfies **all** of these requirements. So what you have to do is pick the place that offers the best **compromise**. You might be able to accept being far from your customers as long as the bulky, hazardous raw materials are nearby. What you compromise on will depend on the exact nature of the chemical plant you're building.

Atom Economy is Important When Choosing **Reactions**

Businesses want to make **efficient** use of their raw materials — especially if they're in limited supply.

1) Atoms from raw materials can end up in **either**: a) products that you can use, **or** b) products that are useless (waste).

2) Industries want to make as **little waste** as possible, since waste products have to be **separated** from the useful ones, and then disposed of **safely** (governments have tight controls on all kinds of **pollution**).

3) Also, they'll probably have paid **good money** for the raw materials, so won't want too much of them ending up as waste.

The atom economy tells you the proportion of atoms from the starting materials that end up in useful products — see p34-35.

4) So where possible, businesses use **reactions** with **high atom economies**.

5) Ideally, they'd also choose reactions where the raw materials, waste products, intermediate products, and the process itself are as **safe** as possible. Apart from reducing the **risks** generally, it also avoids having to take potentially expensive **safety precautions**, which are strictly controlled by **health and safety legislation**.

The Chemical Industry

Reaction Conditions are Often a Compromise

You've got your chemical plant. You've chosen your reaction. Now you need to decide the **reaction conditions**.

1) Reaction conditions will affect your **percentage yield**, the **speed** of the reaction, and the **equipment** you need (high pressures will need expensive **pipes** and **vessels** to withstand it, for example).

> Percentage yield (see p29) compares the amount of product actually produced with the theoretical amount you'd expect according to the reaction equation.

2) Ideally, you'd choose the conditions that give you the **highest percentage yield**, the **fastest reaction** and that **reduce your costs** as much as possible. This will make for the greatest **efficiency**.

3) Unfortunately though, you'll probably have to **compromise** again...

For example, it could be that you can get a really **high percentage yield** and a really **fast reaction** if you use a **high temperature** and **pressure**. Unfortunately, this will mean you need to **spend more** on:
   (i)   **energy costs** (high temperature and pressure are expensive to make),
   (ii) **tougher equipment** (to cope with the high temperatures and pressures),
   (iii) **stricter safety measures** (high temperatures and pressures are more dangerous, requiring more stringent procedures and better training).

So maybe you'll compromise, and choose a **lower temperature and pressure**, meaning:
   (i)   your equipment costs are **cheaper**, and you'll probably need less stringent **safety procedures**, but...
   (ii) you'll have a **slower reaction**, which will **increase** your **costs** anyway (time is money in industry).

Or maybe you could think about how using a high temperature and low pressure would affect things...

4) There's not always an **obvious** answer. In reality, chemists and **accountants** would have to sit down and work out how much the various possible options would cost, and choose the one that works best for the business.

Which do you favour, atom economy or percentage yield?

I don't really care, I'm a used car salesman.

5) One thing that will usually help though is a **catalyst**. Catalysts are great. They can save heaps of money — see pages 104-105. (But you'd still have to think about the time and money needed to **separate** catalysts from the product, the likelihood of the catalyst being **poisoned**, and so on. Nothing's ever straightforward, is it.)

Practice Questions

Q1 Describe an important advantage of using reactions with high atom economies in industry.

Q2 Give two advantages of batch production and two advantages of continuous production.

Q3 Give three factors that affect the siting of a chemical plant.

Exam Questions

Q1 Ethanol can be made by the addition of steam to ethene: $C_2H_{4(g)} + H_2O_{(g)} \rightleftharpoons C_2H_5OH_{(g)}$

   a) Calculate the atom economy of this reaction and use your answer to explain
      why addition reactions are used as often as possible in industry. [2 marks]

   b) Suggest two reasons why the percentage yield of this reaction is always less than 100%? [1 mark]

   c) Ethene is made by cracking oil or natural gas.
      Explain how this might affect the choice of location for a plant producing ethanol. [2 marks]

Q2 Chemical A is used to make chemical B in a reaction with a 90% atom economy.

   a) Starting with 1000 kg of reactants, how much of chemical B would you expect to be produced? [1 mark]

   b) Chemical B is then used to make chemical C. Using 500 kg of chemical B, the reaction equation
      indicates that you should theoretically get 300 kg of Chemical C. You actually get 250 kg.
      Calculate the percentage yield of this reaction. [2 marks]

   c) Chemical A is very cheap. Chemical C is expensive.
      Suggest three factors that might account for this difference in price. [3 marks]

I've got a chemical plant — it's a chemis-tree...

You need to be able to compare different chemical processes by thinking about all the factors mentioned on these pages.
To get rich, all you need is to find a clean, safe chemical process with high atom economy and yield that you can carry out
cheaply and easily anywhere you like, and sell the product for loads of money. And if you can find one, let me know...

Mass Spectrometry

You're fast approaching the thrilling climax of the book — and watch out for the twist at the end of this double page...
These pages are for AQA (Unit 2), OCR A (Unit 2) and Edexcel (Units 1 and 2).

Mass Spectrometry Can Help to Identify Compounds
Not Edexcel (Unit 1)

1) You saw on pages 16-17 how **mass spectrometry** can be used to find **relative isotopic masses**, the **abundance** of different isotopes, and the **relative molecular mass**, M_r, of a compound.

2) Remember — to find the relative molecular mass of a compound you look at the **molecular ion peak** (the **M peak**) on the spectrum. Molecular ions are formed when molecules have **electrons** knocked off. The mass/charge value of the molecular ion peak is the molecular mass.

Assuming the ion has 1+ charge, which it normally will have.

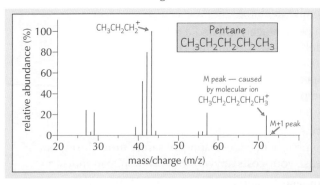

Here's the mass spectrum of pentane. Its M peak is at 72 — so the compound's M_r is 72.

For most <u>organic compounds</u> the M peak is the one with the second highest mass/charge ratio. The smaller peak to the right of the M peak is called the M+1 peak — it's caused by the presence of the carbon isotope ^{13}C (you don't need to worry about this at AS).

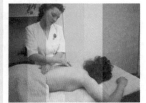

A massage spectrum

The Molecular Ion can be Broken into Smaller Fragments
Not Edexcel (Unit 1)

The bombarding electrons make some of the molecular ions break up into **fragments**. The fragments that are ions show up on the mass spectrum, making a **fragmentation pattern**. Fragmentation patterns are actually pretty cool because you can use them to identify **molecules** and even their **structure**.

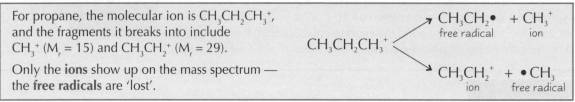

For propane, the molecular ion is $CH_3CH_2CH_3^+$, and the fragments it breaks into include CH_3^+ ($M_r = 15$) and $CH_3CH_2^+$ ($M_r = 29$).

Only the **ions** show up on the mass spectrum — the **free radicals** are 'lost'.

To work out the structural formula, you've got to work out what **ion** could have made each peak from its **m/z value**. (You assume that the m/z value of a peak matches the **mass** of the ion that made it.)

Example: Use this mass spectrum to work out the structure of the molecule:

It's only the m/z values you're interested in — ignore the heights of the bars.

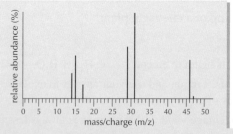

Fragment	Molecular Mass
CH_3	15
C_2H_5	29
C_3H_7	43
OH	17

1. Identify the fragments

This molecule's got a peak at 15 m/z, so it's likely to have a **CH₃** group.

It's also got a peak at 17 m/z, so it's likely to have an **OH** group.

Other ions are matched to the peaks here:

2. Piece them together to form a molecule with the correct M_r

Ethanol has all the fragments on this spectrum.

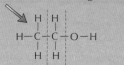

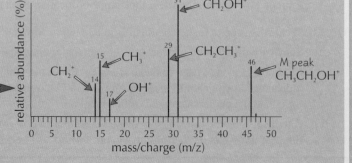

Ethanol's **molecular mass** is 46.
This should be the same as the m/z value of the M peak — it is.

Mass Spectrometry

Mass Spectrometry is Used to **Differentiate** Between **Similar Molecules**

OCR A and Edexcel (Unit 2) only

1) Even if two **different compounds** contain **the same atoms**, you can still tell them apart with mass spectrometry because they won't produce exactly the same set of fragments.

2) The formulas of **propanal** and **propanone** are shown on the right. They've got the same M_r, but different structures, so they produce some **different fragments**. For example, propanal will have a C_2H_5 fragment but propanone won't.

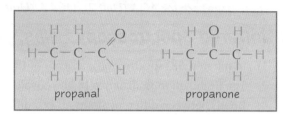
propanal   propanone

3) Every compound produces a different mass spectrum — so the spectrum's like a **fingerprint** for the compound. Large computer **databases** of mass spectra can be used to identify a compound from its spectrum.

Mass Spectrometry Has **Many Uses**   OCR A and Edexcel (Unit 1) only

Mass spectrometry is actually used by scientists out there in the real world. Here are a few examples.

1) **Probes to Mars** have carried small mass spectrometers to study the composition of the surface of Mars and to look for molecules that might suggest that life existed on the planet.

2) Athletes' urine is **tested for drugs** with mass spectrometry. It shows up the presence of **banned substances** such as anabolic steroids by their distinctive spectra.

3) The **pharmaceutical industry** uses mass spectrometry to **identify** the compounds in possible new drugs, and to tell how long drugs stay in the body by finding molecules of the drug in blood and urine samples.

4) **Radiocarbon dating** (see p13) is used by archaeologists to date artefacts they've found. It involves finding out how much of the radioactive isotope ^{14}C an item contains. Traditional methods measure this by measuring the decay rate of the ^{14}C, but it's so slow that the method's not that accurate. But a type of mass spectrometry can be used to measure the proportion of ^{14}C atoms there actually are in a small sample — giving more accurate results.

5) Mass spectrometry can also be used to measure the **levels of pollutants** present in the environment, e.g. the amount of lead or pesticides entering the food chain via vegetables.

Practice Questions

Q1 What is meant by the molecular ion?

Q2 What is the M peak?

Q3 How do fragments get formed?

Q4 How is mass spectrometry used in dating ancient bones?

Exam Question

Q1 Below is the mass spectrum of an organic compound, Q.

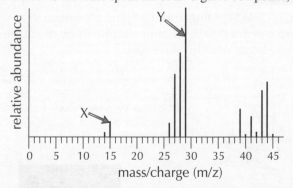

a) What is the M_r of compound Q? [1 mark]

b) What fragments are the peaks marked X and Y most likely to correspond to? [2 marks]

c) Suggest a structure for this compound. [1 mark]

d) Why is it unlikely that this compound is an alcohol? [2 marks]

Use the clues, identify a molecule — mass spectrometry my dear Watson...

It's handy if you can learn the molecular masses of those common fragments, but if you forget them, just take a deep breath and work them out from the relative atomic masses of the atoms in the fragment. And don't worry, I haven't forgotten I said there was twist at the end... erm... hydrogen was my sister all along... and all the elements went to live in Jamaica. The End.

Infrared Spectroscopy

If you've got some stuff and don't know what it is, don't taste it. Stick it in an infrared spectrometer instead. Infrared spectroscopy produces scary looking graphs. But just learn the basics, and you'll be fine.

These pages are for AQA (Unit 2), OCR A (Unit 2), OCR B (Unit 2) and Edexcel (Unit 2).

Infrared Spectroscopy Helps You Identify Organic Molecules

1) In infrared (IR) spectroscopy, a beam of **IR radiation** is passed through a sample of a chemical.

2) The IR radiation is absorbed by the **covalent bonds** in the molecules, increasing their **vibrational** energy (see p143).

3) **Bonds between different atoms** absorb **different frequencies** of IR radiation. Bonds in different **places** in a molecule absorb different frequencies too — so the O–H group in an **alcohol** and the O–H in a **carboxylic acid** absorb different frequencies. This table shows what **frequencies** different bonds absorb:

Functional group	Where it's found	Frequency/ Wavenumber (cm⁻¹)	Type of absorption
C–H	most organic molecules	2800 - 3100	strong, sharp
O–H	alcohols	3200 - 3550	strong, broad
O–H	carboxylic acids	2500 - 3300	medium, broad
N–H	amines (e.g. methylamine, CH_3NH_2)	3200 - 3500	strong, sharp
C=O	aldehydes, ketones, carboxylic acids	1680 - 1750	strong, sharp
C–X	haloalkanes	500 - 1000	strong, sharp

This tells you what the peak on the graph will look like.

You don't need to learn this data, but you do need to understand how to use it.

4) An infrared spectrometer produces a **graph** that shows you what frequencies of radiation the molecules are absorbing. So you can use it to identify the **functional groups** in a molecule:

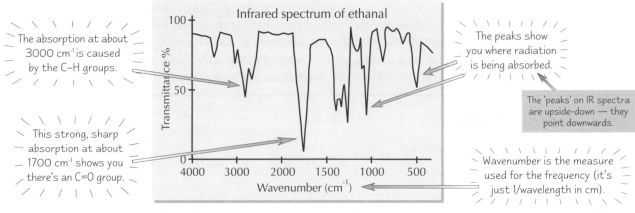

The absorption at about 3000 cm⁻¹ is caused by the C–H groups.

This strong, sharp absorption at about 1700 cm⁻¹ shows you there's an C=O group.

The peaks show you where radiation is being absorbed.

The 'peaks' on IR spectra are upside-down — they point downwards.

Wavenumber is the measure used for the frequency (it's just 1/wavelength in cm).

This also means that you can tell if a functional group has **changed** during a reaction. For example, if you **oxidise** an **alcohol** to an **aldehyde** you'll see the O–H absorption **disappear** from the spectrum, and a C=O absorption **appear**.

The Fingerprint Region Identifies a Molecule   *AQA and OCR B only*

The region between **1000 cm⁻¹** and **1550 cm⁻¹** on the spectrum is called the **fingerprint** region. It's **unique** to a **particular compound**. You can check this region of an unknown compound's IR spectrum against those of known compounds. If it **matches up** with one of them, hey presto — you know what the molecule is.

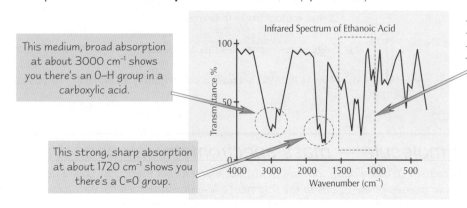

This medium, broad absorption at about 3000 cm⁻¹ shows you there's an O–H group in a carboxylic acid.

This strong, sharp absorption at about 1720 cm⁻¹ shows you there's a C=O group.

This is the fingerprint region. If you see an infrared spectrum of an unknown molecule that has the same pattern in this area, you can be sure that it's ethanoic acid.

Clark began to regret having an infrared mechanism installed in his glasses.

Infrared Spectroscopy

Infrared Spectroscopy Helps Catch **Drunk Drivers**

If a person's suspected of drink driving, they're **breathalysed**.

First a very quick test is done by the roadside — if it says that the driver's over the limit, they're taken into a police station for a more **accurate test** using **infrared spectroscopy**.

The **amount** of **ethanol vapour** in the driver's breath is found by measuring the **intensity** of the peak corresponding to the **C–H bond** in the IR spectrum. It's chosen because it's **not affected** by any **water vapour** in the breath.

OCR A only

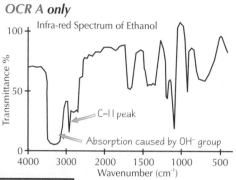

Infrared Spectroscopy is Also Used to **Monitor Air Pollution**

You can use infrared spectroscopy to measure how much of a **polluting gas** is present in the **air**.
Here's an outline of how infrared spectroscopy is used to check how much **carbon monoxide** there is:

1) A **sample of air** is drawn into the spectrometer. A beam of **infrared radiation** of a certain frequency is passed through the sample. Any carbon monoxide that is present will **absorb** some of this radiation.

2) At the same time, a beam of infrared radiation of the **same frequency** is passed through a sample of a gas that **doesn't absorb any infrared**, like N_2. This acts as a kind of **control** reading.

3) The **difference** in the amount of infrared energy absorbed by the gases in the two chambers is a measure of the **amount** of carbon monoxide present in the air sample.

You can use the same technique to monitor the levels of any polluting gas that can absorb infrared, like NO, SO_2 or CH_4.

Remember — only molecules containing at least two different atoms will absorb infrared radiation — see page 143.

Infrared Energy **Absorption** is Linked to **Global Warming**   *AQA and OCR A only*

Some of the electromagnetic radiation emitted by the **Sun** is in the form of **infrared radiation**. Molecules of **greenhouse gases**, like **carbon dioxide**, **methane** and **water vapour**, are really good at absorbing infrared energy — so if the amounts of them in the atmosphere increase, it leads to **global warming**. There's lots more about how this happens on pages 145-148.

Practice Questions

Q1 Which parts of a molecule absorb infrared energy?

Q2 Why do most infrared spectra of organic molecules have a strong, sharp peak at around 3000 cm⁻¹?

Q3 On an infrared spectrum, what is meant by the 'fingerprint region'?

Exam Question

Q1 A molecule with a molecular mass of 74 produces the following IR spectrum.

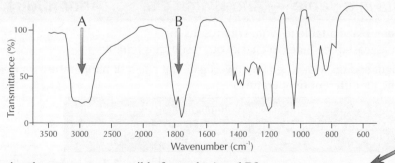

Use the infrared absorption data on the opposite page.

a) Which functional groups are responsible for peaks A and B? [2 marks]

b) Give the molecular formula and name of this molecule. Explain your answer. [3 marks]

I wonder what the infrared spectrum of a fairy cake would look like...

I don't suppose I'll ever know. Very squiggly I imagine. Luckily you don't have to be able to remember what any of the infrared spectrum graphs look like. But you definitely need to know how to interpret them, because sure as eggs are eggs it'll turn up in the exam. And there's only one thing to do to make sure you know how — it's those evil practice questions again...

Practical and Investigative Skills

Whatever exam board you're doing, you're going to have to do some practical work —
and once you've done the practical work, you'll have to make sense of your results.

Make it a **Fair Test** — Control your **Variables**

You probably know this all off by heart but it's easy to get mixed up sometimes. So here's a quick recap:

> **Variable** — A variable is a **quantity** that has the **potential to change**, e.g. mass.
> There are two types of variable commonly referred to in experiments:
> - **Independent variable** — the thing that you **change** in an experiment.
> - **Dependent variable** — the thing that you **measure** in an experiment.

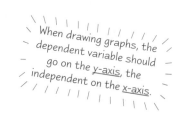

When drawing graphs, the dependent variable should go on the y-axis, the independent on the x-axis.

So, if you're investigating the effect of **temperature** on rate of reaction
(using an experiment like the one on page 102), the variables will be:

Independent variable	Temperature
Dependent variable	Amount of oxygen produced — you can measure this by collecting it in a gas syringe
Other variables — you MUST keep these the same	Concentration and volume of solutions, mass of solids, pressure, the presence of a catalyst and the surface area of any solid reactants

Know Your Different Sorts of **Data**

Experiments always involve some sort of measurement to provide **data**.
There are different types of data — and you need to know what they are.

> **Discrete** — you get discrete data by **counting**. E.g. the number of bubbles produced in a reaction would be discrete. You can't have 1.25 bubbles. That'd be daft. Shoe size is another good example of a discrete variable.

> **Continuous** — a continuous variable can have **any value** on a scale. For example, the volume of gas produced or the mass of products from a reaction. You can never measure the exact value of a continuous variable.

> **Categoric** — a categoric variable has values that can be sorted into **categories**. For example, the colours of solutions might be blue, red and green. Or types of material might be wood, steel, glass.

> **Ordered (ordinal)** — Ordered data is similar to categoric, but the categories can be **put in order**. For example, if you classify reactions as 'slow', 'fairly fast' and 'very fast' you'd have ordered data.

Organise Your Results in a **Table** — And Watch Out For **Anomalous** Ones

Before you start your experiment, make a **table** to write your results in.
You'll need to repeat each test at least three times to check your results are reliable.

This is the sort of table you might end up with when you investigate the effect of **temperature** on **reaction rate**.
(You'd then have to do the same for **different temperatures**.)

Temperature	Time (s)	Volume of gas evolved (cm³) Run 1	Volume of gas evolved (cm³) Run 2	Volume of gas evolved (cm³) Run 3	Average volume of gas evolved (cm³)
	10	8	7	8	7.7
20 °C	20	17	19	20	18.7
	30	28	20	30	29

Find the average of each set of repeated values.

You need to add them all up and divide by how many there are.

E.g.: (8 + 7 + 8) ÷ 3 = 7.7 cm³

Watch out for **anomalous results**. These are ones that don't fit in with the other values and are likely to be wrong.
They're likely to be due to random errors — here the syringe plunger may have got stuck. See page 32 for more on types of error.
Ignore anomalous results when you calculate the average.

Practical and Investigative Skills

Graphs: *Line, Bar or Scatter* — Use the *Best Type*

You'll usually be expected to make a **graph** of your results. Not only are graphs **pretty**, they make your data **easier to understand** — so long as you choose the right type.

Line graphs are best when you have **two sets of continuous data**. For example:

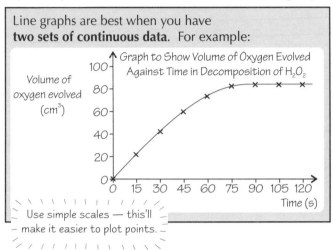

Use simple scales — this'll make it easier to plot points.

You should use a bar chart when one of your data sets is **categoric or ordered data**. For example:

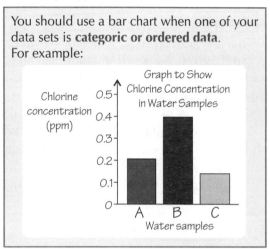

Scatter plots are great for showing how two sets of data are related (or **correlated**).

Don't try to join all the points — draw a **line of best fit** to show the **trend**.

Scatter Graphs Show The Relationship Between Variables

Correlation describes the **relationship** between two variables — the independent one and the dependent one.

Data can show:

1) **Positive correlation** — as one variable **increases** the other **increases**. The graph on the left shows positive correlation.

2) **Negative correlation** — as one variable **increases** the other **decreases**.

3) **No correlation** — there is **no relationship** between the two variables.

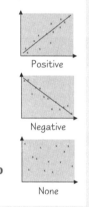

There's also pie charts. These are normally used to display categoric data.

Whatever type of graph you make, you'll ONLY get full marks if you:

- Choose a sensible scale — don't do a tiny graph in the corner of the paper.
- Label both axes — including units.
- Plot your points accurately — using a sharp pencil.

Correlation *Doesn't* Mean *Cause* — Don't Jump to Conclusions

1) Ideally, only **two** quantities would **ever** change in any experiment — everything else would remain **constant**.

2) But in experiments or studies outside the lab, you **can't** usually control all the variables. So even if two variables are correlated, the change in one may **not** be causing the change in the other. Both changes might be caused be a **third variable**.

Watch out for bias too — for instance, a bottled water company might point these studies out to people without mentioning any of the doubts.

Example

For example: Some studies have found a correlation between **drinking chlorinated tap water** and the risk of developing certain cancers. So some people argue that this means water shouldn't have chlorine added.

BUT it's hard to control all the variables between people who drink tap water and people who don't. It could be many lifestyle factors.

Or, the cancer risk could be affected by something else in tap water — or by whatever the non-tap water drinkers drink instead...

Practical and Investigative Skills

Don't Get **Carried Away** When Drawing Conclusions

The **data** should always **support** the conclusion. This may sound obvious but it's easy to **jump** to conclusions. Conclusions have to be **specific** — not make sweeping generalisations.

> **Example**
>
> The rate of an enzyme-controlled reaction was measured at **10 °C, 20 °C, 30 °C, 40 °C, 50 °C and 60 °C**. All other variables were kept constant, and the results are shown in this graph.
>
> A science magazine **concluded** from this data that enzyme X works best at **40 °C**. The data **doesn't** support this.
>
> The enzyme **could** work best at 42 °C or 47 °C but you can't tell from the data because **increases** of **10 °C** at a time were used. The rate of reaction at in-between temperatures **wasn't** measured.
>
> All you know is that it's faster at **40 °C** than at any of the other temperatures tested.

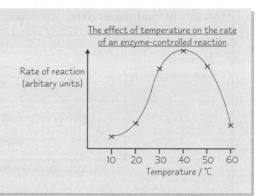

> **Example**
>
> The experiment above **ONLY** gives information about this particular enzyme-controlled reaction. You can't conclude that **all** enzyme-controlled reactions happen faster at a particular temperature — only this one. And you can't say for sure that doing the experiment at, say, a different constant pressure, wouldn't give a different optimum temperature.

You need to Look **Critically** at Your Results

There are a few bits of lingo that you need to understand. They'll be useful when you're evaluating how convincing your results are.

1) **Valid results** — Valid results answer the original question. For example, if you haven't **controlled all the variables** your results won't be valid, because you won't be testing just the thing you wanted to.

2) **Accurate** — Accurate results are those that are **really close** to the **true** answer.

3) **Precise results** — These are results taken using **sensitive instruments** that measure in **small increments**, e.g. pH measured with a meter (pH 7.692) will be **more precise** than pH measured with paper (pH 7).

> It's possible for results to be precise **but not** accurate, e.g. a balance that weighs to 1/1000 th of a gram will give precise results but if it's not **calibrated** properly the results won't be accurate.

4) **Reliable results** — **Reliable** means the results can be **consistently reproduced** in independent experiments. And if the results are reproducible they're more likely to be **true**. If the data isn't reliable for whatever reason you **can't draw** a valid **conclusion**.

    For experiments, the **more repeats** you do, the **more reliable** the data. If you get the **same result** twice, it could be the correct answer. But if you get the same result **20 times**, it'd be much more reliable. And it'd be even more reliable if everyone in the class got about the same results using different apparatus.

Work **Safely** and **Ethically** — Don't Blow Up the Lab or Harm Small Animals

In any experiment you'll be expected to show that you've thought about the **risks and hazards** (see page 141). It's generally a good thing to wear an apron and goggles, but you may need to take additional safety measures, depending on the experiment. For example, anything involving nasty gases will need to be done in a fume cupboard.

You need to make sure you're working **ethically** too. This is most important if there are other people or animals involved. You have to put their welfare first.

Answers

Section One — Atomic Structure

Page 5 — The Atom

1)a) Similarity — They've all got the same number of protons/electrons.
   [1 mark]
   Difference — They all have different numbers of neutrons. [1 mark]
 b) 1 proton [1 mark], 1 neutron (2 – 1) [1 mark], 1 electron [1 mark].
 c) ^{3}H. [1 mark]
   Since tritium has 2 neutrons in the nucleus and also 1 proton, it has a
   mass number of 3. You could also write $^3_1$H but you don't really need the
   atomic number.

2)a) i) Same number of electrons. [1 mark]
     ^{32}S^{2-} has 16 + 2 = 18 electrons. ^{40}Ar has 18 electrons too. [1 mark]
   ii) Same number of protons. [1 mark].
     Each has 16 protons (the atomic number of S must always be the
     same) [1 mark].
   iii)Same number of neutrons. [1 mark]
     ^{40}Ar has 40 – 18 = 22 neutrons. ^{42}Ca has 42 – 20 = 22 neutrons.
     [1 mark]
 b) **A** and **C**. [1 mark] They have the same number of protons but
   different numbers of neutrons. [1 mark].
   It doesn't matter that they have a different number of electrons because
   they are still the same element.

Page 7 — Atomic Models

1)a) Bohr knew that if an electron was freely orbiting the nucleus it would
   spiral into it, causing the atom to collapse [1 mark]. His model only
   allowed electrons to be in fixed shells and not in between them
   [1 mark].
 b) When an electron moves from one shell to another electromagnetic
   radiation is emitted or absorbed [1 mark].
 c) Atoms react in order to gain full shells of electrons [1 mark]. Noble
   gases have full shells and so do not react [1 mark]. (Alternatively: a
   full shell of electrons makes an atom stable [1 mark]; noble gases
   have full shells and do not react because they are stable [1 mark].)

Page 9 — Electronic Structure

1)a) K atom: $1s^2 2s^2 2p^6 3s^2 3p^6 4s^1$ [1 mark]
   K$^+$ ion: $1s^2 2s^2 2p^6 3s^2 3p^6$ [1 mark]
 b)

Oxygen electron Configuration	1s	2s	2p
	↑↓	↑↓	↑↓ ↑ ↑

   1 mark for the correct number of electrons in each sub-shell.
   1 mark for having spin-pairing in one of the p orbitals and parallel
   spins in the other two p orbitals. A box filled with 2 arrows is spin
   pairing — 1 up and 1 down. If you've put the four p electrons into
   just 2 orbitals, it's wrong.
 c) The outer shell electrons in potassium and oxygen can get close to
   the outer shells of other atoms, so they can be transferred or shared
   [1 mark]. The inner shell electrons are tightly held and shielded from
   the electrons in other atoms/molecules [1 mark].
2)a) $1s^2 2s^2 2p^6 3s^2 3p^6 3d^5 4s^2$. [1 mark]
 b) Germanium ($1s^2 2s^2 2p^6 3s^2 3p^6 3d^{10} 4s^2 4p^2$). [1 mark].
   (The 4p sub-shell is partly filled, so it must be a p block element.)
 c) Ar (atom) [1 mark], K$^+$ (positive ion) [1 mark], Cl$^-$ (negative ion)
   [1 mark]. You also could have suggested Ca^{2+}, S^{2-} or P^{3-}.
 d)

Al^{3+} electron Configuration	1s	2s	2p
	↑↓	↑↓	↑↓ ↑↓ ↑↓

   1 mark for the correct number of electrons in each sub-shell.
   1 mark for one arrow in each box pointing up, and one pointing
   down.

Page 11 — Atomic Spectra

1)a) The movement of electrons / an electron [1 mark] from lower to
   higher energy levels [1 mark].
 b) Line E (because it is at the highest frequency) [1 mark].
 c) i) It would consist of bright, not dark, lines [1 mark].
   ii) The lines would be at the same frequencies [1 mark].
 d) Because the energy levels get closer together with increasing energy
   [1 mark].
2) $E = h\nu = (6.626 \times 10^{-34}) \times (5.1 \times 10^{14}) = \textbf{3.38} \times \textbf{10}^{-19}$ **J**
   [1 mark for correct number, and 1 mark for correct unit]

Page 13 — Nuclear Fusion and Radiation

1) $^{216}_{84}$Po $\rightarrow$ $^{212}_{82}$Pb + $^4_2$He [216 – 212 = 4, 84 – 82 = 2] [1 mark]
   $^{212}_{82}$Pb $\rightarrow$ $^{212}_{83}$Bi + $^0_{-1}$e [212 – 0 = 212, 82 – (-1) = 83] [1 mark]

2)a) Atomic number = 12 [1 mark]
   Name is magnesium [1 mark]
   Mass number = 24 [1 mark]
   In beta decay the atomic number increases by 1, but the mass number
   does not change. The atomic number tells you the name of the isotope.
 b) 800 to 50 involves 4 half-lives [1 mark]
   4 × 15 hours = 60 hours [1 mark]

3) Gamma radiation is able to pass through body materials easily
   so it can be detected outside the body, whereas alpha radiation can't
   [1 mark]. Gamma radiation is far less ionising than alpha radiation so
   it causes far less damage [1 mark].

Page 15 — Ionisation Energies

1)a) C$_{(g)}$ $\rightarrow$ C$^+_{(g)}$ + e$^-$
   [1 mark for the correct equation. 1 mark if both state symbols show
   gaseous state.]
 b) First ionisation energy increases as nuclear charge increases [1 mark].
 c) As the nuclear charge increases there is a stronger force of attraction
   between the nucleus and the electron [1 mark] and so more energy is
   required to remove the electron [1 mark].
2)a) Group 3 [1 mark]
   There are three electrons removed before the first big jump in energy.
 b) The electrons are being removed from an increasing positive charge
   [1 mark] so more energy is needed to remove an electron / the force
   of attraction that has to be broken is greater [1 mark].
 c) When an electron is removed from a different shell there is a big
   increase in the energy required (since that shell is closer to the
   nucleus) [1 mark].
 d) There are 3 shells (because there are 2 big jumps in energy) [1 mark].

Section Two — Mass, Moles and Equations

Page 17 — Relative Mass

1)a) First multiply each relative abundance by the relative mass —
   120.8 × 63 = 7610.4, 54.0 × 65 = 3510.0
   Next add up the products —
   7610.4 + 3510.0 = 11 120.4   [1 mark]
   Now divide by the total abundance (120.8 + 54.0 = 174.8)

   $$A_r(Cu) = \frac{11120.4}{174.8} \approx \textbf{63.6}$$ [1 mark]

   You can check your answer by seeing if A$_r$(Cu) is in between 63 and 65
   (the lowest and highest relative isotopic masses).
 b) A sample of copper is a mixture of 2 isotopes of different abundances
   [1 mark]. The weighted average mass of these isotopes isn't a whole
   number [1 mark].
2)a) Mass spectroscopy. [1 mark]
 b) You use pretty much the same method here as for question 1)a).
   93.11 × 39 = 3631.29, 0.12 × 40 = 4.8, 6.77 × 41 = 277.57
   3631.29 + 4.8 + 277.57 = 3913.66   [1 mark]
   This time you divide by 100 because they're percentages.

   $$A_r(K) = \frac{3913.66}{100} \approx \textbf{39.14}$$ [1 mark]

   Again check your answer's between the lowest and highest relative
   isotopic masses, 39 and 41. A$_r$(K) is closer to 39 because most of the
   sample (93.11%) is made up of this isotope.

Page 19 — The Mole

1) M of CH$_3$COOH = (2 x 12) + (4 x 1) + (2 x 16) = 60 g mol^{-1}
   [1 mark]
   so mass of 0.36 moles = 60 × 0.36 = **21.6 g**   [1 mark]

2) No. of moles = $\dfrac{0.25 \times 60}{1000}$ = 0.015 moles H$_2$SO$_4$ [1 mark]

   M of H$_2$SO$_4$ = (2 × 1) + (1 × 32) + (4 × 16) = 98 g mol^{-1}
   Mass of 0.015 mol H$_2$SO$_4$ = 98 × 0.015 = **1.47 g**   [1 mark]

Answers

3) M of $C_3H_8 = (3 \times 12) + (8 \times 1) = 44$ g mol^{-1}

No. of moles of $C_3H_8 = \dfrac{88}{44} = 2$ moles   *[1 mark]*

At r.t.p. 1 mole of gas occupies 24 dm^3
so 2 moles of gas occupies $2 \times 24 = $ **48 dm^3**   *[1 mark]*

Page 21 — Empirical and Molecular Formulas

1) Assume you've got 100 g of the compound so you can turn the % straight into mass.

No. of moles of $C = \dfrac{92.3}{12} = 7.69$ moles

No. of moles of $H = \dfrac{7.7}{1} = 7.7$ moles   *[1 mark]*

Divide both by the smallest number, in this case 7.69.
So ratio $C : H = 1 : 1$
So, the empirical formula = CH *[1 mark]*

The empirical mass $= 12 + 1 = 13$

No. of empirical units in molecule $= \dfrac{78}{13} = 6$

So the molecular formula = **C_6H_6**   *[1 mark]*

2) The magnesium is burning, so it's reacting with oxygen and the product is magnesium oxide.
First work out the number of moles of each element.

No. of moles $Mg = \dfrac{1.2}{24} = 0.05$ moles

Mass of O is everything that isn't Mg: $2 - 1.2 = 0.8$ g

No. of moles $O = \dfrac{0.8}{16} = 0.05$ moles   *[1 mark]*

Ratio $Mg : O = 0.05 : 0.05$
Divide both by the smallest number, in this case 0.05.
So ratio $Mg : O = 1 : 1$
So the empirical formula is **MgO**   *[1 mark]*

3) First calculate the no. of moles of each product and then the mass of C and H:

No. of moles of $CO_2 = \dfrac{33}{44} = 0.75$ moles

Mass of $C = 0.75 \times 12 = 9$ g

No. of moles of $H_2O = \dfrac{10.8}{18} = 0.6$ moles

0.6 moles $H_2O = 1.2$ moles H
Mass of $H = 1.2 \times 1 = 1.2$ g   *[1 mark]*
Organic acids contain C, H and O, so the rest of the mass must be O.
Mass of $O = 19.8 - (9 + 1.2) = 9.6$ g

No. of moles of $O = \dfrac{9.6}{16} = 0.6$ moles   *[1 mark]*

Mole ratio = $C : H : O = $ $0.75 : 1.2 : 0.6$
Divide by smallest $1.25 : 2 : 1$
The carbon ratio isn't a whole number, so you have to multiply them all up until it is. As its fraction is ¼, multiply them all by 4.
So, mole ratio = $C : H : O = 5 : 8 : 4$
Empirical formula = **$C_5H_8O_4$**   *[1 mark]*
Empirical mass $= (12 \times 5) + (1 \times 8) + (16 \times 4) = 132$ g
This is the same as what we're told the molecular mass is,
so the molecular formula is also **$C_5H_8O_4$**.   *[1 mark]*

Page 23 — Equations and Calculations

1) M of $C_2H_5Cl = (2 \times 12) + (5 \times 1) + (1 \times 35.5) = 64.5$ g mol^{-1}
[1 mark]

Number of moles of $C_2H_5Cl = \dfrac{258}{64.5} = 4$ moles   *[1 mark]*

From the equation, 1 mole C_2H_5Cl is made from 1 mole C_2H_4
so, 4 moles C_2H_5Cl is made from 4 moles C_2H_4.   *[1 mark]*
M of $C_2H_4 = (2 \times 12) + (4 \times 1) = 28$ g mol^{-1}
so, the mass of 4 moles $C_2H_4 = 4 \times 28 = $ **112 g**   *[1 mark]*

---

2) a) M of $CaCO_3 = 40 + 12 + (3 \times 16) = 100$ g mol^{-1}

Number of moles of $CaCO_3 = \dfrac{15}{100} = 0.15$ moles

From the equation, 1 mole $CaCO_3$ produces 1 mole CaO
so, 0.15 moles of $CaCO_3$ produces 0.15 moles of CaO.   *[1 mark]*
M of $CaO = 40 + 16 = 56$ g mol^{-1} *[1 mark]*
so, mass of 0.15 moles of $CaO = 56 \times 0.15 = $ **8.4 g**   *[1 mark]*

b) From the equation, 1 mole $CaCO_3$ produces 1 mole CO_2
so, 0.15 moles of $CaCO_3$ produces 0.15 moles of CO_2.   *[1 mark]*
1 mole gas occupies 24 dm^3,   *[1 mark]*
so, 0.15 moles occupies $= 24 \times 0.15 = $ **3.6 dm^3**   *[1 mark]*

3) On the LHS, you need 2 each of K and I, so use 2KI
This makes the final equation: **$2KI + Pb(NO_3)_2 \rightarrow PbI_2 + 2KNO_3$**
     [1 mark]

In this equation, the NO_3 group remains unchanged, so it makes balancing much easier if you treat it as one indivisible lump.

Page 25 — Confirming Equations

1) a) $2NaN_3 \rightarrow 2Na + 3N_2$
LHS correct *[1 mark]*   RHS correct *[1 mark]*
b) i) M of $NaN_3 = 23 + (3 \times 14) = 65$ g mol^{-1} *[1 mark]*
     $0.325/65 = $ **0.005 moles** *[1 mark]*
ii) $180/24000 = $ **0.0075 moles** *[1 mark]*
iii) ratio $NaN_3 : N_2 = 0.005 : 0.0075$ *[1 mark]* = **2:3** *[1 mark]*

2) a) By delivering the gas to an upturned measuring cylinder (or burette) *[1 mark]* filled with water and displacing the water *[1 mark]*
(Alternatively: connecting the conical flask to a gas syringe to measure the volume produced *[2 marks]*)

b) Not all of the hydrogen gas may be collected (some may escape). / The equipment used to measure the mass of magnesium and that used to measure the volume of hydrogen will have a limited precision. / Gas may not be at r.t.p. when volume measured.
[1 mark for each sensible reason, up to a maximum of 2 marks.]

Page 27 — Acids and Bases

1) a) $CaCO_{3(s)} + 2HClO_{4(aq)} \rightarrow Ca(ClO_4)_{2(aq)} + H_2O_{(l)} + CO_{2(g)}$
[1 mark for the state symbols, 1 mark for all the correct formulas and 1 mark for the correct balance.]

b) i) $2Li_{(s)} + 2H^+_{(aq)} \rightarrow 2Li^+_{(aq)} + H_{2(g)}$

     [1 mark for the correct formulas, 1 mark for the correct balance.]
The SO_4^{2-} ions are left out of the ionic equation — they're spectator ions that don't get involved in the reaction.

ii) $2KOH_{(aq)} + H_2SO_{4(aq)} \rightarrow K_2SO_{4(aq)} + 2H_2O_{(l)}$

     [1 mark for the correct formulas, 1 mark for the correct balance.]

iii) $2NH_{3(aq)} + H_2SO_{4(aq)} \rightarrow (NH_4)_2SO_{4(aq)}$

     [1 mark for the correct formulas, 1 mark for the correct balance.]

Page 29 — Salts

1) a) M of $CaSO_4 = 40 + 32 + (4 \times 16) = 136$ g mol^{-1} *[1 mark]*
no. moles $= 1.133$ g$/136 = $ **0.00833 moles** *[1 mark]*
b) mass of water = difference in mass between hydrated and anhydrous salt $= 1.883 - 1.133 = $ **0.750 g** *[1 mark]*
c) no. moles of water = mass/molar mass $= 0.750/18 = 0.04167$
[1 mark]
X = ratio of no. moles water to no. moles salt $= 0.04167/0.00833 = $ 5.002 *[1 mark]*
Rounded to nearest integer **$X = 5$** *[1 mark]*

2) a) no. moles $= 0.2$ mol dm$^{-3} \times 0.05$ dm$^3 = $ **0.01 moles** *[1 mark]*
     (50 cm$^3 = 0.05$ dm^3)
b) molar mass of the hydrated copper(II) sulfate
$= 63.5 + 32 + (4 \times 16) + (5 \times (2 + 16)) = 249.5$ g mol^{-1} *[1 mark]*
ratio of sulfuric acid to copper sulfate = 1:1 (from balanced equation)
so max. no. moles copper sulfate = 0.01 *[1 mark]*
mass of 0.01 moles of hydrated copper sulfate
$= 0.01 \times 249.5 = 2.495$ g *[1 mark]*
percentage yield $= (1.964/2.495) \times 100 = $ **78.72%** *[1 mark]*

Answers

Page 31 — Titrations

1) First write down what you know —
$$CH_3COOH + NaOH \rightarrow CH_3COONa + H_2O$$
$25.4 \, cm^3 \quad 14.6 \, cm^3$
$? \qquad 0.5 \, M$

Number of moles of NaOH $= \dfrac{0.5 \times 14.6}{1000} = 0.0073$ moles [1 mark]

From the equation, you know 1 mole NaOH neutralises 1 mole of CH_3COOH, so if you've used 0.0073 moles NaOH you must have neutralised 0.0073 moles CH_3COOH. [1 mark]

Concentration of $CH_3COOH = \dfrac{0.0073 \times 1000}{25.4} = \textbf{0.287 M}$ [1 mark]

2) First write down what you know again —
$$CaCO_3 + H_2SO_4 \rightarrow CaSO_4 + H_2O + CO_2$$
$0.75 \, g \quad 0.25 \, M$

M of $CaCO_3 = 40 + 12 + (3 \times 16) = 100 \, g \, mol^{-1}$ [1 mark]

Number of moles of $CaCO_3 = \dfrac{0.75}{100} = 7.5 \times 10^{-3}$ moles [1 mark]

From the equation, 1 mole $CaCO_3$ reacts with 1 mole H_2SO_4 so, 7.5×10^{-3} moles $CaCO_3$ reacts with 7.5×10^{-3} moles H_2SO_4. [1 mark]

The volume needed is $= \dfrac{(7.5 \times 10^{-3}) \times 1000}{0.25} = 30 \, cm^3$ [1 mark]

If the question mentions concentration, you can bet your last clean pair of underwear that you'll need to use the formula

no. of moles $= \dfrac{conc. \times volume \, (cm^3)}{1000}$ (or no. moles = conc. × volume (dm^3)).

Page 33 — More About Titrations

1) a) You can make the data more reliable by repeating the titration several more times [1 mark].

b) The titre is calculated by subtracting the initial volume from the final volume. Each of these has an uncertainty of $0.05 \, cm^3$, so the total uncertainty is $0.1 \, cm^3$.
percentage uncertainty = $(0.1/3.1) \times 100 = \textbf{3.23\%}$
[1 mark for correct use of percentage uncertainty formula, 1 mark for using uncertainty of $0.1 \, cm^3$]

c) The percentage error will decrease if the titres are larger [1 mark]. Using a less concentrated solution will result in larger titres [1 mark].

2) a) no. moles of HCl = $0.1 \, mol \, dm^{-3} \times (19.25 \, cm^3/1000) = 0.001925$ [1 mark]
no. moles of NaOH = 0.001925 (since reacting ratio is 1:1) [1 mark]
concentration of NaOH = $0.001925/(25 \, cm^3/1000)$
$= \textbf{0.077 mol dm}^{-3}$ [1 mark]

b) percentage uncertainty in pipette
$= (0.06/25.0) \times 100 = 0.24\%$ [1 mark]
percentage uncertainty in titre = $(0.1/19.25) \times 100 = 0.52\%$ [1 mark]
Total percentage uncertainty = 0.76% [1 mark]
So uncertainty of concentration = 0.76% of 0.077
$= \textbf{0.000585 mol dm}^{-3} \, \textbf{(5.85} \times \textbf{10}^{-4} \, \textbf{mol dm}^{-3})$ [1 mark]

Page 35 — Atom Economy and Percentage Yield

1) a) 2 is an addition reaction [1 mark]

b) For reaction 1: % atom economy
$= M_r(C_2H_5Cl) \div [M_r(C_2H_5Cl) + M_r(POCl_3) + M_r(HCl)]$ [1 mark]
$= [(2 \times 12) + (5 \times 1) + 35.5]$
$\div [(2 \times 12) + (5 \times 1) + 35.5 + 31 + 16 + (3 \times 35.5) +$
$1 + 35.5] \times 100$ [1 mark]
$= (64.5 \div 254.5) \times 100 = 25.3\%$ [1 mark]

c) The atom economy is 100% because there is only one product (there are no by-products) [1 mark]

2) a) There is only one product, so the theoretical yield can be calculated by adding the masses of the reactants [1 mark].
So theoretical yield = 0.275 + 0.142 = 0.417 g [1 mark]

b) percentage yield = $(0.198 \div 0.417) \times 100 = 47.5\%$ [1 mark]

c) Changing reaction conditions will have no effect on atom economy [1 mark]. Since the equation shows that there is only one product, the atom economy will always be 100% [1 mark].
Atom economy is related to the type of reaction — addition, substitution, etc. — not to the quantities of products and reactants.

Section Three — Bonding and Structure

Page 37 — Ionic Bonding

1) a)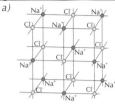

Your diagram should show the following —
• cubic structure with ions at corners [1 mark]
• sodium ions and chloride ions labelled [1 mark]
• alternating sodium ions and chloride ions [1 mark]

b) giant ionic (lattice) [1 mark]

c) You'd expect it to have a high melting point [1 mark]. Because there are strong bonds between the ions [1 mark] due to the electrostatic forces [1 mark]. A lot of energy is required to overcome these bonds [1 mark].

2) a)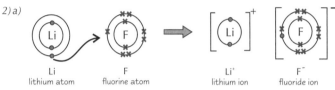

Your diagram should show the following —
• A lithium atom with the correct electron arrangement, and a fluorine atom with the correct electron arrangement [1 mark].
• A clear indication of the transfer of one electron from the outer shell of the lithium atom to the outer shell of the fluorine atom (e.g. an arrow) [1 mark].
• A Li^+ ion with the correct electron arrangement [1 mark].
• An F^- ion with the correct electron arrangement [1 mark].

b) In an ionic solid, ions are held in place by strong ionic bonds [1 mark]. When the solid is heated to melting point, the ions gain enough energy [1 mark] to overcome the forces of attraction [1 mark] so they become mobile [1 mark] and can carry charge (and hence electricity) through the substance [1 mark].

Page 39 — More on Ions and Ionic Bonding

1) a) Neon [1 mark]

b) The O^{2-} ion has a larger ionic radius than the neon atom [1 mark]. The neon atom has two more protons than the O^{2-} ion, so it attracts its ten electrons more strongly [1 mark]. The Na^+ has a smaller ionic radius than the neon atom [1 mark]. The Na^+ ion has one more proton than the neon atom, so it attracts its ten electrons more strongly [1 mark].

2) a) They are colourless [1 mark].
Potassium ions have a 1+ charge. So the potassium ions in the diagram must be moving towards the cathode. Since you can't see a colourful streak moving in that direction, they must be colourless

b) When a current is passed through the solution, the ions/particles move [1 mark] to the oppositely charged electrode [1 mark].

Page 41 — Covalent Bonding

1) a) Covalent [1 mark]

b)

Your diagram should show the following —
• a correct electron arrangement [1 mark]
• all 4 overlaps correct (one dot + one cross in each) [1 mark]

2) Ethene has a (C=C) double bond, made up of a σ and a π bond [1 mark]. Ethane only has a σ bond [1 mark]. The π bond is less tightly bound to the nuclei than the σ bond, so it is more reactive [1 mark].

Answers

3 a) *Dative covalent/coordinate bond [1 mark]*
  b) *One atom [1 mark] donates a pair of/both the electrons to the bond [1 mark].*

Page 43 — Giant Covalent Structures
1)a) *Giant molecular/macromolecular/giant covalent [1 mark]*

  b)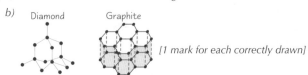

Diamond   Graphite

[1 mark for each correctly drawn]

  Diamond's a bit awkward to draw without it looking like a bunch of ballet-dancing spiders — just make sure each central carbon is connected to four others.
  c) *All of the outer electrons in a molecule of diamond are involved in covalent bonds [1 mark], so it is a poor electrical conductor [1 mark]. Graphite has delocalised electrons [1 mark], which can flow within the sheets, making it a good electrical conductor [1 mark].*
2) *Any two from: Very hard [1 mark] — down to the network of strong covalent bonds [1 mark]. / Good thermal conductor [1 mark] — the covalent lattice is very stiff, so vibrations travel through it easily [1 mark]. / High melting point [1 mark] — requires lots of energy to break all the strong covalent bonds in the lattice [1 mark]. / Doesn't conduct electricity [1 mark] — all the bonding electrons are held in localised covalent bonds [1 mark]. / Insoluble in any solvent [1 mark] — the covalent bonds are too strong to be overcome by intermolecular forces [1 mark].*

Page 45 — Nanostructures and Metallic Bonding
1)a)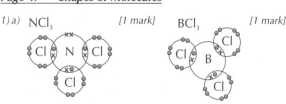

delocalised electron sea   lattice of +ve metal ions

  [1 mark for showing any closely packed metal ions and 1 mark for showing a sea of delocalised electrons.]
  Metallic bonding results from the attraction between positive metal ions [1 mark] and a sea of delocalised electrons between them [1 mark].
  b) *Calcium (Ca^{2+}) has two delocalised electrons per atom [1 mark], while potassium (K^+) has only one delocalised electron per atom [1 mark]. So calcium has more delocalised electrons [1 mark], and therefore stronger metallic bonding [1 mark].*
2)a) *Sixty carbon atoms [1 mark], with each carbon atom bonded to three other carbon atoms [1 mark], to form a hollow ball [1 mark].*
  b) *One of two or more different structural forms of the same element (in the same state) [1 mark].*
  c) *E.g. any one from: Small wires in circuits [1 mark] — the structure contains free electrons that can conduct electricity [1 mark]. / Making building materials or sports equipment [1 mark] — network of covalent bonds gives a very strong material, that is also light since the molecules are hollow [1 mark]. / Drug delivery mechanism [1 mark] — the hollow tube can be used to cage another molecule, such as a drug molecule, and carry it to the cells of the body [1 mark].*

Page 47 — Shapes of Molecules
1)a)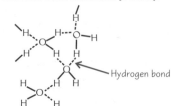

NCl_3 *[1 mark]* BCl_3 *[1 mark]*

Cl   N   Cl   Cl   B   Cl
Cl   Cl

  b) NCl_3

shape: *trigonal pyramidal [1 mark],*
bond angle: *107° (accept between 105° and 109°) [1 mark]*

BCl_3 Cl   Cl   *[1 mark]*
          B   120°
          Cl

(It must be a reasonable "Y" shaped molecule.)
shape: *trigonal planar [1 mark], bond angle: 120° exactly [1 mark]*
  c) *BCl_3 has three electron pairs around the central B atom. [1 mark] NCl_3 has four electron pairs around N [1 mark], including one lone pair. [1 mark]*

Page 49 — Polarisation of Molecules and Ions
1)a) *The power of an atom to withdraw electron density [1 mark] from a covalent bond [1 mark] OR the ability of an atom to attract the bonding electrons [1 mark] in a covalent bond [1 mark].*

  b) (i)   Br — Br
          non-polar
          (or no dipole)

     (ii)   O
           δ−
        δ+ H   H δ+
           polar
           (or dipole)

     (iii)   Cl δ−
            C δ+
        δ− Cl   Cl δ−
            Cl δ−
            non-polar
            (or no dipole)

     (iv)   N δ−
         H   H   H
        δ+ δ+ δ+
           polar
           (or dipole)

  [For each molecule: 1 mark for correct shape and bond polarities, 1 mark for correct overall polarity].
  To help you decide if the molecule's polar or not, imagine the atoms are having a tug of war with the electrons. If they're all pulling the same amount in opposite directions, the electrons aren't going to go anywhere.
2) *Al^{3+} has a high charge/volume ratio (or a small radius AND a large positive charge) [1 mark], so it has a high polarising ability [1 mark] and can pull electron density away from Cl^- [1 mark] to create a bond with mostly covalent characteristics [1 mark]. (Alternatively Cl^- is relatively large [1 mark] and easily polarised [1 mark] so its electrons can be pulled away from Cl^- [1 mark] to create a bond with mostly covalent characteristics [1 mark].)*

Page 51 — Intermolecular forces
1)a) *Van der Waals OR instantaneous/temporary dipole-induced dipole OR dispersion forces.*
  Permanent dipole-dipole interactions/forces.
  Hydrogen bonding.
  Permanent dipole-induced dipole interactions.
  [1 mark each for any three]
  b) *Except for water, there's an increase in boiling point going down the group [1 mark], because the increase in the size of the molecule/M_r [1 mark] leads to an increase in van der Waals OR instantaneous/ temporary dipole-induced dipole OR dispersion forces [1 mark]. More energy [1 mark] is needed to break the hydrogen bonds between water molecules [1 mark].*
  c)

  H   H   O   H
  H   O   H   H
      H   O   H   ← Hydrogen bond
  H   O   H
  H   H

Your diagram should show the following —
  • *Labelled hydrogen bonds between the water molecules [1 mark].*
  • *At least two hydrogen bonds between an oxygen atom and a hydrogen atom on adjacent molecules [1 mark].*

Answers

Page 53 — Properties of Structures

1) a) A — Ionic   B — (Simple) molecular
   C — Metallic   D — Giant molecular (macromolecular)
   [1 mark for each]
   b) i) Diamond — D   ii) Aluminium — C
   iii) Sodium chloride — A   iv) Iodine — B   [1 mark for each]
2) **Magnesium** has a metallic crystal lattice/metallic bonding
   [1 mark]. It has positive ions [1 mark] and a sea of electrons/
   delocalised electrons/free electrons [1 mark], which allow it to
   conduct electricity in the solid or liquid state [1 mark].
   Sodium chloride has a (giant) ionic lattice [1 mark]. It doesn't
   conduct electricity when it's solid [1 mark] because the ions are held
   in place by strong ionic bonds [1 mark]. But it does conduct
   electricity when liquid/molten [1 mark] or in aqueous solution [1
   mark] because it has freely moving ions (not electrons) [1 mark].
   Graphite has a giant covalent/macromolecular structure [1 mark]. It
   has delocalised/free electrons [1 mark] within the layers [1 mark] so it
   can conduct electricity in the solid state [1 mark].

Section Four — Elements of the Periodic Table

Page 55 — The Periodic Table

1) a) He arranged the elements in order of atomic mass [1 mark].
   b) The word 'octaves' was used because elements with similar properties
   occurred at regular intervals [1 mark], and the similarities occurred
   every eighth element [1 mark].
   c) The pattern broke down on the third row of elements [1 mark].
2) a) He left blanks for undiscovered elements [1 mark].
   b) Mendeleev used the table to predict the properties of 'missing'/
   undiscovered elements [1 mark]. When the missing elements were
   discovered his predictions were proved to be very accurate [1 mark].

Page 58 — Periodic Trends

1) The regular repeating patterns of variations of the properties of
   elements with increasing atomic number [1 mark] across each period
   of the periodic table [1 mark].
2) Mg has more delocalised electrons per atom [1 mark] and the ion has
   a greater charge density due to its smaller ionic radius (because of the
   greater nuclear charge) [1 mark]. This gives Mg a stronger metal-
   metal bond, resulting in a higher boiling point [1 mark].
3) a) Increasing number of protons means a stronger pull from the
   positively charged nucleus [1 mark] making it harder to remove an
   electron from the outer shell [1 mark]. There are no extra inner
   electrons to add to the shielding effect [1 mark].
   b) (i) Boron has the configuration $1s^2 2s^2 2p_x^1$ compared to $1s^2 2s^2$ for
   beryllium [1 mark]. The 2p shell is at a slightly higher energy level
   than the 2s shell. As a result, the extra distance and partial
   shielding of the 2s orbital make it easier to remove the outer
   electron [1 mark].
   (ii) Oxygen has the configuration $1s^2 2s^2 2p_x^2 2p_y^1 2p_z^1$ compared to
   $1s^2 2s^2 2p_x^1 2p_y^1 2p_z^1$ for nitrogen [1 mark]. Electron repulsion in the
   $2p_x$ sub-shell makes it easier to remove an electron in oxygen
   [1 mark].
4) The atomic radius decreases across the period from left to right
   [1 mark]. The number of protons increases, so nuclear charge
   increases [1 mark], meaning electrons are pulled closer to the nucleus
   [1 mark]. (The electrons are all added to the same outer shell, so
   there's little effect on shielding) [1 mark].
5) Neon has the configuration $1s^2 2s^2 2p^6$ and sodium $1s^2 2s^2 2p^6 3s^1$.
   [1 mark] The extra distance of sodium's outer electron from the
   nucleus and the extra electron shielding make it easier to remove than
   one of neon's 2p electrons [1 mark].

Page 61 — Oxidation and Reduction

1) a) $H_2SO_{4\,(aq)} + 8HI_{(g)} \rightarrow H_2S_{(g)} + 4I_{2\,(s)} + 4H_2O_{(l)}$ [1 mark]
   b) Ox. No. of S in H_2SO_4 = +6   [1 mark]
   Ox. No. of S in H_2S = -2   [1 mark]
   c) $2I^- \rightarrow I_2 + 2e^-$ [1 mark]
   d) $H_2SO_4 + 8H^+ + 8e^- \rightarrow H_2S + 4H_2O$
   [all species correct — 1 mark, balancing — 1 mark]

e) Iodide [1 mark] — it donates electrons / its oxidation number
   increases [1 mark]
   The ionic equations here are pretty tricky. Use the equation you're given
   as much as possible. For part d), sulfur is being reduced from +6 to –2,
   so it's gaining 8 electrons. You also need to add H⁺s and H₂O's to
   balance it. With ionic equations, always make sure the charges balance.
   E.g. in part d), charge on left = +8 – 8 = 0 = right-hand side.
2) a) (i) $FeSO_4$ (ii) $Fe(OH)_2$ (iii) $Fe_2(SO_4)_3$ (iv) $Fe(OH)_3$
   [1 mark for each]
   b) The oxygen in the atmosphere would oxidise iron(II) compounds to
   iron(III) compounds. [1 mark]

Page 63 — Group 2 — The Alkaline Earth Metals

1) Mg $1s^2\ 2s^2\ 2p^6\ 3s^2$ Ca $1s^2\ 2s^2 2p^6 3s^2 3p^6\ 4s^2$ [1 mark]
   First ionisation energy of Ca is smaller [1 mark]
   because Ca has (one) more electron shell(s) [1 mark]. This
   reduces the attraction between the nucleus and the outer electrons
   because it increases the shielding effect [1 mark] and because the
   outer shell of Ca is further from the nucleus [1 mark].
2) a) $Ca_{(s)} + Cl_{2(g)} \rightarrow CaCl_{2(s)}$ [1 mark]
   b) From 0 to +2 [1 mark]
   c) White [1 mark] solid [1 mark]
   d) Ionic [1 mark]
   ...because as everybody who's anybody knows, Group 2 compounds
   (including oxides) are generally white ionic solids.
3) a) Y [1 mark]
   b) Y has the largest radius [1 mark] so it will have the smallest ionisation
   energy [1 mark].

Page 65 — Compounds of Group 2 Metals

1) a) $NaHCO_3 + HCl \rightarrow NaCl + H_2O + CO_2$ [1 mark]
   b) Wind/burping etc. [1 mark]
   c) Magnesium hydroxide [1 mark] – NB many of the other compounds
   would be either toxic or otherwise harmful.
   $Mg(OH)_2 + 2HCl \rightarrow MgCl_2 + 2H_2O$ [1 mark]
2) Add barium chloride (or nitrate) solution to both [1 mark]
   Zinc chloride would change/no reaction [1 mark]
   Zinc sulfate solution would give a white precipitate [1 mark]
   $BaCl_{2(aq)} + ZnSO_{4(aq)} \rightarrow BaSO_{4(s)} + ZnCl_{2(aq)}$ [1 mark]
   (or suitable equation using $Ba(NO_3)_{2(aq)}$)
   OR $Ba^{2+}_{(aq)} + SO_4^{2-}_{(aq)} \rightarrow BaSO_{4(s)}$ [1 mark]
   (or a test with silver nitrate for the chloride ions could be done.)
3) Test A $BaCl_2$ [1 mark]. Most soluble hydroxide. [1 mark]
   Test B $MgSO_4$ [1 mark]. Addition of $BaCl_{2(aq)}$ to a sulfate
           gives a white precipitate of $BaSO_4$ [1 mark].
   It's getting really hard now. Question 3 is a real stinker, so don't cry if
   you got stuck. The trick is to realise that it's about solubilities — then if
   you know the info on the page you're most of the way there.

Page 67 — Compounds of S-block Metals

1) **A** = CO_2 [1 mark] (it turns limewater cloudy)
   B = CaO [1 mark] (CO_2 is released when a carbonate is heated,
   leaving an oxide)
   C = $CaCO_3$ [1 mark] (the precipitate formed in the reaction between
   CO_2 and limewater)
   Original compound = $CaCO_3$ [1 mark] (CO_2 is released when a
   carbonate is heated, so the original compound must have been
   calcium carbonate)
   ...the easiest one to get is gas A because it's just describing the
   limewater test for CO_2. Getting the others isn't hard either, but you've
   got to really know all equations from page 66 — or you'll get muddled up.
2) a) $2NaNO_{3(s)} \rightarrow 2NaNO_{2(s)} + O_{2(g)}$ [1 mark]
   b) O_2 gas relights a glowing splint. [1 mark]
   c) magnesium nitrate   sodium nitrate   potassium nitrate [1 mark]
   Group 2 nitrates decompose more easily than Group 1 (the greater
   the charge on the cation, the less stable the nitrate anion) [1 mark].
   The further down the group, the more stable the nitrate (the larger
   the cation, the less distortion to the nitrate anion) [1 mark].
3) a) Energy is absorbed and electrons move to higher energy levels.
   [1 mark] Energy is released in the form of coloured light when the
   electrons fall back to the lower levels [1 mark].
   b) caesium [1 mark]

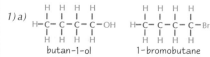
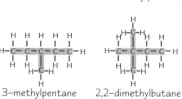

Answers

Page 83 — Alkanes and Petroleum

1) a) **A** [1 mark].
Straight-chain alkanes can pack very closely together / **A** has a larger molecular surface area [1 mark] — thus the van der Waals forces are greater [1 mark].

b) The longer carbon chain in decane [1 mark], means stronger van der Waals forces between the decane molecules [1 mark].
This is due to a greater molecular surface area/more electrons to interact [1 mark].

c) $C_5H_{12} + 8O_2 \rightarrow 5CO_2 + 6H_2O$ [1 mark for correct reactants and products, 1 mark for correct balancing]

2) a) (i) There's greater demand for smaller fractions [1 mark] for motor fuels [1 mark]. Or alternatively: There's greater demand for alkenes [1 mark] to make petrochemicals/polymers [1 mark].

(ii) E.g. $C_{12}H_{26} \rightarrow C_2H_4 + C_{10}H_{22}$ [1 mark].
There are loads of possible answers — just make sure the C's and H's balance and there's an alkane and an alkene.

b) (i) A measure [1 mark] of the tendency of the petrol to auto-ignite [1 mark] — the higher the number, the lower the tendency [1 mark].

(ii) Branched-chain alkanes, cycloalkanes and arenes [1 mark for each]. They promote efficient combustion/reduce knocking (autoignition) [1 mark].

(iii)

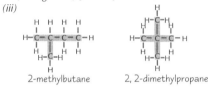

2-methylbutane   2, 2-dimethylpropane

[1 mark for each structure, 1 mark for each name]
2,2-dimethylpropane would increase the octane rating most [1 mark].
This is cos shorter, more branched alkanes increase the octane rating more. Don't worry about why — just remember that they do.

Page 85 — Alkanes as Fuels

1) a) $N_{2(g)} + O_{2(g)} \rightarrow 2NO_{(g)}$ [1 mark for correct reactants and products, 1 mark for correct balancing]

b) $2NO_{(g)} + O_{2(g)} \rightarrow 2NO_{2(g)}$ [1 mark for correct reactants and products, 1 mark for correct balancing]

c) Acid rain OR smog [1 mark]

2) a) Carbon dioxide is released, which was removed from the atmosphere millions of years ago [1 mark].

b) It will eventually run out [1 mark]

c) (i) Fermentation [1 mark]
(ii) Every bit of carbon that is released into the atmosphere when the fuel is burned is removed [1 mark] when the next crop of sugar cane is grown / was removed by the crop as it grew [1 mark]

Page 87 — Alkanes — Substitution Reactions

1) a) Free radical substitution [1 mark]

b) $CH_4 + Br_2 \xrightarrow{\text{UV light}} CH_3Br + HBr$ [1 mark]

c) $Br\cdot + CH_4 \rightarrow HBr + CH_3\cdot$ [1 mark]
$CH_3\cdot + Br_2 \rightarrow CH_3Br + Br\cdot$ [1 mark]

d) (i) $CH_3\cdot + CH_3\cdot \rightarrow CH_3CH_3$ [1 mark]
(ii) Termination step [1 mark]

e) Tetrabromomethane [1 mark]

2) $CH_3CH_3 + Br_2 \xrightarrow{\text{UV}} CH_3CH_2Br + HBr$ [1 mark]
Initiation: $Br_2 \xrightarrow{\text{UV}} 2Br\cdot$ [1 mark]
Propagation: $CH_3CH_3 + Br\cdot \rightarrow CH_3CH_2\cdot + HBr$ [1 mark]
   $CH_3CH_2\cdot + Br_2 \rightarrow CH_3CH_2Br + Br\cdot$ [1 mark]
Termination: $CH_3CH_2\cdot + Br\cdot \rightarrow CH_3CH_2Br$
Or: $CH_3CH_2\cdot + CH_3CH_2\cdot \rightarrow CH_3CH_2CH_2CH_3$ [1 mark]
[1 mark for mentioning UV]
Watch out — you're asked for the reaction with ethane here. It's just the same as the methane reaction though.

Section Six — Energetics

Page 89 — Enthalpy Changes

1)

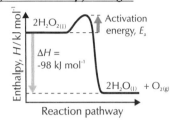

Reactants lower in energy than products [1 mark]. Activation energy correctly labelled [1 mark]. ΔH correctly labelled with arrow pointing **downwards** [1 mark].
For an exothermic reaction, the ΔH arrow points downwards, but for an endothermic reaction it points upwards. The activation energy arrow always points upwards though.

2) a) $CH_3OH_{(l)} + 1\frac{1}{2}O_{2(g)} \rightarrow CO_{2(g)} + 2H_2O_{(l)}$
Correct balanced equation [1 mark]. Correct state symbols [1 mark].
It is perfectly OK to use halves to balance equations. Make sure that only 1 mole of CH_3OH is combusted, as it says in the definition for $\Delta H_c^{\ominus}$.

b) $C_{(s)} + 2H_{2(g)} + \frac{1}{2}O_{2(g)} \rightarrow CH_3OH_{(l)}$
Correct balanced equation [1 mark]. Correct state symbols [1 mark].

c) H_2O should be formed under standard conditions (i.e. liquid, not gas) [1 mark]. Only 1 mole of C_3H_8 should be shown according to the definition of $\Delta H_c^{\ominus}$ [1 mark].

You really need to know the definitions of the standard enthalpy changes off by heart. There are loads of nit-picky little details they could ask you questions about.

Page 91 — Measuring Enthalpy Changes Directly

1) $\Delta T = 25.5 - 19 = 6.5\ °C$ [1 mark]
$m = 25 + 25 = 50\ cm^3$ of solution which has a mass of 50 g (assume density to be 1.0 g cm^{-3}) [1 mark]
Heat produced by reaction $= mc\Delta T$
$$= 50 \times 4.18 \times 6.5 = 1358.5\ J\ \text{[1 mark]}$$

No. of moles of HCl $= \dfrac{1 \times 25}{1000} = 0.025$ moles [1 mark]

0.025 moles of HCl produces 1358.5 J of heat, therefore 1 mole of

HCl produces $\dfrac{1358.5}{0.025}$ [1 mark] $= 54\ 340\ J \approx 54.3\ kJ$

So the enthalpy change is **–54.3 kJ mol^{-1}** [1 mark for correct number, 1 mark for minus sign].
You need the minus sign because it's exothermic.

2) a) No. of moles of $CuSO_4 = \dfrac{0.2 \times 50}{1000} = 0.01$ moles [1 mark]

From the equation, 1 mole of $CuSO_4$ reacts with 1 mole of Zn.
So, 0.01 moles of $CuSO_4$ reacts with 0.01 moles of Zn [1 mark].
Heat produced by reaction $= mc\Delta T$
$$= 50 \times 4.18 \times 2.6 = 543.4\ J\ \text{[1 mark]}$$
0.01 moles of zinc produces 543.4 J of heat, therefore 1 mole of zinc

produces $\dfrac{543.4}{0.01}$ [1 mark] $= 54\ 340\ J \approx 54.3\ kJ$

So the enthalpy change is **–54.3 kJ mol^{-1}** (you need the minus sign because it's exothermic) [1 mark for correct number, 1 mark for minus sign].
It'd be dead easy to work out the heat produced by the reaction, breathe a sigh of relief and sail on to the next question. But you need to find out the enthalpy change when 1 mole of zinc reacts. It's always a good idea to reread the question and check you've actually answered it.

b) Any sensible suggestion [1 mark], and whether it will cause results to be too high or too low [1 mark]. E.g. Some heat will be absorbed by the container (or lost to the environment) [1 mark]. This will make the experimental results lower than they should be [1 mark].

Answers

Page 93 — Hess's Law

1) $\Delta H_r^{\ominus}$ = sum of $\Delta H_f^{\ominus}$ (products) – sum of $\Delta H_f^{\ominus}$ (reactants)

= [0 + (3 × –602)] [1 mark] – [–1676 + (3 × 0)] [1 mark]

= **–130 kJ mol⁻¹** [1 mark]

Don't forget the units. It's a daft way to lose marks.

2) $\Delta H_f^{\ominus}$ = $\Delta H_c^{\ominus}$(glucose) – 2 × $\Delta H_c^{\ominus}$(ethanol) [1 mark]

= [–2820] – [(2 × –1367)] [1 mark]

= **–86 kJ mol⁻¹** [1 mark]

Page 96 — Ions and Born-Haber Cycles

1) a) $\Delta H_f^{\ominus}$ = +177 + 590 + 1100 + 249 – 141 + 790 – 3401

[2 marks. Deduct 1 mark for each error.]

= –636 kJ mol⁻¹ [1 mark]

b) Energy is required [1 mark] for the addition of the electron to the O⁻ ion due to the repulsion between the electron and the negatively charged O⁻ ion [1 mark].

2) $\Delta H_{latt}^{\ominus}$ = –641 – 148 – 738 – 1451 [1 mark] – (122 × 2) [1 mark]

(–349 × 2) [1 mark] = –2524 kJ mol⁻¹ [1 mark]

Page 99 — Bond Enthalpies

1) The negative charge density [1 mark] between carbon and oxygen in C=O is greater than in C–O [1 mark].

Attraction between the positive nuclei [1 mark] of carbon and oxygen for this electron density is stronger for C=O. [1 mark].

So the bond enthalpy of C=O is higher [1 mark] and the atoms are closer together in C=O [1 mark], giving a shorter bond length.

2) a)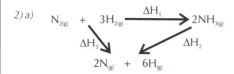

$\Delta H_1 = 2\Delta H_f^{\ominus}(NH_{3(g)})$

$\Delta H_2 = 6E(N–H)$

$\Delta H_3 = 2\Delta H_{at}^{\ominus}(N_{(g)}) + 6\Delta H_{at}^{\ominus}(H_{(g)})$

[1 mark for correctly drawing Hess cycle. 1 mark for correctly defining each of ΔH_1, ΔH_2 and ΔH_3. Award marks if all of the quantities are halved.]

b) $2\Delta H_f^{\ominus}(NH_3) = (2 × +473) + (6 × +218) – (6 × +391)$ [1 mark]

$2\Delta H_f^{\ominus}(NH_3) = +946 + 1308 – 2346 = –92$ kJ mol⁻¹ [1 mark]

$\Delta H_f^{\ominus}(NH_3) = \dfrac{-92}{2}$ [1 mark] = –46 kJ mol⁻¹ [1 mark]

Remember — there's 6 N–H bonds to be broken in $2NH_3$.

c) 391 kJ mol⁻¹ is the average N–H bond energy in ammonia.

The data book value of N–H is an average of N–H bond energies in many molecules [1 mark], like amines and acid amides.

Section Seven — Kinetics

Page 101 — Reaction Rates

1) The molecules don't always have enough energy [1 mark].

Collisions don't always happen in the right orientation (the molecules mightn't be facing each other in the best way and will just bounce off each other) [1 mark].

2) The particles in a liquid move freely and all of them are able to collide with the solid particles [1 mark]. Particles in solids just vibrate about fixed positions, so only those on the touching surfaces between the two solids will be able to react [1 mark].

3) a) X

The X curve shows the same total number of molecules as the 25°C curve, but more of them have lower energy.

b) The smaller area to the right of the activation energy line shows fewer molecules [1 mark] will have enough energy to react [1 mark]. / The shape of the curve shows fewer molecules [1 mark] have the required activation energy [1 mark].

Page 103 — More on Reaction Rates

1) Catalysts lower the activation energy [1 mark]

by providing a different pathway for the reaction [1 mark]

2) a) (i) Curve Y

(ii) Curve Z

b) Curve X is steeper (faster reaction) so greater concentration of acid [1 mark] but produces the same amount of gas in the end [1 mark]. Curve Z is less steep (slower reaction) [1 mark].

Page 105 — Catalysts

1) a)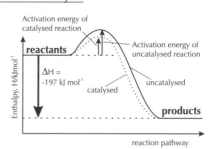

Curve showing activation energy [1 mark]. This must link reactants and products. Showing exothermic change (products lower in energy than reactants), with ΔH correctly labelled and a downward arrow [1 mark]. Correctly labelling activation energy (from reactants to highest energy peak) [1 mark].

Label your axes correctly. (No, not the sharp tools for chopping wood or heads off — you know what I mean.)

b) See the diagram above. Reaction profile showing a greater activation energy than for the catalysed reaction [1 mark].

Remember — catalysts lower the activation energy. So uncatalysed reactions have greater activation energies.

c) Catalysts increase the rate of the reaction by providing an alternative reaction pathway [1 mark], with a lower activation energy [1 mark].

d) The arsenic probably clings to the surface of the platinum [1 mark] and stops it getting involved in the reaction [1 mark].

Vanadium(V) oxide's solid, but the reactants are gases — so it's a heterogeneous catalyst. This is how they're normally poisoned.

2) a) $2H_2O_{2(l)} \rightarrow 2H_2O_{(l)} + O_{2(g)}$

Correct symbols [1 mark] and balancing equation [1 mark]. You get the marks even if you forgot the state symbols.

b)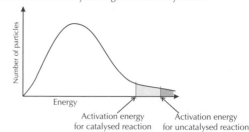

Correct general shape of the curve [1 mark]. Correctly labelling the axes [1 mark]. Activation energies marked on the horizontal axis — the catalysed activation energy must be lower than the uncatalysed activation energy [1 mark].

You don't have to draw another curve for the catalysed reaction. Just mark the lower activation energy on the one you've already done.

c) Manganese(IV) oxide lowers the activation energy by providing an alternative reaction pathway [1 mark]. So, more reactant molecules have energies greater than the activation energy [1 mark], meaning there are more successful collisions in a given period of time, and so the rate increases [1 mark].

Answers

Page 107 — Homogeneous and Heterogeneous Catalysts

1)

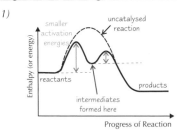

Curve for uncatalysed reaction. [1 mark]
Curve for catalysed reaction with lower activation energy. [1 mark]
Two humps and label for intermediate. [1 mark]
Both axes correctly labelled. [1 mark]

2) In heterogeneous catalysis, the solid catalyst provides a surface where the reaction can take place and be speeded up [1 mark].
The iron needs to be finely divided so that it provides the largest possible surface area where the reaction can proceed [1 mark].

Section Eight — Equilibria

Page 109 — Reversible Reactions

1) a) If a reaction at equilibrium is subjected to a change in concentration, pressure or temperature, the equilibrium will shift to try to oppose (counteract) the change [1 mark].
Examiners are always asking for definitions so learn them — they're easy marks.

b) (i) There's no change [1 mark]. There's the same number of molecules/moles on each side of the equation [1 mark].
(ii) Reducing temperature removes heat. So the equilibrium shifts in the exothermic direction to release heat [1 mark]. The reverse reaction is exothermic (since the forward reaction is endothermic). So, the position of equilibrium shifts left [1 mark].
(iii) Removing nitrogen monoxide reduces its concentration. The equilibrium position shifts right to try and increase the nitrogen monoxide concentration again [1 mark].

c) No effect [1 mark].
Catalysts don't affect the equilibrium position.
They just help the reaction to get there sooner.

Page 112 — More About Equilibria

1) a) At low temperature the particles move more slowly [1 mark].
This means fewer successful collisions [1 mark] and a slower rate of reaction [1 mark].

b) High pressure is expensive. [1 mark] The cost of the extra pressure is greater than the value of the extra yield. [1 mark]

c) (i) The rate of production of ethanol is increased [1 mark] because the catalyst provides an alternative reaction route [1 mark] of lower activation energy [1 mark]
(ii) The amount of ethanol in the equilibrium mixture stays the same [1 mark] because a catalyst has no effect on the position of equilibrium [1 mark]

d) Unreacted ethene is recycled through the catalyst [1 mark]

Section Nine — Bits and Bobs

Page 115 — Extracting Metals From Their Ores

1) a) $Fe_3O_4 + 4CO \rightarrow 3Fe + 4CO_2$ [1 mark]
b) $Fe_3O_4 + 2C \rightarrow 3Fe + 2CO_2$
OR $Fe_3O_4 + 4C \rightarrow 3Fe + 4CO$ [1 mark]

2) Advantage: the tungsten produced is purer [1 mark]
Disadvantage: hydrogen is more expensive
OR hydrogen is highly explosive [1 mark]

3) a) Aluminium oxide dissolved [1 mark] in molten cryolite [1 mark]
b) Cathode: $Al^{3+} + 3e^- \rightarrow Al$ [1 mark]
Anode: $2O^{2-} \rightarrow O_2 + 4e^-$ [1 mark]
c) High energy costs of extracting Al [1 mark].

Page 117 — Dissolving and Entropy

1) a) Hydrogen bonding [1 mark]
b) The polar O-H bonds in the alcohol [1 mark] are attracted to the polar water molecules [1 mark].
The (hydrogen) bonds between water molecules are stronger [1 mark] than bonds that would form between water and the haloalkane molecules [1 mark].
OR
The haloalkanes do not contain δ+H or δ-O atoms [1 mark] and so cannot form hydrogen bonds with water [1 mark].

2) a) Water [1 mark] and hexane (or other non-polar solvent) [1 mark]
If X is non-polar, it is likely to dissolve in hexane [1 mark], but not in water [1 mark].
Remember 'like dissolves like' — in other words, substances usually dissolve best in solvents that have similar bonding.
b) X and hexane have van der Waals forces between their molecules [1 mark] and form similar bonds with each other [1 mark].
Water has hydrogen bonds [1 mark].

3) Increase in entropy [1 mark]
The reactants contain a solid (Na) while the products contain a gas (H_2). [1 mark]
Gases have a higher entropy than solids. [1 mark]
Entropy just means 'how disordered the particles are'.

Section Ten — More Organic Chemistry

Page 119 — Alkenes

1) It's unsaturated because more atoms can be added [1 mark] across the double bond [1 mark]. (It doesn't have as many bonds as it can.)

2) a) $C_{10}H_{16}$ [1 mark]
b) Three [1 mark]
The equivalent alkane would be $C_{10}H_{22}$, and each double bond removes 2 hydrogens.
c) [2 marks. Lose 1 mark for each error.]

3) a) $CH_3CH_2CH_2CH=CH_2$ (or $CH_2=CHCH_2CH_2CH_3$), pent-1-ene [1 mark]
$CH_3CH_2CH=CHCH_3$ (or $CH_3CH=CHCH_2CH_3$), pent-2-ene [1 mark]
You don't need to show the double bond as long as the number of hydrogen atoms on each carbon is correct.
b) $CH_3CH_2CH_2CH=CH_2 + H_2 \rightarrow CH_3CH_2CH_2CH_2CH_3$ [1 mark]
c) Less reactive [1 mark] because product is a saturated hydrocarbon/ alkene is unsaturated or alkene has a C=C double bond/area of high electron density/π-bond [1 mark].

Page 121 — Reactions of Alkenes

1) a) Shake the alkene with bromine water [1 mark], and the solution goes colourless if a double bond is present [1 mark].
b) Electrophilic [1 mark] addition [1 mark].

c) (i) 2-bromobutane
[1 mark] [1 mark for correct intermediate] [1 mark]

Check that your curly arrows are exactly right, or you'll lose marks. They have to go from exactly where the electrons are from, to where they're going to.
(ii) The secondary carbocation OR the carbocation with the most attached alkyl groups [1 mark] is the most stable intermediate and so is the most likely to form [1 mark].

Answers

Page 123 — E/Z Isomerism

1) a)

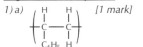

E-pent-2-ene *[1 mark]* *[1 mark]*

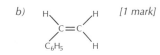

Z-pent-2-ene *[1 mark]* *[1 mark]*

b) *E/Z isomers occur because atoms can't rotate about C=C double bonds [1 mark]. Alkenes contain C=C double bonds and alkanes don't, so alkenes can form E/Z isomers and alkanes can't [1 mark].*

2) 2 *[1 mark]*

Page 125 — Polymers

1) a) *[1 mark]* b) *[1 mark]*

2) a) *[1 mark]*

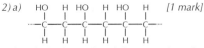

b) *The hydrogen bonds between the polymer molecules are broken [1 mark] and the polymer molecules form hydrogen bonds with water molecules instead [1 mark].*

c) *A polymer with many -OH groups will not dissolve in water because the hydrogen bonding between its molecules will be very strong [1 mark] so too much energy is needed to separate them [1 mark].*

3) *[2 marks for any two of the following]*
Polymer A will be stronger/harder/more rigid than polymer B.
Polymer B can be easily melted and remoulded, but polymer A won't.

Page 127 — More About Polymers

1) a) *Saves on landfill*
OR Energy can be used to generate electricity [1 mark for either]
b) *Toxic gases produced [1 mark].*
Scrubbers can be used [1 mark] to remove these toxic gases.
2) *Melted [1 mark] and remoulded [1 mark]*
OR Cracked [1 mark] and processed [1 mark] to make a new object.
3) *Renewable raw material / Less energy used (in manufacture) /*
Less CO_2 produced (over lifetime of polymer)
[1 mark for each, up to a maximum of 2 marks]

Page 129 — Alcohols

1) a) *Butan-1-ol [1 mark], primary [1 mark]*
b) *2-methylpropan-2-ol [1 mark], tertiary [1 mark]*
c) *Butan-2-ol [1 mark], secondary [1 mark]*
d) *2-methylpropan-1-ol [1 mark], primary [1 mark]*
2) a) *Primary [1 mark]. The -OH group is bonded to a carbon with one alkyl group/other carbon atom attached [1 mark].*
b) (i) $C_6H_{12}O_{6(aq)} \rightarrow 2C_2H_5OH_{(aq)} + 2CO_{2(g)}$ *[1 mark]*
(ii) *Yeast [1 mark], temperature between 30 and 40 °C [1 mark],*
Anaerobic conditions OR air/oxygen excluded [1 mark]
c) *Ethene is cheap and abundantly available / It's a low-cost process / it's a high-yield process / Very pure ethanol is produced / Fast reaction [1 mark each for up to two of these reasons]. This might change in the future as crude oil reserves run out or become more expensive [1 mark].*
d) *The -OH group can hydrogen-bond [1 mark] so ethanol can dissolve polar compounds [1 mark]. Its non-polar hydrocarbon part [1 mark] allows it to dissolve non-polar compounds too [1 mark].*
e) *It is produced from a renewable resource [1 mark].*
The equipment used is relatively inexpensive [1 mark].

Page 131 — Reactions of Alcohols

1) a) C_2H_5ONa / CH_3CH_2ONa *(sodium ethoxide) AND* H_2 *[1 mark]*
b) $CH_2=CH_2$ *(accept* C_2H_4*) AND* H_2O *[1 mark]*
2) a) $C_2H_5OH + PCl_5$ *[1 mark]* $\rightarrow C_2H_5Cl + HCl + POCl_3$ *[1 mark]*
b) *Steamy/misty fumes [1 mark] which turn blue litmus red [1 mark].*

Page 133 — Oxidation of Alcohols

1) a)

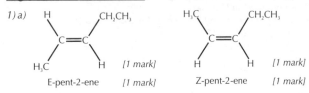

water out
Liebig condenser
water in
round bottomed flask
anti-bumping granules and reaction mixture
heat
[1 mark for diagram]

You set up reflux apparatus in this way so that the reaction can be heated to boiling point [1 mark] without losing any materials/reactants/products OR so vapour will condense and drip back into the flask [1 mark].

b) (i) *Warm with Fehling's/Benedict's solution: turns from blue to brick-red OR warm with Tollen's reagent: a silver mirror is produced [1 mark for test, 1 mark for result]*

(ii) *Propanoic acid [1 mark]*

(iii) $CH_3CH_2CH_2OH + [O] \rightarrow CH_3CH_2CHO + H_2O$ *[1 mark]*
$CH_3CH_2CHO + [O] \rightarrow CH_3CH_2COOH$ *[1 mark]*

(iv) *Distillation [1 mark]. This is so aldehyde is removed immediately as it forms [1 mark].*
If you don't get the aldehyde out quick-smart, it'll be a carboxylic acid before you know it.

c) (i)

[1 mark]

(ii) *2-methylpropan-2-ol is a tertiary alcohol (which is more stable) [1 mark].*

Page 135 — Haloalkanes

1) a) primary secondary tertiary

C_3H_7 C_2H_5 CH_3

[1 mark for each – if not labelled or incorrectly labelled then 1 mark only for all 3 correct structures.]
b) *Tertiary [1 mark]*
c) $CH_3CH_2CH_2CH_2I + 2H_2O$ *[1 mark]* $\rightarrow$
$CH_3CH_2CH_2CH_2OH + H_3O^+ + I^-$ *[1 mark]*
OR: $CH_3CH_2CH_2CH_2I + H_2O$ *[1 mark]* $\rightarrow$
$CH_3CH_2CH_2CH_2OH + HI$ *[1 mark]*
2) *Tube A = 1-bromopropane, Tube B = 1-chloropropane,*
Tube C = 1-iodopropane [1 mark for all correct]
The larger the halogen/more electrons the halogen has [1 mark] the stronger the van der Waals forces [1 mark] and the more energy required to overcome them [1 mark].

Page 137 — More About Haloalkanes

1) a) (i) *hydrolysis / nucleophilic substitution*
(ii) *propan-2-ol [2 marks for correct answer. Allow 1 mark for just propanol.]*
b) *The reaction would be faster with 2-iodopropane [1 mark]. This is because the C-I bond is weaker than the C-Br bond [1 mark].*

c)

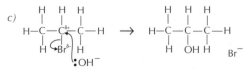

[1 mark for each curly arrow – one must start on C-Br bond and go to Br. The other must start on lone pair on O and go towards correct C. 1 mark for correct structures of reactants and product, including charge on OH.]

Answers

Page 139 — Haloalkanes and Reaction Types

1) **Reaction 1**
   Reagent — NaOH/KOH/OH⁻ *[1 mark]*
   Solvent — Aqueous solution/water *[1 mark]*
   Reaction 2
   Reagent — Ammonia/NH_3 *[1 mark]*
   Solvent — Ethanol/alcohol *[1 mark]*

2) a) KOH or NaOH *[1 mark]*, ethanol or anhydrous *[1 mark]*,
   reflux *[1 mark]*
   b) Elimination *[1 mark]*
   c) $CH_3CHBrCH_3 + KOH \xrightarrow[\text{reflux}]{\text{ethanol/anhydrous}} CH_2=CHCH_3 + H_2O + KBr$

   or $CH_3CHBrCH_3 + NaOH \xrightarrow[\text{reflux}]{\text{ethanol/anhydrous}} CH_2=CHCH_3 + H_2O + NaBr$

   [1 mark for correct formula for 2-bromopropane, 1 mark for correct product for propene, and 1 mark for other reactants and products.]

Page 141 — Doing Organic Chemistry

1) Reflux is continuous boiling/evaporation and condensation. *[1 mark]*
   It is done to prevent loss of volatile liquids while heating. *[1 mark]*
2) Each liquid in a mixture has a different boiling point. *[1 mark]*
   Collecting only the liquid (fraction) that boils at a particular temperature will separate it from the mixture. *[1 mark]*
3) E.g. Keep away from naked flames / Use a fume cupboard / In case of contact with skin rinse well with water *[1 mark for each, up to a maximum of 2 marks]*

Section Eleven — Environmental and Analytical Chemistry

Page 143 — The Atmosphere

1) a) The Sun mainly emits visible radiation/light and infrared radiation. *[1 mark]* The Earth mainly emits infrared radiation. *[1 mark]*
   b) Vibrational energy increases / bonds vibrate more *[1 mark]*.
2) $E = h\nu$
   $E = (6.63 \times 10^{-34}) \times (8.19 \times 10^{13})$ *[1 mark]*
   $E = \mathbf{5.43 \times 10^{-20}}$ **J** *[1 mark]*

Page 145 — The Ozone Layer

1) a) Ozone is formed by the effect of UV radiation from the Sun on oxygen molecules. *[1 mark]* The oxygen molecules split to form oxygen free radicals *[1 mark]* which react with more oxygen molecules to form ozone. *[1 mark]*
   b) E.g. UV radiation can cause skin cancer. *[1 mark]* The ozone layer prevents most harmful UV radiation from the Sun from reaching the Earth's surface. *[1 mark]*
   c) The ozone molecules interact with UV radiation to form an oxygen molecule and a free oxygen radical ($O_3 + h\nu \rightarrow O_2 + O\bullet$) *[1 mark]*
   The radical produced then forms more ozone with an O_2 molecule. ($O_2 + O\bullet \rightarrow O_3$) *[1 mark]*
2) a) Coolants in fridges / aerosol propellants / fire extinguishers / foaming plastics *[1 mark each use, up to a maximum of 3 marks]*
   b) They are unreactive/chemically stable *[1 mark]*
   They are non-flammable *[1 mark]*
   They are non-toxic *[1 mark]*
   c) Because they were destroying the ozone layer. *[1 mark]*
   d) e.g. HCFCs *[1 mark]* — still damage the ozone layer
   OR are greenhouse gases *[1 mark]*
   HFCs *[1 mark]* — are greenhouse gases *[1 mark]*
   Hydrocarbons *[1 mark]* — are greenhouse gases *[1 mark]*

Page 148 — The Greenhouse Effect

1) a) Water vapour *[1 mark]*, carbon dioxide *[1 mark]*, methane *[1 mark]*
   b) The molecule/bond absorbs infrared radiation and the bond's vibrational energy increases. *[1 mark]*
   Energy is transferred to other molecules by collision. *[1 mark]*
   The average kinetic energy of the molecules increases, so the temperature increases. *[1 mark]*
   c) How much radiation one molecule of the gas absorbs *[1 mark]*
   How much of the gas there is in the atmosphere *[1 mark]*

2) a) Increased use of fossil fuels *[1 mark]*
   Increased deforestation *[1 mark]*
   b) Increased CO_2 levels in remote, unpolluted places / Oceans have become more acidic as more CO_2 dissolves (forming carbonic acid) / Lower levels of CO_2 found in air trapped for many years in polar ice *[1 mark]*
   c) Capturing CO_2 and storing it in underground rock formations/storing it deep in the ocean/converting it to stable minerals / Developing alternative fuels / Increasing photosynthesis e.g. by increasing growth of phytoplankton *[1 mark each method, up to a maximum of 2 marks]*

Page 151 — Green Chemistry

1) a) Ethanol is from a renewable resource (sugar cane) but petrol is from crude oil, which is non-renewable. *[1 mark]*
   Ethanol from sugar cane can be a carbon neutral fuel. *[1 mark]*
   b) The climate in some countries is unsuitable for growing sugar cane. *[1 mark]*
   c) Land used for food production may be taken up growing the sugar cane, increasing the cost of food. *[1 mark]*
   Forests may be cleared to plant sugar cane. *[1 mark]*
2) a) If a catalyst is used:
   less energy is needed for the process *[1 mark]*
   more efficient processes are made possible *[1 mark]*
   b) The process has 100% atom economy as only one product is made *[1 mark]* so no waste is produced *[1 mark]*.

Page 153 — The Chemical Industry

1) a) 100% as there is only 1 product. *[1 mark]*
   Addition reactions produce no waste products, so they make better use of resources / avoid waste disposal. *[1 mark]*
   b) It is a reversible reaction so some starting material will always remain. *[1 mark]*
   c) You would expect to find an ethanol plant near an oil refinery *[1 mark]* so that ethene produced at the refinery can be easily transported to the ethanol plant *[1 mark]*.
2) a) 900 kg *[1 mark]*
   b) $(250 \div 300) \times 100$ *[1 mark]* = 83.3% *[1 mark]*
   c) High energy costs / Expensive plant needed / A labour intensive process / Batch process needed / Special safety measures needed *[1 mark for each factor, up to a maximum of 3 marks]*

Page 155 — Mass Spectrometry

1) a) 44 *[1 mark]*
   b) X has a mass of 15. It is probably a methyl group/CH_3. *[1 mark]*
   Y has a mass of 29. It is probably an ethyl group/C_2H_5. *[1 mark]*
   c) *[1 mark]*
   H H H
   H–C–C–C–H
   H H H
   d) If the compound was an alcohol, you would expect a peak with m/z ratio of 17 *[1 mark]*, caused by the OH fragment *[1 mark]*.

Page 157 — Infrared Spectroscopy

1 a) A's due to an O–H group in a carboxylic acid *[1 mark]*.
   B's due to a C=O as in an aldehyde, ketone, acid or ester *[1 mark]*.
   b) The spectrum suggests it's a carboxylic acid — it's got a COOH group *[1 mark]*. This group has a mass of 45, so the rest of the molecule has a mass of 29 (74 – 45), which is likely to be C_2H_5 *[1 mark]*. So the molecule could be C_2H_5COOH — propanoic acid *[1 mark]*.

Index

Index

Index